OUTER SPACE

UNFAIR
TO
HUMANS

JOB
TRAINING
ROLL HERE

LEISURE

N. SCHNEIDER

AUTOMATION, EDUCATION,

AND

HUMAN VALUES

BOOKS BY WILLIAM W. BRICKMAN AND STANLEY LEHRER

John Dewey: Master Educator
(First and Second Editions)

The Countdown on Segregated Education

Religion, Government, and Education

A Century of Higher Education:
Classical Citadel to Collegiate Colossus

AUTOMATION, EDUCATION, AND HUMAN VALUES

Edited by

William W. Brickman

Professor of Educational History and Comparative Education, Graduate School of Education, University of Pennsylvania; Editor, School and Society

and

Stanley Lehrer

Vice-President and Managing Editor, School and Society; Publisher, School & Society Books

INTRODUCTION BY MAXWELL H. GOLDBERG

Associate Director for Humanities, Center for Continuing Liberal Education, and Professor of Humanities, The Pennsylvania State University

New York • SCHOOL & SOCIETY BOOKS • *1966*

To

DOROTHY and PHILIP STEINBERG

humane, gentle people in a dehumanizing world

and to

LOUISE ANTZ

humanist and scholar

Contents

Illustrations

Introduction

AUTOMATION, EDUCATION, AND THE HUMANITY OF MAN

MAXWELL H. GOLDBERG

MOST OF THE CHAPTERS that make up this volume have been developed in connection with a major project of the Center for Continuing Liberal Education (CCLE), College of the Liberal Arts, The Pennsylvania State University. This project is concerned with the impact of technological change on the individual, in terms of human values and public response and responsibility. It is being developed under my direction and in cooperation with the International Business Machines Corporation and with its partial support. In common with other CCLE projects, this one has the general encouragement and guidance of Cyril F. Hager, associate dean of liberal arts and CCLE director, and it has the enthusiastic endorsement of Pres. Eric A. Walker, Dean Kenneth R. Roose of the College of Liberal Arts, and other university and state government administrative officers, as well as of alumni and faculty leaders.

Under the editorship of William W. Brickman and Stanley Lehrer, most of the present collection have been selected from a much larger number of papers connected with two of the CCLE project's main public events thus far: the December, 1963, CCLE Humanities Conference on Technological Change and Human Values and the June, 1964, CCLE Humanities Seminar on Work, Leisure, and Edu-

11

cation in a Changing Industrialized Democracy.[1] The papers are
offered as part of the fulfillment of one of the important purposes of
the project—to provide, simultaneously, regional and national stimulus to sustained study and reflection about the far-reaching and
pervasive impact and implications of exponential technological
change, generally, and of vaulting developments in automation, in
particular. Indeed, one of the most rewarding outcomes of the efforts
of the project thus far has been the lively display of interest the
programs have evoked both within Pennsylvania and outside its
boundaries and both in the United States and abroad. Certainly,
this outcome corroborates the estimate that Seymour L. Wolfbein,
Director of Manpower, Automation, and Training, U. S. Department of Labor, made, some time ago, of the meaning of this project:
"Programs such as the Project on Technological Change and Human
Values make a real contribution toward establishing responsible
attitudes, and are of invaluable assistance in the formulation of
positive policies aimed at achieving full employment in a dynamic
economy."

Especially since the papers that make up this volume are drawn
from such varied occasional sources and thematic and programmatic
contexts, they defy the strict ordering and the tight imbrication—even
if this were deemed desirable—that characterize the severely intensive
or the definitive work. Actually, the several chapters constitute, rather,
so many alarums and excursions, so many reconnaissance probes and
thrusts into vast, rough, and as yet uncertainly mapped terrain, with
jutting rocks and treacherous, spongy areas of communal and personal thought, feeling, imagining, and attitude. Some of the chapters,
moreover, speak much more narrowly and precisely than others to
the main question posed for the volume, which is: *What are the
humanistic implications for education of the pervasive impact of
exponentially accelerating technological change—specifically through
the marriage of sophisticated producing and processing machinery
with the computer, itself developing advanced sophistication with
astonishing speed and ingenuity?*

---

[1] For reports on the conference and the seminar, see the following: Alan
Trachtenberg, "Technology, Education, and Human Values," *School and Society*,
92: 316-318, Oct. 31, 1964; *idem*, "Technology and Human Values: The Penn State
CCLE Conference," *Technology and Culture*, 5: 359-76, Summer, 1964; Frank H.
Weir, "Mankind's Most Momentous Revolution; Changing America's Way of Life,"
The Philadelphia Inquirer, June 28, 1964; "The Labor Month in Review," edited
by Phyllis Groom, *Monthly Labor Review*, 87: iv, July, 1964; *General Director's
Letter*, American Association of University Women, September, 1964 (report and
commentary by Mary-Averett Seelye, staff associate for cultural interests).

Other chapters help provide background and context for the more specific observations and explorations. Together, it is hoped, they help evoke a sense of the complex "field," the glacial or, better, the galactic drift, the vector thrust of the massive, yet extraordinarily delicate and ubiquitously insinuative, cultural phenomenon of radical technological change and its social and personal concomitants. Together, it is further hoped, the several chapters of this volume will provide both the stimulus—or provocation—and the incentive—or inspiration—for further study and discussion as to how, particularly on leadership levels, we most effectively may confront drastic technological change. This is a confrontation which calls, minimally, for containment—in the military sense—of the explosive thrust of surging technological change, and, maximally, for that sort of creative accommodation which will work for the benefit of the individual and society, even while it reaffirms the dignity of the human spirit and redounds to the glory of mankind.

While the several chapters of this volume do not have the tightness of a suit of chain-linked armor, they are arranged in four main suggestive groupings that should provide a sense of order and progression. The first group is brought together with reference to time point of view: Outlook; the second focuses upon the Humanities[2]; the third, upon Education comprehensively considered; the fourth, upon Man, Mind and Soul. Running through the volume, furthermore, is something of a dialectic set-up between those implications of advanced technological change which bear upon education in its more practical, *more immediately* applied and useful aspects, and those implications which bear upon education in its *less immediately* useful aspects. I stress the terms, *more immediately* and *less immediately*, because, thereby, I suggest one of the modes of resolving the oppositions set up by this dialectic. This is, namely, that, as Jacques Barzun has urged us, we must cease the fruitless debate between so-called useful and so-called useless education and seek to set up a sort of hierarchy among utilities. One way of setting up such a hierarchy is to grant,

---

[2] Other humanities-related papers from the CCLE Humanities Conference and the Seminar related to technological change are appearing in periodicals: Charles T. Davis, "Humanistic Imperatives in an Age of Technology," *PLA Bulletin*, 20: 7-11, August, 1964; Ralph W. Burhoe, "Human Values in an Age of Science and Technology," *Current Issues in Higher Education* (Washington: Association for Higher Education, 1964), pp. 33-35; Melvin Kranzberg, "Technology and Human Values," *Virginia Quarterly Review*, 40: 578-592, Autumn, 1964; Richard A. Gibboney (deputy superintendent for research and development, Department of Public Instruction, Commonwealth of Pennsylvania), "The Pennsylvania Humanities Course," *Phi Delta Kappan*, 46: 58-59, October, 1964.

for example, that both education for the world of work and education for the world of leisure may legitimately be expected to be useful, and then to distinguish between the education that is immediately useful, say to the individual's and society's economy, in the bread-and-butter, nuts-and-bolts sense, and that which is conducive to the individual's enduring *psychic* economy—including his ethico-spiritual and his esthetic economy—as well as to the over-arching value goals of society.

TECHNOLOGICAL CHANGE, AUTOMATION, AND THE SET TOWARD TOTALISM

How can we freshly sense the unprecedented urgency of the basic question posed in this volume, and the host of further questions that the several contributions cogently force upon us as our unfinished agenda? We face Hollywood's mounting problem of yesteryear. *Magnificent, dazzling, glorious, tremendous, stupendous, colossal*—to try to gain the same massive audience response, the Hollywood publicists had to keep stepping up the voltage of the laudatory epithets employed. Yet, eventually, they could gain no higher voltage. And, worse, the jaded public proved duckbacks to the exclamatory superlatives worn trite.

So it is with our attempts to convey the wizardry, the radically progressive magnitude, novelty, and pervasiveness of the technological changes with which we deal. Nothing less than the lexicon of superlatives and absolutes will do; and, as the term *wizardry* itself suggests, nothing less will do than a vocabulary borrowed from the never-never land of high romance. *Radical, revolutionary, unprecedented, sweeping, mushrooming, explosive, catastrophic, titanic, gigantic, astronomic, meteoric, cosmic, phenomenal, breathtaking, astounding, astonishing, fascinating, wonderful, marvelous, magical, miraculous, fabulous, incredible, fantastic, limitless, boundless, infinite*—these are some of the highest-powered and most gorgeously colored terms that are used, soberly, to suggest, modestly, the present preludial accomplishments and the predicted or guaranteed infinite potentialities of the phenomenon with which this volume is most deeply concerned. It is the phenomenon of radically and exponentially accelerating technological change, as momentarily climaxed in that recent marriage of mind and machine—the synergistic combination of enhanced brawn-power and enhanced brain-power—the "cybernated combine."

Yet, all too often, the superlatives fail to touch or stir their listeners. What they try to signal is either inconceivable, or unbelievable, or now unavailable because the terms employed to signal them are already worn trite. Take a new IBM computer which exhibits a versatility making that of the Renaissance Universal Man dwarf into insignificance. We hear an expert tell us that this machine has the capacity to absorb 1,000,000,000 "bits" for storage. We try to picture 1,000,000,000 "bits." Our imagination fails us. And, as we try, we are told that the "echo principle" of the Laser Ray may make this storage capacity sound paltry. We are dealing with orders of magnitude which our minds, however we stretch them, cannot encompass—let alone visualize.

Even if we can achieve, momentarily, the requisite degree of high excitement to be evoked by the terms from high romance which are used to describe our present and coming technological feats, we cannot long sustain our feelings at this pitch; and with the waning of the excitement, there is the waning, also, of the momentarily roused sense of critical urgency. We fall back into the apathy of indifference, exhaustion, or fatalistic resignation. We often lose the excitation of will sufficiently powerful to confront and seek to master, through creative accommodation, the twofold challenge of radical and exponential technological change—to dominate its threats and to exploit its promises. Yet, nothing short of such Herculean—or, better still, Promethean and Apolline—excitations and exertions will do.

This we no longer need the scholarly and technical treatises to tell us. The signs, in bewildering plethora, are all about us; and each day's outpouring from the presses and over the airwaves adds new items to this already bulging store. The problem is, from the many, to limit oneself to the few that space permits.

Here, then, is an item that shows how the vocabulary of superlatives and absolutes extends to the socio-economic and, hence, to the educational implications of radical and exponential technological change. This is an article by A. H. Raskin in *Saturday Review* (Nov. 28, 1964). The very title has one of these terms of all-inclusiveness: "Automation: Road to Lifetime Jobs." In the note about the author that follows, another such term matches the "Lifetime" of the title: "A noted American authority on American labor describes a growing movement that is revolutionizing man's relation to his work." The text itself provides further instances of this idiom of superlatives and absolutes that has become the hallmark of even the most realistic treatments of our dramatic theme.

Let a few illustrative excerpts suffice (italics added by this writer):

Automation, that *most dreaded* of job-killers in labor's Domesday Book, is proving a powerful union ally in moving toward *the ultimate in job security. Lifetime income guarantees* for industrial workers will be the next big goal on the bargaining front. . . . Technological change, proceeding at an ever *more meteoric* pace, provides both the spur for these demands to safeguard earnings and the increased efficiency out of which the cost of extra protection must come.

Elsewhere the benefits *have mushroomed.* The concept that employers have an obligation to workers "too old to work and too young to die" has become just one facet of *a unique system* of social security under the union label that grows *more inclusive* with each cycle of collective bargaining. Programs of health, hospital, and life insurance, established to protect workers, have been extended to cover not only their wives and children but a broad range of convalescent and psychiatric services. . . .

But the newest extension of the security principle is the one that carries blue-collar workers dramatically close to *the promised land of lifetime jobs.*

Essentially, what the convention [United Steelworkers] voted for was a plan under which anyone who had worked for a company long enough to be considered *a permanent employee* would have *the certainty* of an appropriate job opportunity and income for *the rest of his work life.*[3]

In the 200-odd words of the preceding excerpts, note the yield of superlatives and absolutes—expressions that we might well describe as part of the vocabulary of "totalism" so frequently employed in the burgeoning literature of our subject: Automation, that *most dreaded of job-killers;* toward the *ultimate in job security; Lifetime income guarantees;* Technological change, proceeding at *an ever more meteoric pace;* the *benefits have mushroomed;* a *unique system* of social security . . . that grows *more inclusive;* carries blue-collar workers dramatically close to the *promised land of lifetime jobs;* the *certainty* of an appropriate job opportunity and income for *the rest of his work life.*

---

[3] A number of the papers of the December, 1963, CCLE Humanities Conference on Technological Change and Human Values and of the June, 1964, CCLE Humanities Seminar on Work, Leisure, and Education in a Changing Industrialized Democracy focused upon the matter of technological change and national manpower, but in such a way as to project implications for the individual in terms of human values and the quality of American living. Several of these papers, some in adapted form, have been published: Robert Theobald, "Human Rights in a Cybernated Age," *Educational Record,* 45: 113-121, June, 1964; Garth L. Mangum, "Automation, Employment, and Human Values," *ibid.,* 122-127; and Stanley Foster Reed, "Entrepreneurship and the Depressed Area," *Yale Review,* 54: 31-40, Fall, 1964. The last-named article is an outgrowth, in part, of the June CCLE Humanities Seminar's experimental discussion series which Mr. Reed led on the theme of "Creativity, Entrepreneurship, and the Depressed (or Stratified) Community." See, also, Mr. Reed's December CCLE Humanities Conference keynoting paper, "Innovation and Human Values: The Interaction Spectrum," *The Gadfly* (University of Colorado), April 10, 1964.

It is this twin thrust toward totalism—the thrust of radical and exponentially accelerating technological change and the counter-thrust of socio-economic reaction—that we educators have to take into account as we try to visualize the tasks and opportunities of education in the years ahead of us. And our vocabulary for the discussion of these tasks and opportunities similarly becomes totalistic, for the problems and promises with which we deal are similarly totalistic. Indeed, for American educators, the semantics and the conceptualizations of totalism are not new. The conference rhetoric of the profession, for more than a decade, has been shot through with terms from the lexicon of absolutes and superlatives.

Yet, nowadays, it is not American educators alone who use this idiom. We find it among our colleagues abroad. We find it among our English colleagues, for example; and this is all the more note-worthy, since, at least on the college and university level, the English, in their educational pronouncements, have been noted for their restraint. Hence, we find the following remarks by Albert E. Sloman, vice-chancellor of the newly established University of Essex, England, all the more dramatically illustrative of the point we are making:

. . . The university ideal, which derives from the corporation of masters and scholars of the Middle Ages, is of a self-governing community concerned with advancing and disseminating knowledge. This conception is still cherished, but in conditions of today, conditions *undreamt of* only a few years ago, it is in jeopardy. Long before the Robbins report it was clear that universities, as we have known them, are threatened by the pressures not only of expanding numbers but also of rapidly expanding knowledge. This two-fold threat can be met, I believe, only by *radical innovation*.[4]

Another item to which I wish to call attention, as a means of freshly vivifying our sense of the scope and the urgency of the main concerns of this volume, comes from the Business Section of *The New York Times* (Nov. 22, 1964). It is an extended and copiously illustrated feature article by William D. Smith. The headline itself suggests the inclusiveness and the ultimate pervasiveness of the cyber-cultural revolution. It reads: "Blue-Collar Computers Run Plants, Roll Steel, Grind Pulp and Mix Cake." A subhead adds: "Systems

---

[4] "A University in the Making," The BBC Reith Lectures, 1963 (New York: Oxford University Press, 1964), pp. 9-10. (Italics added by this writer.) Toward the end of the same lecture, Mr. Sloman reiterates that "radical innovation is needed if we are still to preserve the university ideal." He adds that his own university "has been given the freedom and the scope to make its own attempt at preserving the essential nature of a university in face of a double explosion of knowledge and numbers" (pp. 21-22). *Cf.*, too, a newspaper item of Dec. 4, 1964, with the following headline: "Steelworkers List Total Job Securtiy in 5-Point Demand," and with the following lead: "Total job security for the steelworkers —just a concept for the past few months—today is a 5-point program and goal." In the details, the vocabulary of totalism is dominant (*Centre Daily Times*, State College and Bellefonte, Pa.).

for Process-Control Operate Top U. S. Concerns." Heading the spill-over of this article are equally emphatic captions: "Computers Are Moving into New Fields of Manufacturing"; "Systems in Use in 50 Industries"; "400 Installations Operating in the Nation—Baking Is One of the Latest." The text of this feature article continues to suggest the totalistic impulsion, if not totalistic logic of development, in the cybercultural transformation of modern industry.

At a plant in Deerfield, Illinois, Sara Lee, Inc., a subsidiary of the Consolidated Foods Company, has started a three-year program to make a Honeywell 601 computer the head baker. Within that time the company will gradually automate the plant to the point where the computer system takes almost complete control of the baking process. The computer will control equipment, speeds, humidities in key areas, temperatures of ingredients and ovens and the flow of baking materials into giant mixers.

While the computer keeps tabs on what is going into the ovens it also oversees the movement of cakes into the company's freezers.[5]

Thus, cake joins steel, cement, gasoline, electricity and many other items produced with computers as foremen.

Process-control computers, the blue-collar cousins of the more glamorous white-collar data-processing computers, have become big business in their own right in recent years.

Sales of digital process-control computers have climbed from $10 million in 1960 to $25 million in 1963. Volume is expected to reach $40 million this year.

Both here and abroad the day still has not arrived when huge plants are run by a handful of men sitting in a control room. The foundations are there, however, and the reality may not be too far behind.

What is education doing to prepare the individual and the community for "The Day" of dominant, if not pervasive or total, industrial cybernation? What will education be called upon to do when that day actually arrives? For the handful of men no longer needed

---

[5] In her June CCLE Seminar paper, "Cyberculture—The Age of Abundance and Leisure," Alice Mary Hilton, president, Institute for Cybercultural Research, presents a far more detailed picture of just how inclusive this bakery cybernation is. For it "also performs management functions for the business end of the bakery operation by controlling and monitoring the component machines to calculate, for example, the optimum number of rolls to be delivered on any day to each customer"; to process "the payroll for the company's diminishing number of employees and the invoices for its increasing number of customers; to compute market prognosis, adjusted in accordance with trends in taste, seasons, advertising, and any other influences the programmers have thought of . . .," etc. Dr. Hilton adds: "The few human beings still inside the 'black box' are only nursing the infant cybernation to maturity. They are no longer an integral part of the production process." She observes, further, that, "Contrary to popular opinion and nostalgic reminiscences, the machine bakes delicious bread if the recipe calls for the right proportions of excellent raw materials" *(Michigan Quarterly Review*, 3: 218-220, Fall, 1964). In his January, 1965, *Fortune* article (p. 221) on "The Real News about Automation," Charles E. Silberman observes, concerning this picture presented in Dr. Hilton's "awestruck report": ". . . people are still required to perform a wide range of activities—*e.g.*, braiding Danish pastry dough and spreading chocolate icing. And, 'the few human beings still inside the "black box"' come to about 450 per shift—300 of them in direct labor."

even to sit in that control room? For the youth who are to grow up into such a condition? The totalistic vector drift of the recent *New York Times* report needs to be matched by similar totalist thinking and imagining by the educator. The present volume seeks to make a contribution to this end.

Still another item is here submitted for freshness of appreciation of the seriousness of the problems with which this volume deals. This, too, is a feature article. *The Centre Daily Times,* of State College and Bellefonte, Pa. (Sept. 29, 1964), announces that "New York Computer Will Act as Tutor for University," and it reports, in part, as follows:

A computer located near New York City will be tested for its effectiveness as a tutor of students in college-level courses at the University this year.

Via 250 miles of telephone cable from University Park to the Thomas J. Watson Research Center of International Business Machines Corporation in Yorktown Heights, N. Y., Penn State students will experiment with the computer system which can give individual instruction to a number of students simultaneously in a variety of subjects.

Four faculty members are in the process of preparing their lecture notes, quizzes and favorite jokes for the computer pilot program.

The four courses written for the computer are one-term, three-credit courses normally offered at the University.

The "tutor" for the four courses will be an intermediate sized IBM computer.

The instructions to the computer have been written in a language which is close to every-day human language, a vocabulary which was devised by IBM scientists in Yorktown Heights. The faculty members were not versed in computer technology; nor have they had to learn a highly technical language.

The professors intend to document their findings as to whether or not a computer is effective, feasible, economical and useful in providing what educators as far back as Socrates and Plato have hoped for—an individual tutor for every learner.

Let us make allowances in the preceding for that "heightened and telling way" which headline writers have of drawing attention to the story that follows and for the similarly heightened and telling way the reporter has of spicing up his feature. Let us suppose that the term "tutor" is at least semi-metaphoric and that the allusion to Socrates and Plato is but a half-fanciful trope of the historic fancy. We know, at least, that a computer cannot do what, according to Stephen Leacock, the Oxford tutor used to do. We know that it cannot smoke at the student until he becomes a seasoned scholar. This sort of educational process, in the words of that computer-inspired TV series, "My Living Doll," "doesn't compute."

Even so, we just cannot dismiss the story with a shrug of the shoulders and a whimsical chuckle. Back of the playfulness and the journalistic fun lies a basic seriousness. The article reports that the computer-tutor "analyzes how far the student has progressed," "starts the program in the appropriate spot, just as an instructor would begin a new day's class work," "instructs the student to read certain subject matter," or "administers a text, assisting and correcting the student as he progresses through the material." It "gives directions to the student"; and it "analyzes the reply and then reacts to the student's performance in accordance with the plan laid out by the teacher, responding with clues, questions, remedial study matter, drills, on the next assignment." It "also can record such data as response times and errors." Thus "an extensive evaluation of both student performance and the adequacy of the course is possible."

Here, once again, we get a sense of totalistic set. Lest we hastily conclude, however, that the computer will eliminate altogether the living teacher, we are given an assurance: "We do not expect computer-assisted instruction to eliminate the need for the teacher; on the contrary, using computers may make it possible for teachers to spend more time with the students individually and in small groups." We note that the computer merely assists in the instruction. We note the hope—we almost said "pious hope"—that, instead of being put on reduced time and pay, the computer-assisted teachers "may" be given the opportunity to spend more time with their students—individually and in small groups. In short, we note the assurance that our teachers themselves will not be dispensed with altogether, but will be enfranchised to serve in that ideal teaching role that goes back to that mother of humanistic and liberal education in the Western world—the Academy of Ancient Athens. This is the role of the tutor, teaching the individual or, at most, the small group. But —and especially for the future of humanistic or liberal education, this is a momentous *but*—we also note that the article ends by attributing, not to the living voice and the living countenance, but to the mechanism, the computer, the role of Platonic or Socratic teacher.[6]

---

[6] *Cf.*, Terry Ferrer, "Teaching Machines, Computers, TV, in Our Changing Colleges" and "For Learning—A Center of Electronics Hardware," *New York Herald-Tribune,* Dec. 7, 1964, p. 11. "There are 1,000 students, each plugged into the mother computer. They are studying eight different lessons. Each of the students is having a 'dialogue' with the computer through two sets of electronic keys, one to answer questions and one to tell the machine to 'continue,' 'reverse,' or 'judge' his answer. The student watches his individual television screen. On it appear both slides operated by the computer and machine-drawn characters and diagrams on the electronic blackboard." Note that here, too, we have the computer depicted as playing a key role in a teaching-learning process called "a dialogue."

Even if this is said partly with tongue in cheek, it cannot just be tossed aside. Many a truth is said in jest. Many an intention, it might be added, is revealed in jest—or many a doubt or misgiving, many a hope or aspiration, many a tendency or drift of thought and feeling, many a flight of projective imagining. The tendency or drift of imaginative projection suggested here is what calls for more than passing comment. This concluding allusion ventures to intimate that, contrary to reiterated denials, the computer, as well as other instrumentalities of programmed learning, may be expected, sooner or later, to invade that last sanctuary of humanistic and liberal education, as it already has penetrated into the cubicles of humanistic scholarship and research.[7] It may be expected to insinuate itself into the domain of the dialogue—"The Great Conversation"—that great non-mechanical instrument of intellectual growth and enlightenment of which the Platonic Socrates is the prototypic practitioner and of which the Platonic dialogue remains the ideal model.[8]

The conclusion of this article reminds us of the claim of that expert on the advanced human replacement functions and potentialities of the computers—Prof. Herbert A. Simon, Graduate School of Industrial Administration, the Carnegie Institute of Technology. This claim was advanced by Dr. Simon in a comment after his keynoting address at the Program on Technological and Social Change, Human Values, and the Library, co-sponsored by the CCLE and the Pennsylvania Library Association in connection with the 1964 Annual PLA Conference at Pittsburgh. In his comment, Dr. Simon maintained that, in time, our computers will become so versatile, efficient, sophisticated, ingenious, and gifted that, systematically, they will be able to produce those traditionally designated "flashes of creative intuition" or of "creative insight" which have yielded such great contributions to the march of intellect as a Newton's theory of gravitation or an Einstein's theory of relativity. The realm of the

---

[7] *Cf.*, Three-day meeting on "literary data processing," held at the International Business Machines Corporation's research center in Yorktown Heights, N. Y., in September, 1964. *New York Times* articles on the conference carried such headlines and subheads as "Computers Offer Humanities Help," "Meeting Explores Ways to Sharpen Literary Ideas" (Sept. 13, 1964); "Computers Turn to Poetry Study," "Milton's Influence on Shelley Appraised Through Tapes" (Sept. 11, 1964); "Scholars Praise Computer's Uses," "Literary Problems Found Easier With Machines" (Sept. 10, 1964).

[8] *Cf.*, Robert Redfield, "The Educational Experience" (Pasadena, Calif.: Fund for Adult Education, 1953), *passim*, but note Lecture 2, "Conversation," pp. 24-40. *Cf.*, too, William Orville Douglas, "Freedom of the Mind" (New York: Doubleday, 1964), *passim*.

creative process, the instrumentality of the creative dialogue—both of them have been regarded as central concerns of the humanities and the liberal arts—permanently discrete from so much else involved in the teaching-learning process that appropriately and efficiently can be taken over by the machine. Now, the penetration of the computer into both these realms is being talked of as imminent, if not actually under way.

At the same conference of librarians, Ruth Nanda Anshen, editor of several series—"The Science of Culture," "World Perspectives," "Religious Perspectives," and "Credo"—and now at work on a book on "The Nature of Evil," presented a searching paper on "Automation, the Individual, and Human Values." In it she sought, through rigorous and subtle, though severely particularized, analysis of perception and other aspects of experiencing, to demonstrate that computers, however sophisticated and gifted, never could take over totally man's distinctive modes, up to now, of knowledge and of humanistically evaluating experience.

In her argument, Dr. Anshen, who was soon to develop her views at greater length in a series of lectures at the University of Geneva, Switzerland, stressed, among other things, the crucial role for full perceptive experience and for humanistically normative experience of "tacit knowledge." This, she insisted, by its very nature eludes and will continue to elude the programming of the computers; and it seems to suggest what others have called that "clinical intuition," say, of the psychiatrist as he gains his full impression, diagnostically, of his patient. The speaker, in closely reasoned argument, stressed aspects of experience which we apprehend as the reality of the *Gestalt* or "field" rather than as a discretely limited entity, which we apprehend as the reality not of a mere aggregation of separate particles or entities, but rather as the reality of an organic whole subsuming its parts and greater than their sum. Dr. Anshen further maintained that this tacit knowledge, this awareness of the field, this awareness of the subsuming vital whole all are crucial for our distinctly human function of humanistic evaluating and purposive decision and action. As she put it in an interview with Ruth Heimbuecher of the *Pittsburgh Press*: "The great clue we have to a valid experience is seeing another person's face. We do not attend to the particulars as a machine would do—the eyes, nose, ears or mouth—but we have the experience of the totality of the face. No machine will give us this kind of certainty."[9]

Where do the practitioners of the humanities stand on this momentous ontological and metaphysical issue, with its far-reaching ethical and social reverberations? Where do the scientists and technologists stand with regard to it? Several of the contributors to this book address themselves to these questions, which seem at first very abstruse, very "academic," but which have a way of bobbing up, critically, at moments of major decision-making in our personal, professional, and public lives.

Vice Admiral Hyman G. Rickover recently has assigned to the liberal arts the function of providing the traditional humanistic, ethical norms for the public policy decisions made or crucially influenced by scientist-technologists. This serves to underscore just how serious and searching these questions are.[10]

TECHNOLOGICAL CHANGE AND LIBERAL EDUCATION FOR ADULTS

Those of us who are seeking to win, for continuing liberal education, the recognition, the status (both within and without the university), the support, and the dedicated professional talent (scholarly and pedagogic) it deserves—and soon must have—should resort to the idiom of totalism in responding to the educational challenge of radical and exponentially accelerating technological change.

For more than a decade now, lip service has been offered at educational conferences, in educational papers, articles, reports, and books to the exponentially increasing *immediate* needs for adult liberal studies. These are the needs to cope with the problems of vaulting technology, to take strategic advantage, on behalf of Adm. Rickover's humanized decisions based on humanistic values and humanized ends, of what the humanities and other liberal arts, refurbished, renovated, and made freshly relevant, may offer. We

---

[9] This comment reminds one of Martin Buber. The full text of Dr. Simon's address, "The Promise of Automation," appeared in the *Bulletin* of the Pennsylvania Library Association, February, 1965.

[10] *Cf.*, John W. Finney's report, in the *New York Times* for Nov. 20, 1964, of Adm. Rickover's address at the symposium on Cybernetics and Society, held in connection with the 175th anniversary celebration of Georgetown University. The headline reads: "Technological Decisions Ignore Human Factors . . . "; the subhead adds: "Admiral Asserts Traditional Concepts of Ethics and Morals Must Rule." The story itself reports, among other things, that, referring to engineering schools as now "mere trade schools though often excellent in their narrow field," Adm. Rickover suggested, "as one step in humanizing technology, . . . that students be required to have a liberal arts education before going on to engineering."

cannot rest content with applying this to the oncoming generations of students. Our present adults right now are being called upon to make decisions, fraught with humanistic implications, and, hopefully, grounded upon humanistic values and norms, which will have far-reaching implications for the future of modern man's—that is, Faustian man's—high and fateful romance with the Promethean fire of technology and its concomitant Protean social changes. We cannot wait for the oncoming crops of youngsters—even if they are bumper crops—to mature. We need humane leadership—*now*—from the present generation of adults.[11]

We have to take time by the forelock. We have to do some educational leapfrogging, and this means that far more systematically than in the past, far more attractively yet rigorously, far more vigorously yet critically do we have to develop innovational programs in the humanities and other liberal studies—formal and informal, credit and non-credit—for the adults. We have to do this particularly for the adults who have professionally arrived and who suddenly find themselves in positions of heavy public responsibility.

Indeed, we have to strengthen humanistic studies for adults all along the line. As the late Pres. Griswold of Yale insisted, and as the new humanities programs in the high schools suggest,[12] we need to lay the groundwork long before adulthood.[13] Certainly, as Pres. Francis Horn of the University of Rhode Island recently has reminded us, we need to give attention to this in the undergraduate years. Yet, we must not stop here, because a

. . . truly liberal education is the product of a lifetime of learning, study, reflection. Even then few individuals attain it. The best the college can do is to lay the foundation for a liberal education, to inculcate the habits of mind, breadth of interest, and enlargement of spirit which, when continued and enriched during

---

[11] *Cf.*, Martha B. Zeigler, "Creative Education," *Christian Standard*, Aug. 29, 1964, pp. 9-10, and Sept. 5, 1964, pp. 5-6 (working paper for June, 1964, CCLE Humanities Seminar); and Maxwell H. Goldberg, "Library Services to Adults, The Educational Challenge of Technological Change," *PLA Bulletin*, 19: 17-19, May, 1964.

[12] *Cf.*, A. Whitney Griswold, "Liberal Education and the Democratic Ideal" (New Haven, Conn.: Yale University Press, 1959). Also, *The English Leaflet*, LXIII, Fall, 1964. This entire issue is devoted to articles on the humanities in the schools—including one by Charles R. Keller, director of the John Hay Fellows program.

[13] *Cf.*, Robert T. Oliver, "Education in the Year 2000 A.D.," *Michigan Quarterly Review*, 3: 233-236, Fall, 1964. Head of the department of speech, the Pennsylvania State University, and president, the Speech Association of America. Dr. Oliver contributed this paper as a resource for the CCLE June, 1964, Humanities Seminar.

the later years—and there will be more of these later years for most of us—can result in a true liberal education. . . .[14]

In justifying his bill "for the Establishment of a National Foundation for the Humanities,"[15] Congressman William S. Moorhead has pinpointed the increasingly important role the humanities are expected to play in counteracting some of the adverse outcomes of cybernetic change and in advancing the gains for the dignity and meaningfulness of individual lives:

Science is bringing greater and greater leisure to America. "What shall I do with my spare time?" all too quickly becomes the question, "Who am I? What shall I make of my life?" When men and women find nothing within themselves they turn to trivialities and the society to which they belong becomes socially delinquent and potentially unstable. The humanities are the time-tested answer to man's questing and his need for self-expression.

It is up to us who profess the humanities, or who profess to be friends of the humanities, to make certain that the humanities prove to be not only a time-tested answer, but an answer functionally expressive in terms meaningful in and for the new times ahead. As Dean Cyril F. Hager, CCLE director, has observed, all of us engaged in the development of continuing liberal studies for adults in the face of radically and exponentially accelerating technological changes must heed G. B. Shaw's warning: "Unlimited leisure is a definition of hell."

ACKNOWLEDGMENTS: A PARTIAL LIST

The entire CCLE Project, for which most of the papers of this volume originally were produced, is one sustained effort to take time by the forelock and to apply the developing ways of liberal studies for adults at the leadership levels to the social and humanistic crisis connected with radical and exponential technological change. For the response, far beyond expectation, to this effort to contribute toward adult liberal education for personal, professional, and civic

---

[14] "Improving the Humanities," p. 2. A paper presented at the final session of the seminar on "Education for Human Competence in the Face of Technological Change," co-sponsored by the Humanities Center for Liberal Education in an Industrial Society and the University of Delaware, Oct. 30-Nov. 1, 1964. Excerpts from other papers at this seminar appear under the title, "Technology's Challenge to Education: A Symposium," *Saturday Review*, Dec. 12, 1964, pp. 21-25, 78-79; also in *Michigan Quarterly Review*, Spring, 1965, pp. 82-94.

[15] H. R. 1204, introduced into the House of Representatives, Aug. 17, 1964, and then referred to the Committee on Education and Labor. By July 2, 1965, the Committee had approved a new version of the Moorhead bill (H. R. 9482). A "clean bill" (H. R. 9460), introduced by Rep. Frank Thompson, Jr., was passed by the House on Sept. 15. The next day the Senate sent the bill to the President, who signed it on Sept. 29, 1965.

responsibility and leadership, thanks should go to many who have contributed and cooperated.

For the many, a few names must suffice. Chief among these, in addition to Dean Cyril F. Hager, are Charles R. Bowen, manager, educational projects, and Ormsbee W. Robinson, director of educational affairs, International Business Machines Corporation. The latter have been heartening advisers who scrupulously have avoided intrusion on our initiative and autonomy.

I cannot end without mentioning, with appreciation, the following: Ralph W. Baldwin, of Ralph W. Baldwin Associates, New York City; Marie A. Davis, coordinator, Work with Adults and Young Adults, the Free Library of Philadelphia; Melvin Kranzberg, secretary, the Society for the History of Technology, and editor-in-chief, *Technology and Culture;* Pauline Tompkins, general director, American Association of University Women; and from the Pennsylvania State University—Roy C. Buck, CCLE associate director for the social sciences and professor of social science and rural sociology; Harold K. Schilling, author, "Science and Religion: An Interpretation of Two Communities," and now newly honored as University Professor; M. Nelson McGeary, dean, Graduate School; Ben Euwema, former dean, College of the Liberal Arts; Frederick R. Matson, assistant dean for research, College of the Liberal Arts; Henry W. Sams, head, department of English, and chairman, Humanities Council; Ralph W. McComb, librarian, and chairman, Planning Committee, CCLE-Pennsylvania Library Association program on Technological and Social Change, Human Values, and the Library; Alan Trachtenberg, assistant professor of English and CCLE staff associate (1963-64); Stephen Knox and John Low, graduate assistants in English and CCLE staff assistants; Richard Bunnell, Continuing Education Services, and coordinator of the December, 1963, CCLE Humanities Conference and the June, 1964, Humanities Seminar; and last, but by no means least, my wife, Ethel.

As for the preparation of this volume, the creative contributions of the editors, William W. Brickman and Stanley Lehrer, are so obvious as to render explicit acknowledgement almost superfluous. The idea for this particular volume was theirs; theirs has been the role of selecting and pruning; theirs has been the drive needed to meet imminent deadlines without sacrifice of scope or quality.

Acknowledgments

DESPITE what some people think, the acknowledgment section of a book is not always a joy to write because it is a challenge to a writer's ability to express his appreciation adequately to everyone who has helped in the preparation of the volume. Nevertheless, the editors of this book will make an attempt to record their appreciation. After all, in the words of Samuel Johnson, "gratitude is a fruit of great cultivation" and was regarded by Aesop as "the sign of noble souls."

The following contributors deserve all the credit for creating the substance of this book:

GEORGE E. ARNSTEIN, Associate Director, Project on Educational Implications of Automation, National Education Association

EMERY F. BACON, Director, Department of Education, United Steelworkers of America, Pittsburgh, Pa.

JOHN W. BALL, President, Resources Development Corporation, East Lansing, Mich.

ARNOLD B. BARACH, Senior Editor, Changing Times

MYRON B. BLOY, JR., Chaplain, Massachusetts Institute of Technology

CHARLES R. BOWEN, Manager, Educational Projects, IBM Corporation

27

ROY C. BUCK, Associate Director for Social Sciences, Center for Continuing Liberal Education, and Professor of Social Sciences and Rural Sociology, The Pennsylvania State University

RALPH WENDELL BURHOE, Professor and Chairman, Theology and the Frontiers of Learning, Meadville Theological School of Lombard College, affiliated with the University of Chicago

ANTHONY J. CELEBREZZE, Federal Judge, U.S. Court of Appeals for the Sixth Circuit, Cincinnati, Ohio; former Secretary of Health, Education, and Welfare

ALBERT J. CROFT, Vice President, Training, Resources Development Corporation, East Lansing, Mich.

WALTER L. DAVIS, Area Director, Committee on Political Education, AFL-CIO

G. BRUCE DEARING, President, State University of New York at Binghamton

JAMES A. DONOVAN, JR., Staff Director, United States Advisory Commission on International Educational and Cultural Affairs, Washington, D. C.

LUTHER H. EVANS, Director of International and Legal Collections, Columbia University

MAXWELL H. GOLDBERG, Associate Director for Humanities, Center for Continuing Liberal Education, and Professor of Humanities, The Pennsylvania State University

DALE B. HARRIS, Professor and Head, Department of Psychology, The Pennsylvania State University

LUTHER H. HARSHBARGER, Professor of Humanities and Religious Studies and Head, Department of Religious Studies, College of the Liberal Arts, The Pennsylvania State University

AUGUST HECKSCHER, Director, The Twentieth Century Fund

HUBERT H. HUMPHREY, The Vice President of the United States

FRANCIS KEPPEL, U. S. Commissioner of Education

NORMAN D. KURLAND, Director, Center on Innovation in Education, New York State Education Department

DONALD J. LLOYD, Editor, Program Press Division, Resources Development Corporation, East Lansing, Mich.

JOHN MacIVER, Assistant Medical Director, United States Steel Corporation, Pittsburgh, Pa.

WILLIAM G. MATHER, Research Professor of Sociology, The Pennsylvania State University

MARGARET MEAD, *Curator of Ethnology, American Museum of Natural History, New York City*

DONALD N. MICHAEL, *Resident Fellow, Institute for Policy Studies, Washington, D. C.*

C. M. D. PETERS, *Assistant Manager, Shell Oil Company, New York City*

STANLEY FOSTER REED, *President, The Reed Research Institute for Creative Studies, and Chairman of the Board and President, Technology Audit Corporation, Washington, D. C.*

WARNER G. RICE, *Chairman, Department of English Language and Literature, University of Michigan*

VIRGIL M. ROGERS, *Director, Project on Educational Implications of Automation, National Education Association*

PETER E. SIEGLE, *Staff Associate, Center for the Study of Liberal Education for Adults, Boston University*

LAWRENCE K. WILLIAMS, *Associate Professor, New York State School of Industrial and Labor Relations, Cornell University*

Various sources were consulted and many viewpoints, conditioned by professional experiences and/or observations, were expressed before this book became a reality. The contributors did their tasks well.

To Maxwell H. Goldberg, more than any other single person, belongs the editors' gratitude for making the book possible. Dr. Goldberg is the 19th and 20th century all in one—a literary fireball whose sparks as a classical scholar light up the corners of men's minds and keep alive the humanistic spirit of years gone by. To know Dr. Goldberg is to touch the rampart of humanism in a world overwhelmed—but not yet completely subjugated—by technology. The editors are indebted to him for his untiring help in the preparation of this book. His voluminous letters and personal discussions with the editors offered invaluable suggestions on improving the book's contents. He has the distinction of laying the basic groundwork for this book as a result of the humanities conference and seminar on technological change, education, and human values which he directed as part of the Humanities Project of the Center for Continuing Liberal Education, The Pennsylvania State University. Dr. Goldberg's unselfish, enthusiastic devotion to the editors, offering them any assistance required, is a credit to his sincerity as a scholar in an age of mass indifference.

The editors also are grateful to the Center for Continuing Liberal Education and its staff for handling much of the correspondence to and from contributors, especially during the crucial revision of certain manuscripts, and for gaining clearances for publication of quotations and other material.

The editors wish to thank Robert S. Rothenberg of the Society for the Advancement of Education for his work on the index and for his excellent assistance in checking proof, particularly his adeptness in spotting typographical errors occasionally overlooked even by those closest to the writing—the contributors.

Mrs. Nancy Schneider was kind enough to devote her artistic ability to illustrating the end papers of the book. Her illustration was previewed on the cover of the Oct. 31, 1964, issue of *School and Society*.

Frequently consulted was this writer's wife, Laurel, whenever questions arose concerning the simplification of involved sentences. Her greatest help came in the form of encouragement during those occasional moments when the book seemed to be progressing too slowly, and she obligingly served meals at ungodly hours when the creative process required an irregular schedule.

STANLEY LEHRER

New Hyde Park, N. Y.
August, 1965

AUTOMATION,
EDUCATION,
AND
HUMAN VALUES

The greatest task before civilization at present is to make machines what they ought to be, the slaves, instead of the masters of men.

—HAVELOCK ELLIS (1859-1939)

Part I

OUTLOOK

I. MAN, AUTOMATION, AND DIGNITY

STANLEY LEHRER

MAN, the precocious Earth creature with the restive impulse to seek the Good Life, awoke from the slumber of the Stone Age and, through the vision of his creative genius, fashioned his destiny out of the vigor of the Iron Age, the inspiration and guidance of God's Commandments, the cultural enthusiasm of the Renaissance, the power of steam and electricity, the mass productivity of the Industrial Revolution, the strength of labor unions, the explosive promise of the Nuclear Age, and the silence and mystery of outer space. In his miracle world of blinking computers and electronic work-saving gadgetry, after centuries of creativity, the highest form of life found what he was looking for in the lowest form of activity—indolence.

But was idleness the great dream of man, the reward for his technological inventiveness, or a nightmarish exile from usefulness in the name of Progress? Certainly, the impetuous spirit of man in anxious pursuit of happiness will not find fruition in an unproductive way of life.

Between the dawn of man's potentialities and the sunset of his individual usefulness in the technological world of the electronic brain, man created the means for bettering his life with time to enjoy it. Work and leisure became the traditional pattern of life in that social phenomenon—civilization. As Benjamin Disraeli reasoned in 1872, "Increased means and increased leisure are the two civilizers of man." What the Earl of Beaconsfield did not envision, of course, was the leisure-time explosion to be touched off nearly 100 years later by automation. The mass production of labor-saving devices made the Better Life the Easy Life. Yet, the gradual replacement of man by machine was a blow to his pride and left him with excess leisure to bemoan his fate.

But man's desire to pursue progress was as intense as his impulse to pursue happiness, so he could not remain idle and be content without a purpose for living. Man now marches on to his greatest glory, creating more mechanical marvels to do his work and leaving himself one vital function to perform—to push buttons to prepare his meals, to switch television channels, to shift the gears of his car, to activate teaching machines, and to conduct other similarly strenuous activities of the Easy Life.

Many believe that a push-button world would be a good thing. But with its inevitable elimination of human purposefulness and pride of accomplishment, it might not be the best of all possible worlds. Unquestionably, education holds the answer to a better life where man is master of automation and not mastered by it. Just as education equipped man for the challenge of the race for space, education will help man to meet the challenge of leisure.

Man must awaken from his dream world and initiate effective planning for the Age of Automation over whose threshold he already has crossed. As the shorter working day creates more and more leisure time, man will think more and more about continuing his education, developing new skills, and retraining to channel his inherent abilities. By preparing for automation as early as possible, rather than surrendering to it and compromising the human spirit, man stands on the brink of a new and fuller life with dignity.

2. WHEN MEN AND MACHINES WORK TOGETHER

WILLIAM G. MATHER

THERE USED TO BE a clever little quip to the effect that automation consists of making a man's work so simple that a woman can do it. With several thousand elevator operators out of work in New York City—and replaced not by women but by tin boxes in the attic —it somehow does not seem very funny any more. We might as well face it; the first move toward automation, the use of machines, was for the purpose of reducing the need for human labor, thereby reducing the cost of production. When men and machines work together, fewer men are needed per unit of output. It is still an important motive.

Time (Oct. 5, 1962) carried a story of the growth of the ship building industry in Sweden against terrific competition from Japan, Britain, and West Germany, a competition met by raising the hourly wage and slashing the daily number of workers. It was with the approval of the shipyard workers' union. The not-so-secret method is an assembly-line shipyard, with steel ships moving stern first down the ways in 45-foot sections, everything from deck plates to cabin carpets installed en route, and 40,000 ton tankers being floated, not in 40 weeks but 20.

This always has been true, this saving of human labor by the use of machines. Even when the machine was merely a chipped stone, held in the hand, it skinned the hide from an animal faster and easier than the prehistoric fingernail. Man, even very early man, has been a rather frail creature when stripped to the buff and pitted against the other animals. The horse can run faster, the tiger can scratch deeper, the fish can swim longer, the bird can fly higher. But by using his clever brain to devise machines, and his remarkably generalized and dexterous hands to make the machines, man can do all of those things better than any of the animals.

It is rather important that we recognize that the use of machines, especially the increasing use of machines, is an essentially *human* characteristic. It is found wherever men are found—simple machines in the case of the "simpler" men, and much more complex and self-operating machines in the case of industrialized men.

AUTOMATION AFFECTS ALL ECONOMIC AREAS

We tend to see the increasing use of machines exclusively as a feature of modern manufacturing, but that is not the case. It is found in all endeavors of life—even the modern kitchen stove that is programmed to turn itself on at a certain hour, heat to a certain temperature, maintain the heat for a certain time, and then reduce the heat and hold the cooked food at a steady warmth until the housewife comes and removes it. If the delay is too long, it even may ring a bell and summon her—gently at first, and then with an angry clangor. Even the woman works with machines.

But not so well known is it that modern *farming* is an increasingly mechanized process. Farm output per man-hour between 1947 and 1959 increased nearly 100%, while non-farm productivity increased only 36.5%.[1] In consequence, at the time when more food has been produced than ever before, to the extent that our surplus storage bins are bursting, the number of farmers and farmworkers are declining not only in percentage of the working force, but in actual numbers. The farm worker displaced by the machine milker, the machine feeder, the machine barn cleaner, the machine tiller, the machine harvester, and the machine processer leans against the porch of the small-town store along with the strip mine worker displaced by the electric shovel.

This has happened before, and we have survived. It has been tough on a few, but generally our population grew and our frontiers

[1] A. R. Mangus and J. B. Mitchell, "Our Farm Labor Force—Where Is It Going?" *Better Farming Methods*, September, 1962, p. 12.

expanded, the economy as a whole thrived, and displaced workers either found other and new jobs or starved quietly without fuss.

What we face that is new about automation today is that it strikes all segments of industry at once, and very swiftly, with such impact that there is no time to sweep it under the rug. Neil W. Chamberlain, professor of economics at Yale, quotes an estimate that 200,000 persons a year will lose their jobs for the next decade.[2] This is too large a number to leave to chance, hoping that "something will turn up." For these displaced will not be young, would-be workers for whom unemployment will mean only a disappointing prolongation of a period of loafing before accepting responsibilities of wife, children, and citizenship; these will be people who already have such responsibilities. These lost jobs will not be the result of temporary lay-offs for a few months until that line of work picks up again; these will be jobs that are gone permanently, that will not reappear no matter what happens to the rest of the economy, and that will take with them the livelihood of families.

THE UNSKILLED AND AUTOMATION

Automation probably has had its greatest effect on the unskilled, the hand laborers whose only marketable assets are strong backs and willing minds. Machines that do the heavy digging and lifting already have taken their places, at least on the big jobs. Some more may be displaced by small machines for small jobs, as powered garden tools have replaced hand spading and raking; but the U. S. Bureau of Labor Statistics[3] estimates that during the remaining years of the present decade, aside from a loss of 15% more of the farmers and farm workers, the need for unskilled non-farm labor will hold at about the same number it is now, in spite of the population growth of 28,000,000 people.

The problem here will come mainly with the children of the unskilled. The families of unskilled workers tend to be much larger than those of skilled workers. The old adage is in general true, that "the rich get richer and the poor get children." It is also true that the children of the poor do not receive much encouragement to stay in school and to learn a trade, so that, even if unskilled jobs remain

---

[2] Neil W. Chamberlain, "Job Obsolescence—Challenge and Opportunity." Address, Illinois Chamber of Commerce, October, 1962, Chicago.

[3] "Manpower, Challenge of the 1960's" (Washington: U. S. Department of Labor, 1961).

steady as they are, we will have more workers of this class than we need. The alternative, aside from population reduction by war, would appear to be a radically revised and expanded school system that will move the unskilled workers' children up and out of the unskilled group. If local school districts cannot do this, state and Federal powers must intervene, for we cannot afford the irresponsible flooding of the labor market with unfit citizens any longer. A real emergency exists in that automation is getting into its stride just as the biggest baby crop of all time hits our high schools and colleges.

THE SKILLED AND AUTOMATION

Education of the unskilled to make them skilled has its pitfalls, however, because in the immediate future it is precisely some of the skilled jobs which automation is going to strike with the greatest force. The first to go already have been plainly marked—the man whose only skill is that of "operative"—that is, tender of an individual machine that does one or two simple operations on a part of a product. Automated, fully programmed machines already are making complete products and even inspecting them—light bulbs, Christmas tree ornaments, printed circuits, for example, and in the heavy industry we have automated sheet steel rolling and wire mills and petroleum refineries. Here, however, some of the displaced jobs will be replaced by jobs of still higher skill that will work with the much larger, more complex, and vastly more expensive machines. These jobs will be fewer in number but better paid, commensurate with training and responsibility, for a mistake here really will cost money. As automation spreads from industry to industry, human dislocations will come. Some can be retrained for the new kind of skill; but some will find the pressure of the accompanying responsibility too great to stand and break under the strain. Machines of this type are monumental, fast, relentless, superbly accurate, and precise when running well; they do not get nerves, they do not count the hours or the holidays, and it is sometimes cheaper to keep them going than to stop them and start them again. Three shifts will be commonplace. And always, when they require attention, the needs of the machine must be met instantly, skillfully, and adequately. Pay may well be tied inversely to the amount of "down time." When men and machines of that kind work together, human flesh will be put to a severe test.

As these are in the unionized industries, labor unions and management will have some interesting new experiences. I look for more joint planning and consultation, more cooperation, more profit-sharing, more job security, and expanded fringe benefits. There also will be more on-the-job retraining and up-grading, for today's skills, whatever they may be, in 10 years may be obsolete. It will not be enough for an industry to hire a bright high school graduate; it will need to provide for his *continuing* training.

CLERICAL, SALES, AND SERVICE TRADES

There has been a trend for some time away from the "production" industries, which now, as a group, employ 26,000,000, and toward the "service" industries, which now employ 32,500,000. The production industries are manufacturing, agriculture, construction, and mining; the service industries are trade, government, transportation, public utilities, finance, insurance, and real estate. This reflects the fact that we are getting to be well supplied with *things* but are asking for more mobility, more security, more travel and exchange of goods, more government control, and even more hair cuts, beauty parlor treatments, and recreation. We could predict that this trend will continue, as it is the most conspicuous part of the affluent society; we are becoming less concerned about food and shelter and more concerned about being, or living.

But automation will come here also, with the usual displacement of jobs. Television can be regarded as automated recreation, as can the juke box and the high fidelity set; but our appetite for these things is so great that as yet their spread has increased jobs in general, in the sale and service of equipment, the making and distribution of records and tapes, and other things of that kind. The location and reservation of space on trains and airplanes is becoming automated, with speed as the motive, but here again lost jobs are presently countered by more positions in travel bureaus and airports.

The spread of automatic telephone dialing would have displaced operators, but the consequent increase in number of phone calls seems to have created enough new work to make up for that. It will bear watching, however. For one thing, travellers and talkers are beginning to complain, of all things, about the psychological effect of all this speed. One reaches his party in San Diego from Harrisburg before he has had time to phrase what he has to say properly, and, in consequence, long-distance conversations often are carried on at a pretty inefficient level. The man who travels much has occasions, usually around daybreak, when he has difficulty identifying himself, his location, and the reason for his being there—and this without alcohol as the confusing agent. These things we may become accustomed to, but for the interim some of us have a feeling that our bodies are moving too fast for our souls to keep up.

The automatic or semi-automatic supermarket and self-service establishments will have their effect also. Eventually, they may reduce the over-all total of employed; but right now their rapid spread seems to have more effect on the pocketbooks of their clients. Their open and colorful layout of good things is a great temptation to the customer to buy; he usually goes in for a loaf of bread and a head of lettuce but comes out with green cheese, tomatoes out of season, calves brains, pickled onions, and a drip-dry shirt. We can look for a growing sales resistance, perhaps to the point of cynicism, to advertising and other public information releases, unless we become a nation of sheep and meekly follow the well-modulated advice of four out of five New York doctors or, better still, unless advertising develops more dependable and visible ethics than it seems inclined to now.

The increasing use of self-service methods of selling, when applied to the teen-age market, does put great strain upon the not-well-organized conscience of the adolescent. A lot of goods are spread out within easy reach of youthful customers, who as a rule do not have a corresponding lot of money. Even those who are well supplied may shoplift for the fun of it or because they feel they will be gypped by low quality if they should buy. It is a problem to determine where the blame lies, but communities should give the whole emerging system a long, hard look. They might properly ask: If great steel, electrical, milling and brokerage firms break the laws, should they complain if their customers do?

One interesting feature of automation in this general field is the development of the automatic, coin-in-slot washing and dry cleaning stores. It has been observed that certain people habitually take their clothes to these cleaning machines at certain times each week, and a deal of gossip and socializing goes on among the members of these informal groups. It is remindful of the groups of peasant women at the river bank or the village well, and it may serve the same purpose of neighboring, much needed to offset the growing impersonality of our culture.

THE MANAGERIAL, PROFESSIONAL, AND TECHNICAL LEVELS

It is difficult to classify some of the new jobs that automation will bring. Take the rapid spread of computers, for example. These machines can perform arithmetical computations of truly awesome size in a few moments—and do them more accurately—that would take a clerk years to perform even with an electric adding machine. But they are not really very bright. They have to be told what to do, at every step, by a series of orders given in the language of that particular kind of computer. The language can be punched holes on a card, or punched holes on a ribbon of tape, or printed as symbols quite like the usual letters of the alphabet. But it has to be accurate and precise. One remembers the spoiling of one of our space probes by the omission of a hyphen from the set of instructions given to the controlling mechanism. To a computer, a hyphen is not just a little bar separating two parts of a word; it is an order for a complex maneuver. The people who talk with computers, who give them their instructions, are known as "programmers." Their skills are narrow but very important, requiring a most orderly mind and close concentration. It is mental, not manual, dexterity. Are the programmers skilled labor or are they clerks? They are neither, but their hourly wages are higher than most skilled labor, and they do what clerks used to do. The term "technician" is as good a title as any. They are not managers; they boss only the machines. They are not professionals; they do not have trained, free judgment like that of the doctor, the lawyer, the college professor. The professional, the manager, will make the judgment on a basis of the factual data served up to him by the machine.

There is some evidence that some programmers, after a few years, become dissatisfied with being interpreters between professionals and machines and go back to school to learn the "what" and "why" of the things they have been doing; the "how" has become a bore.

It is worth noting what this teaming of man and computer means to us. To begin with, the computer has value only in that it can run through a tremendous number of facts, arrange them as instructed, and present to the real decision-maker a set of figures to help him make this decision. For example, at the Agricultural College of the Pennsylvania State University a computer has been used successfully for several years to figure what grains, at prevailing prices, should be bought in what amounts to make the cheapest mixture that will give a herd of cows the proper amount of carbohydrates, proteins, fats, and the like that it needs to have for producing the optimum amount of milk at the present prices for milk of a certain butterfat content. But it does not make the farmer do it. Maybe, after he reads the results of the computer's work, he says to himself, "John needs money bad for his wife's operation, and I think I'll buy his corn rather than ship in soybeans from Ohio; it won't cost me much more." Now, is that farmer doing right or wrong, ethically and morally? Even if we could program such a kind of decision into the machine, would it be fair to the farmer to deprive him of the need for making it himself?

One trouble with computers is that they have no ethics, no morals. They are pure materialists. But life is worth more than food, and the body more than clothing.[4] Managers and professionals always must be able to see the people behind the figures. Edmund Berkeley has referred to this partnership of man and computer as "thinking without thought" and suggests that it also may be thinking without social responsibility.[5] Arthur B. Watson, president, I.B.M. World Trade Corporation, largest of the computer distributors, has asked, "When the big computer systems come, will there be room for dynamism, for imagination, for creativity and for human trust in business?" and urged his hearers to make sure that this coming new age is "a good age to live in."[6]

There may be some real significance to the joy with which Walter Schirra, Jr., reported, after his six-orbit flight in space, that for a time he had turned off the automatic control to prove that "it was my capsule" and he could maneuver it at his will.

For the executive, automation presents serious problems. They are matters of plant reorganization and of decision-making.

Automated plants require a different system of division of labor than do the traditional plants. For example, the on-the-job managerial function shifts its center from the plant floor to the main office. The Boeing Aero-Space Division plant in Seattle, Wash., has installed a system whereby each floor worker carries a punch-card both as an identification badge and as a sort of time card.[7] Each time an employee starts a new task, he runs his card through a small

---

[4] Matthew, 5: 25 (Revised Standard Version).

[5] Edmund C. Berkeley, "The Computer Revolution" (New York: Doubleday, 1962).

[6] Talk, 8th Congress of Accountants, New York City, Sept. 24, 1962 *(New York Times)*.

[7] *New York Times*, Nov. 4, 1962, sect. F, p. 1.

machine on the working floor. This reports at once, on tape in the office, that he is busy on this task. When finished, he does it again and the report is given that he is now free for another assignment. By this means, "the office" can know in a few seconds where each employee is and what he is doing. This makes for precise cost accounting and increased efficiency in the use of manpower skills. But it makes a change in the foreman's role because it by-passes him, and it tempts the manager to spend too much time checking on details he should delegate to someone else. (There is something a bit disturbing about this; it would be a very handy system for citizen control in a totalitarian state.)

The net effect of all the mechanization of work, communication, and control is, for management, not a decrease in the number of decisions to be made, but an *increase*. More details are ready for the manager in a shorter time than ever before. Therefore, he is forced to make his response quicker than before. He will have little time for putting his feet on the desk—a healthful change of posture—and for leisurely digestion of facts and slow but sure weighing of the possible alternatives and their consequences. The *New York Times* (Nov. 4, 1962) carried an advertisement for program analysts, systems implementation engineers, and information engineers for work upon a remarkable new machine. Development already has started. Its purpose was "to inform the military commander" in the Strategic Air Command.

In order to further multiply the effectiveness of the Military Commander, faced with the crucial task of assimilating vast quantities of information projected on the screens in front of him, ITT engineers have recently added a remarkable new capability to 465-L: data presentation in color. . . . Operating at speeds that appeared incredible only a short time ago, the system enables computer outputs to be converted to alpha-numeric form. . . . photographed . . . developed and projected on control-center screens in as many as seven colors in a matter of seconds. . . . This new capability opens up a whole new field of data format techniques to be explored. An obvious and immediate value is the enhancement of human perception through color changes denoting different degrees of situation criticality.[8]

If this should become the pattern for all administrators, it would be tragic. Decision-making under such conditions is not only dictatorial in the extreme, but must take place at such speed as to be not reflective, but reflexive. The machine might as well do it itself. But before that looks attractive, one should remember Oct. 5, 1960, when the Thule Early Warning System interpreted the moon as a missile flight toward America. Only Air Marshall Slemon's refusal to flap saved civilization then.

---

[8] *New York Times*, Nov. 4, 1962, sect. F, p. 17.

It is somewhat reassuring to know that about two weeks following
the *Times* advertisement for personnel to work on the seven-color
job, Brockway McMillan, an Assistant Secretary of the Air Force,
warned a Hot Springs electronic systems conference that electronic
systems for command and control were intended "to support the
commander, not to supplant him." "Above all," said he, "let us not
design too much into our systems."[9]

FEARFUL LEISURE

When we began the consideration of the effects of teamwork between men and machines, we spoke of the displacement of human
labor by mechanical labor. To the degree this takes the strain from
human arms and backs, it is good. If a heavy job, or a monotonous
and repetitive job, can be done by machines as well as or better than
by man or woman, let the machines have it. Theoretically, the result
should give man more time to grow roses or go fishing.

To some extent, this is happening and can be expected to increase. The standard work week since 1850 has dropped from 70
hours to 39 hours. This includes part-time workers, however, but
when these are removed we still have a true standard work week of
46 or 47 hours, and a gain of about 25 hours of "free time." Coupled
with this is a large increase in expenditures for bowling balls, golf
clubs, swim fins, skis, motorboats, and vacation travel. This is an
opportunity that the machine has helped to give man.

But we run into a clash of values here. We have operated on the
theory that work is good—good in itself and for itself, that is, in
contrast to non-work, which is not good but instead is thriftless and
evidence of laziness. We have the parable of the ant and the grass-
hopper and the proverb that Satan finds mischief for idle hands. We
compliment a person by saying he is hard-working, and we arrest
people for having "no visible means of support." Is it "good" to
have so much free time?

Apparently, some think it is not good. At least 3,750,000 American
workers have more than one job[10] and are known as "moonlighters."
Their financial or other needs are such that they take a second job
rather than a rest. Of those who have only one regular job, the 25
hours of "free time" rapidly disappears. An average of 8½ hours
is spent going to and from work; five hours in mowing the lawn,

[9] *New York Times,* Nov. 20, 1962.
[10] Ewan Clague, "Demographic Trends and Their Significance," in H. S.
Simpson, editor, "The Changing American Population" (New York: Institute of
Life Insurance, 1962), p. 73.

painting the house, tending the garden; and two hours in washing dishes, shopping, and the like, leaving only 10 hours as the net gain over the year 1850 for doing anything one wants to do, not something that has to be done. This, says Sebastian de Grazia, is pure leisure, "a state of being, a condition of man, which few desire and fewer achieve."[11] De Grazia calls attention to the fact that this leisure was regarded by the ancient Greeks as "the brightest of all activities, the single one in which man was revealed as related to the gods, and in the exercise of which he celebrated the gods. Politics and religion were at the heart of leisure."

David Sarnoff is almost equally poetic when he writes that ". . . the machine in the year 2000 will still be the servant of man. The real promise of technology is that it will release man from routine drudgeries of mind and body and will remove the final imprint of the cave. . . . Man's mind will then be free for the creative thinking that must be done if the impact of science is to be harmonized with man's enduring spiritual, social, and political needs."[12]

That has an appealing sweetness. But it overlooks the obvious fact that the average man at the present time is little interested in being given such freedom. We are not only inured to, we are absorbed in, the beloved drudgery of the daily struggle for bread. Curse it we may, but when the factory whistle blows in the morning for others than us, we do not respond with a whoop of joyful derision; we whimper that we are still as good as we ever were and beg to be taken back for one more year. Our society has prepared us for work, not for leisure—and least of all, not for constructive leisure, for anything beyond beer, bowling, and boating. To be released suddenly from routine drudgeries is an apalling thing to happen to a man who has learned to master his job but not himself.

EDUCATION FOR LEISURE

"Education for leisure" is too easy an answer. To begin with, what would be the response to any request (for such a purpose) to taxpayers in any American community, struggling under the burden of keeping its flood of children simply dammed up out of mischief for six hours a day? The problem is far deeper.

Because of the need for skills to build our country, we have

[11] Sebastian de Grazia and August Heckscher, "Of Time, Work and Leisure" (New York: Twentieth Century Fund, 1962).
[12] David Sarnoff, "By the End of the Twentieth Century," *Fortune*, May, 1964, p. 116.

viewed education as preparation for a job. Parents send their young
to schools, at all levels of education, to acquire a skill with which to
earn money. They are resentful of spending money for any purpose
other than for education, and they measure the success of the process
by the average beginning salary of the senior class. If it is high, they
are pleased, for the future of their offspring is secure. They believe
this delusion even though grandfather was a blacksmith and father
is an unemployed coal miner.

We now must accept the fact that modern technology greatly will
accelerate the obsolescence of skills and cease to make their teaching
the main end of education. Skills in the future will be taught *on*
the job and retaught continuously through the span of a worker's
employment. (M. I. T. is already in a program for such retraining
of mid-career engineers.[13]) One never again will be said to have "finished school."

What schools will teach will be the great basic facts (so far as
known) about the world, the universe, man, and his life on earth
among his fellows—the physical and biological sciences, mathematics,
the social sciences, including anthropology, the humanities, and arts
as means of expression and communication—not as "pre-medical,"
or "pre-social work," or "pre-engineering," but as a means of learning
the nature of man and his worlds. A student should leave school, if
he likes especially the "life sciences," not a laboratory technician, but
a biologist—and not just a biologist, but rather a person who has entered the temple of knowledge through a particular door, which,
after all, is only a door.

With such a base, the learning of techniques and skills, the keeping of them alive and useful, and the transfer from one skill to
another will be relatively easy. But the teaching of the skill never
again must be confused with education.[14]

TECHNOLOGY AND THE MASS SOCIETY

Technology often is accused, and I think justly, of being the
breeder of conformity, and social scientists have come to regard
with apprehension a coming "mass society"—if it has not already
arrived. Without doubt, the first impacts of the automobile, the
radio and television, the large-circulation magazines, and the great
corporations have been in that direction. This may have been due

---

[13] *New York Times,* May 10, 1964, sect. F, p. 1.
[14] Frederick Harbison and Charles A. Myers, "Education, Manpower, and
Economic Growth" (New York: McGraw-Hill, 1964).

more to their use than to their nature, for the same mass media that propagandize also can be used to educate and to present issues for discussion. The experience of closed-circuit television instruction, where the classrooms are wired for student interruption of the instructor for questions, as at the Pennsylvania State University, has established that mass media communication does not necessarily have to be one-way. The development of electronic recording and tabulating of votes already has made the once-necessary "electoral college" system of determining the national choice of an American president a mere ritual genuflection to the days when "express" meant a string of fast ponies. There is only one reason why, by such means, the public cannot discuss and decide great issues by 21st-century town meetings.

The one reason is our distrust of submitting vital questions to an uninformed and gullible public. It has been a well-founded distrust because, in parts of the country, there is no tolerance of dissent, full participation in citizenship has been restricted to a few, and real education has been rare. But we are looking to the future, when technology will have given us the need for a broader, more "liberal" education, and the money and time for acquiring it. To the future, when our major education will be for living and only our training will be for work. To the future, when our work will not run us down and exhaust us so that we do not, as now, have time and strength beyond the immediate weariness, the immediate hunger, the immediate confusion. To the future, when we will have the time and the means and the inner resources to communicate with and understand our fellows and become intelligent and responsible citizens.

We will have problems still with us, but they will be different problems, dealing with a different set of values. As an example, waste-disposal for a city or an industrial plant will not be approached from the point of view of, "How can we get rid of this stuff the cheapest and quickest?" but, "How can we get rid of this stuff the cheapest and quickest without poisoning the air about us or hurting the people down stream?" Because then we will know the people downstream as people and, in all probability, as fellow members of our own expanded community.

This will have some implication for municipal government and political science, for economics and business, but underlying all of these will be new developments in ethics and religion. That sort of thinking, on national and international scales, can lead to a very different world.

3. CHANGING TECHNOLOGY AND CHANGING CULTURE

ARNOLD B. BARACH

THE COUNTRY is in the midst of one of its great periods of transition and churning change. Nothing quite comparable to it has occurred since the heroic forward movements of the last century when the frontier was conquered, the Industrial Revolution was brought to full flower, and the millions of immigrants from Europe were absorbed in a welcoming land.

Then the ingredients of growth were physical expansion, technological advance, and a bursting population. Today the stimulants of change are not much different. Only this time the frontiers are those of outer space and the atom, the technology is in such unfamiliar disciplines as solid state physics and micromodular electronics, and the population growth results from greater longevity and the upward trend in births.

Together, they create an excitement about the future that is part rational expectancy and part pure fantasy. Many Americans are prone to find escape from present problems and frustrations in happy speculation on the changes ahead. It is a pleasant exercise, for it tends to accent the promises while obscuring the problems. In some circles it is fashionable to pooh-pooh present difficulties with assurances that the brave, new tomorrow will take care of everything.

There is no certainty that it will. But what is crystal clear is that the country we live in a decade or so hence will be in many respects as strange and different as the rapidly receding decade of the '40's is from the present. When World War II ended, television was a controversial infant, atomic energy a hazy promise, polio vaccines a laboratory idea, split rambler a California oddity, transistor radios a speculative possibility, and modern supermarkets strictly a blue-print concept.

In that half-remembered period, the school crisis was just in an embryonic stage. Suburbia and all its accompanying problems were not yet a matter of national import. People looked forward to a cut in taxes and reduction in the national budget. As for putting a man into orbit, the idea was simply preposterous.

Progress since then has been at breakneck speed—far too fast for those with a nostalgic feeling for the more relaxed pace of yore. And there are no signs that it will slow down. If anything, the tempo of change will increase as tomorrow unfolds.

The psychological setting, if it can be called that, already has been established. Nothing in the past has excited the public imagination as much as the advances in rocketry and space exploration. Almost as provocative but now eclipsed by the drama of rocket launchings is the probing of the atom's secrets. These two together persuade people that almost anything is possible and likely. If man can land on the moon or launch a ship powered by atomic fission, then what can he not do? It is a question that can be challenging or disturbing, depending on where one sits.

Given this mood, it is possible to concoct a whole never-never land of incredible feats—from transport to Mars to prolongation of life to double the Biblical three score and 10. As of now, however, these are more in the province of the science-fiction creator than the practical visionary. A more down-to-earth appraisal has to be limited to what is possible or even probable in the foreseeable future.

The outlines of what is to come already are well defined. Present trends foreshadow future events, and that is true whether one is concerned with the nation's population or traffic snarls in metropolis. Much of what follows has its roots in these trends and is simply the logical fulfillment of what now is taking place.

In 1961, I attempted a projection of tomorrow* based on what were then the apparent directions of the national course in such a diversity of areas as population, transportation, technology, communications, medicine, education, living standards, and the like. The

---

* Arnold B. Barach, "1975 and the Changes to Come" (New York: Harper & Row, 1961).

take-off point was approximately 1960; the target date was 1975. This choice was not as arbitrary as it seems. It was selected deliberately for two reasons: first, to embrace for as many readers as possible the remembered past and the anticipated future; and, second, as a device to see where the nation had come since the end of World War II and where it was likely to be at a time equidistant in the future from the half-way year of 1960.

A re-examination of this particular projection demonstrates the fallibility of being a seer in a period of history when change proceeds at such a dazzling pace as to make even the most heady optimist seem conservative in his tenets. Now, only about four years after the original effort, it can be demonstrated that many of those projections were inhibited by a refusal to acknowledge the speed at which transition occurs. Some of the developments expected in the next decade are already at hand. Much of the technology foreseen for the future is so close to fulfillment that it is no longer a part of the '70's but, instead, very much an ingredient of the '60's. In the area of science and advanced technical progress, in particular, there has been a speed-up of development. The year 1964 seems to be the one when the real breakout to the world of tomorrow was ready to ripen. In retrospect, 1964 may be the year when the nation first became aware of where its "Third Revolution" was leading it.

The speed of technological progress is one measurement of the advance into the 1970's. The other is the confrontation of problems— social and economic in nature—which in many respects are the product of the revolutionary upheavals in our domestic scene. Here, again, 1964 ultimately may be viewed as the year when, for the first time, the solid impact of such problems as automation, unemployed youth, inadequate education, shifting population mix, poverty amid plenty, and reappraisal of old values really was felt. Until then, there had been an acknowledgement of them. But only then did the urgent need for their solution take its place with other major issues of our times.

CHANGES IN POPULATION

What about this nation that we are to become? The place to begin is with the population—the people. And here the projections can be firm and consistent, since the patterns of population growth are well-defined and directed to easily predictable goals.

By 1975, this nation—now less than 6,000,000 shy of 200,000,000 —probably will total 235,000,000 people, give or take a few million.

It will be a country in which the young predominate, with more than half the population this side of 26. One of the more significant changes—and most hopeful from a business point of view—will be the rapid increase among those in the 25 to 34 segment of the population. There will be about 40% more people in the 25-34 segment in 1975 than in 1965, and since these form the acquisitive group—the group involved in buying everything from houses to diaper services—they inevitably will represent an economic stimulant to business and to the country.

Coincident with the increase of young people, there will be a considerable expansion of that part of the population over 65. More than 22,000,000 Americans will find themselves in this category of the retired citizen, or the semi-retired. Will they be geriatric problems? Or will they represent an expanding market for the promoters of retirement communities? Both, probably, depending on their resources, their health, and their economic status.

No examination of the population of the 1970's can ignore the fact that from the big birth waves of the 1940's will emerge a whole new generation of marrying and multiplying Americans. By 1975, the annual number of marriages will approximate 2,000,000, with all this implies for housing, community development, and family formation. And, in the natural course of events, another baby boom will ensue from this marriage boom. Conservatively speaking, instead of the current 4,000,000 or more babies being born a year, the 1975 count is likely to be up over the 5,000,000 level.

What all this means is that by 1975 the nation's households will number approximately 67,000,000. In only 10 years, family growth in this country will take a sharp and unprecedented step upward.

PROSPEROUS NATION

Qualified by the usual conditions of no war, no national disasters, and no devastating economic debacle, it can be stated confidently that Americans a decade or so hence will be much better off, materially, than they ever imagined themselves to be. A report by the Twentieth Century Fund—in which I had a hand—concludes that disposable personal income, which came to $376,000,000,000 in 1962, will be $626,000,000,000 in 1975. Those are 1960 dollars; the inflation factor has been discounted. When this figure is reduced to the amount to be made available for the average family unit in 1975, it comes to $9,525 per family, compared to 1962's $7,011. By 1975, it is estimated that about two out of every five families will have a $10,000 annual income, figured in 1960 dollars.

The source of this impressive upgrading of the national living standard will be the nation's productive plant, and here is where the dynamic nature of the economy can best be sensed. The growth in 1964 alone in the Gross National Product was in excess of $27,000,000,000, or more than 5%. It is not an insignificant sum. But the more meaningful statistic is the comparison of 1964's GNP of $622,000,000,000-plus with that of only four years before, when it was $120,000,000,000 less. If, in less than four years, the country can add $120,000,000,000 to the value of all the goods and services it produces, how well can it do in the next 10 or 11 years?

Again, in 1960 dollars, a conservative estimate is that from the beginning of 1964 to the end of 1975, roughly $400,000,000,000 will be added to the GNP—an average of about $35,000,000,000 a year. Thus, by 1975, the per capita GNP, which in 1962 was $2,894, will be in excess of $4,000 a year. With that kind of growth, there can be little doubt that the average American family will find that its material wealth is constantly increasing in quantity, quality, and variety.

Such an economy can be expected to create millions of new jobs as it expands and elevates. Almost 20,000,000 individuals will be added to the work force by 1975. The need to provide jobs will be unprecedented; never before has any nation found itself on the verge of an economic surge in which an average of 2,000,000 new jobs will be found each year to absorb the able-bodied workers in the work force.

Can it be done? Probably the more important question is, can there be an alternative to the proposition that it must be done? Obviously not. And given a decade in which to cope with the gnawing problem of an unemployment rate that for six years in a row has averaged 5% or better, the optimistic view is that the nation will find the ways and means of reducing this rate to the desired maximum of about 4%. It is an attainable goal. As recently as 1956-57, the unemployment rate was close to this figure, and there seems to be no reason why it should not drop to this level again.

TECHNOLOGICAL REVOLUTION

Such growth, whether of population or of national wealth, is but a backdrop to the most drastic upheaval of all in the economic structure—the scientific and technological revolution. There was recognition of this interrelationship in Sen. Joseph Clark's comment during hearings of the Senate Subcommittee on Employment and Manpower in 1963 when he expressed concern whether "change, not only in the field of cybernation, but in terms of population growth, perhaps in a good many areas of human life, has not suddenly begun to shift into an almost geometric progression of speed and we are just not prepared to cope with it all."

One of the current fashions in economic prognostication is to relate the expansion of knowledge to time. Thus, one reads that knowledge increases "at exponential rates varying between the power of three and the power of nine." It took 200,000 years for man to move out of the Stone Age. Metal tools appeared on the civilized scene only 10,000 years ago. And the Industrial Revolution, which is supposed to be covered with cobwebs by now, is hardly a century old.

In every decade, the amount of knowledge compressed in the mind of man doubles and redoubles, and redoubles again. The effects of so swift a change have staggering implications when looked at from the perspective of the scientist who now is confronted with the need to be expert not only in his own discipline, but in related disciplines as well. Thus, the biologist no longer can limit himself to just the study of biology; he must know chemistry, physics, mathematics, genetics, biochemistry, and so on to keep abreast of modern developments. The computer operator not only must be skilled in electronics; it is equally important that he be versed in such subjects as physics, mathematics, and psychology if he is to be master of the machine.

The speed with which technical knowledge is acquired and applied challenges even the most active imagination. No better symbols of this pace exist than two key exhibits in the Smithsonian Institution. One is the first commercial computer—now an ancient 16 years old. The other is John Glenn's space capsule, not much over three years old and already a museum piece. The future that has been talked about and speculated about already has reached the stage of its development where it can regard its genealogical roots as being in a museum.

It is none too soon to examine the proposition that much of what has been termed the future is already upon us. It is manifested in one way or another in every sector of the nation's economy and culture that is investigated.

Consider communications. There had been vague talk of a commercial satellite service for the transmission of telephone communications and TV programs from one spot of the globe to another. In the spring of 1965, the nation saw such a service become a reality and the day came closer when, as Robert Sarnoff, chairman of the National Broadcasting Company, puts it, a billion people on the globe will be able to watch one telecast simultaneously. Should there be any reservations as to the business community's expectations of such a service, consider the desperate problem confronting Comsat in its efforts to distribute its stock ownership equitably to a pack of enthusiastic investors.

Consider transportation. We ride in our jets six miles in the air, 10 miles a minute, and marvel at the miracle that man has wrought. But the 600-mile-an-hour jet already is being readied to join the assemblage of the planes whose hour has come and gone. For, by 1970, the British and the French will have put into commercial use their supersonic passenger planes, flying at 1,500 miles an hour. And, if the breaks are with us, the U. S. shortly will have its own supersonic transport in service. It can come none too soon. There already are orders for 88 of the planes on the books, each accompanied with a hard cash advance of $200,000.

The computer, of course, occupies a position all its own as an early arrival to symbolize the world of tomorrow. Is there anything the computer cannot do now? It brings together in one communications web the far-flung offices and branches of a major corporation such as Westinghouse. It handles Eastern's and American's airline business with such deftness and speed that it is no longer a problem to determine space availability or routing no matter how involved the query. In New York, there is a legal reference firm which, for a fee, will provide lawyers with fast retrieval of legal precedents, rulings, and references in a few hours at the most—all of this information being available from a master computer. At the University of California Medical Center, at the George Washington Medical School, and at a dozen other medical research facilities around the country, computer technology rapidly is being adapted to the task of medical diagnosis, keeping medical records, and backstopping physicians in keeping abreast of the mass of medical knowledge that pours out of laboratories and institutes.

These are a smattering of the developments that only a few years ago were being offered as predictions of a tomorrow that is already here, or is just over the horizon. If we have come so far so fast, what about the future ahead—the very close future of 1975?

Let us go back to the observation that the relationship of technical development to time becomes narrower and narrower with every year that passes. What was impossible yesterday is likely today and inevitable for tomorrow.

CHALLENGES AHEAD

Who is to say what is to come as the scientist begins to unravel, strand by strand, the secret inner structures of the genes and chromosomes—the mysteries of deoxyribonucleic acid? What unknown and undreamed-of application will be made of mastering the mystery of the atomic nucleus, the rearrangement of the particles within it, or the harnessing of its power to less cumbersome tasks than powering a reactor or propelling a submarine? Why should one not predict a new world of materials and products to come out of current exploration into the behavior of substances at very low temperatures and very high ones?

The laser, which was a laboratory oddity only yesterday, now is talked of as the most versatile scientific tool to be developed for the use of man since the invention of the wheel. In the not-too-distant tomorrow it will be used for the most delicate of surgical procedures. It has application as a device to slice through steel. One of its greatest sources of promise is in communications; it is not inconceivable that a single laser beam could transmit as many phone conversations and TV programs as now require an entire communications network.

Electronics is a wonder-world all its own. Probably the most rapid development in electronic technology is in the field of microminiaturization. The transistor replaced the vacuum tube. And now chemically grown crystals and other microscopic-sized components are being used to replace bulky condensers and other components. William D. Murray, research manager of the Burroughs Corporation, is quoted as saying, "We've learned to make electronic circuits made up of resistors, capacitors, and diodes as small as pencil dots." Philco Corporation has demonstrated entire electrical circuits for use in radios or appliances packed together in a space no bigger than a postage stamp.

In a few years' time, these developments truly will make possible the cigar-box computer or the radio set as big as one's fingernail. For industry, they will solve much of the problem of working space for machines and electronic installations. In the home, they will take much of the bulk out of TV sets, appliances, and even the telephone.

There have been predictions of electroluminescent light as the new form of illumination, replacing the incandescent and fluorescent bulbs. Such light fixtures today are available in their embryonic forms—one as a night light, the other as long ribbons which illuminate when plugged into an electric socket.

Thermoelectricity has been another new development for which much has been predicted in the refrigeration and air-conditioning field. But already, small—two cubic-foot—thermoelectric refrigerators are on the market. And the first commercial installation of a thermoelectric air-conditioning system was announced recently.

AUTOMATION'S IMPACT

Robert Oppenheimer has said this is an age "in which our work, our leisure, our economy and an increasingly large part of the very quality of our lives are all based on the application of newly-acquired knowledge of nature to practical human problems." In no better way can this be observed than in the world of work and in the way machines increasingly do the jobs of men.

There is nothing new about displacement of people by machines. It has been a worry since the Rev. William Lee invented the automatic knitting machine in 1589. But when one reflects that, in less than 15 years, 3,000,000 men have been replaced by machines in the coal mines, over 130,000 have been made surplus in the steel mills, and that only half as many man-hours now are needed to produce a car, the effects of the march of automation become crystal clear.

Today, two workers do the job of 200 in making 1,000 radio sets each day. Ten men do the job of a previous 400 in producing auto motor blocks with an automated machine. Only 14 operators are needed to preside over the glass-blowing machines that make 90% of all our light bulbs.

In Samuel Butler's fictitious land of Erewhon, workers destroyed all their machines because a philosopher warned them that the machines were threatening to outdo men and eventually might take charge. Are we approaching the reality of such a fantasy today? Will "Rossum's Universal Robots" eventually overtake us?

I think not. But the march of the machine is in measured cadence, steadily, persistently, indubitably moving forward. By 1975, automation or cybernation or mechanization or whatever you choose to call it will have displaced not thousands but millions of workers from their jobs. And this will occur at a time when 2,000,000 people a year are being added to the work force. No better recognition of the imminence of the problem can be cited than IBM's grant of $5,000,000 to Harvard for a 10-year study of the social impact of technological change and automation.

EDUCATION TOMORROW

There is one other area where the prospects of tomorrow are beginning to fall into focus, and that is education. Public school enrollments are mounting at a rate of close to 1,000,000 a year, and it is not inconceivable that, by 1975, the total public school enrollment will be close to 54,000,000, compared to today's approximately 42,000,000. College enrollments, which only a year or two back were predicted to reach about 8,000,000 in 1975, are increasing so fast that an enrollment figure of 9,000,000 or more a decade hence is not an unrealistic estimate.

Along with the revolution in technology, communications, transportation, living standards, and the rest, profound changes can be anticipated in our educational process. Not long ago, the Educational Facilities Laboratories, a Ford Foundation offshoot, examined the problem of expanding student bodies and concluded that the current tentative experiments with such educational techniques as the electronic carrel or the group of huge lecture halls addressed by a single professor via television point the way to future innovations. The supply of teachers—particularly in higher education—will be so limited as to demand such a solution to the educational process. The proposition that the student is best taught in small groups by gifted teachers is one that rapidly assumes the character of true luxury.

No mention of education in the future can ignore the tortuous problem of the uneducated—the dropout, the unskilled, the individual who has neither the training nor the resources to cope with a world in such rapid transition. There is no question that it must be solved—and will be. But as to the methods, I can only cite the establishment of a domestic Peace Corps and the organization of facilities tailored to provide education for the rejects of our society as evidence of what trends will be found in the future.

These are but a few of the promises and problems of tomorrow. They highlight the nature and the substance of some of the things to come. There is nothing that the nation cannot solve, given its resources and its demonstrated ingenuity. Probably the initial responsibility is to develop an awareness of what is to come, and then to design a program that recognizes that much of what is to come is new and in many ways not a part of the nation's traditions.

One can be an optimist about the future. Or one might be pessimistically oriented. I prefer to stand with Max Lerner, who has coined a new word for those who look expectantly upon the future: "possibilist." For the "possibilist," tomorrow provides the setting for beneficial change and improvement in the condition of man. The trend has been set. Now the question is: what, within the realm of possibility, will we do with it?

4. THE MIXED BLESSINGS OF AUTOMATION

GEORGE E. ARNSTEIN

MOST SERIOUS STUDENTS of automation deal with it in ambivalent terms. Boon or Bane, says one writer; Threat or Promise, another; while a popular article talked about Friend or Foe. In theory, of course, automation should be an unmixed blessing, leading us to higher production, better health and safety, and a higher standard of living. To put it briefly, automation makes possible the more effective use of our resources and speeds their distribution. In practice, all of these achievements are being accomplished, but at a social cost which is not yet fully known. Man, within limits, is conquering nature, but he is laggard in his conquest of the social environment. Automation, by speeding up the conquest of nature, tends to enlarge the lag in social amelioration.

The problems of automation are largely the same as the problems we would have without the rapid technological advances we now are witnessing. Our shortage of teachers has continued for more than two decades; our system of transportation was congested and inadequate even before World War II; and our scientific know-how is ahead of our willingness to pay for its application, for otherwise we would have less pollution, no malnutrition, greater safety, and less noise and dirt.

This gap between invention and science on the one hand and the social consequences of technological progress on the other is what made the Industrial Revolution so painful; it is also what makes the present Technological Revolution such a double-edged weapon.

It is ironic that we suffer from agricultural surpluses, produced in part by better chemicals, better farming methods, and better machinery, while some of our population is underfed; that we face a shortage of water resources even though we have the means of producing and distributing an abundant supply; that our highways, airways, and railways are subject to accidents which could be prevented by means of better electronic and other controls; and that our cities are congested, and too much of our housing is substandard, although we have the knowledge and means of overcoming these deficiencies.

What has happened, of course, is that we have mobilized our resources, but have done so unevenly. In the middle of the last century, we decided, as a nation, that agriculture should be stimulated. Accordingly, we arranged for a series of measures, ranging from land-grant colleges to county agricultural extension services, to strengthen the farmer and his knowledge. Our success has been great —so much so that it, in turn, has produced new problems of abundance.

Earlier in this century, when secondary education was too academic, the Congress sought to redress the balance by stimulating a program of vocational education. Its success, too, probably has outlived its original purpose and has made some school programs the prisoners of an existing obsolescent orientation.[1]

Then, about 1940, we started a series of deliberate increases in funding research and development of new products, new techniques, and greater scientific knowledge. Research-and-development expenditures have grown from about $1,000,000,000 in 1941 to an estimated $16,000,000,000 in 1963, with visible and spectacular results. A projection reported by James Killian of the Massachusetts Institute of Technology puts the total for 1970 at $40,000,000,000 or more.[2]

These efforts usually have been stimulated and financed by the Federal government in response to specific needs. After the launching of the first Soviet satellite in 1957, there was a renewed impetus for scientific progress, ranging from the National Defense Education Act of 1958 to the present program to put a man on the moon.

The resulting programs have given the United States a command-

---

[1] See George E. Arnstein, "Quo Vadis, Vocational Education?" *Phi Delta Kappan*, 44:326-330, April, 1963.

[2] James R. Killian, Jr., "The Crisis in Research," *Atlantic Monthly*, 211:69-72, March, 1963.

ing lead in many fields of science and have produced vast technological progress, to the accompaniment of quiet protests from the social sciences and the humanities that there has been a disproportionate emphasis on the physical sciences and a neglect of the rest of our society and culture. This imbalance, in part, explains the negative implications of automation—the fear that it means a dehumanization of our culture; high social costs of job displacement; potential dynamite among unemployed youth in our urban centers; and vague, gnawing doubts about the efficacy of our economic system.

The negative effects cannot be denied, no matter how much we may appreciate the relatively low cost of automobiles, the wonders of new cookware derived from ceramic nosecones, the glories of irradiated food, synthetic tubeless tires, and colored self-dialing telephones.

Just to complicate things, there are some important educational implications arising from automation.

First of all, every change calls for a *new* skill which calls for retraining or re-education. Thus, the market for education would expand, even if we did not have a built-in expansion based on our high birth rate. Because of this, there are increasing demands for adult education, for education is the key to maintaining skills needed on a changing and evolving job, to better mastery of the environment through understanding of the economic system and science, and to the enjoyment of leisure. Further, education has been shown to pay off in lifetime income so much that there is increasing recognition of education as an investment as well as a consumer "good."[3] Above all, there is evidence to suggest that lifelong learning is the prerequisite for the continuing ability of older persons to learn new skills.[4]

Secondly, unemployment has been running at approximately 5% for the past six years. In the face of this problem, the primary educational responsibility must be in the area of salable skills. However, this task is complicated by the large number of entrants into the labor force in the face of relatively slow economic growth. The U. S. Department of Labor, in the so-called Black Book, published a forecast dealing with the decade 1960-1970 in which it estimated that some 26,000,000 young people would enter the labor force in that decade; but the number of departures was estimated at only

---

[3] See Harold M. Groves, "Education and Economic Growth" (Washington, D. C.: National Education Association, 1961).

[4] Wilma T. Donahue, "Adult Learning: Limits and Potentialities," in Luther H. Evans and George E. Arnstein, editors, "Automation and the Challenge to Education" (Washington, D. C.: National Education Association, 1962), pp. 19-37.

13,000,000.[5] This leaves a net deficit of 13,000,000 jobs still to be created. While the economic task may be tremendous in creating 13,000,000 jobs, the educational task has another dimension because it means that 26,000,000 young people must be given an education.

By way of complicating this assignment, we must keep in mind that the jobs do not yet exist, that they call for changes in skill, and that the data underlying our indications of the speed and direction of these changes are grossly inadequate. The question thus becomes one of how the schools can prepare students for a future which is as yet unknown.

Automation is part of the explosion of knowledge we now are witnessing. The usual measure of this explosion is the quotation attributed to J. Robert Oppenheimer that our scientific knowledge doubles approximately every eight years. This is good, insofar as it increases man's mastery over his environment. In some respects it is bad, because it makes for greater specialization and militates against our goal of making well-rounded citizens in a democratic society who have to understand many things in order to take an active and informed part in the decision-making process. The explosion of knowledge is the source of our inability to arrive at rational, independent judgments about such complex problems as the TFX fighter, the effect of fallout on our food, or who was to blame for the New York newspaper strike. In effect, the increase in knowledge and complexity means an increasing tendency to delegate some of our own decisions to others—to a trade association, consumer group, political party, or lobby. No longer can we follow in the footsteps of Francis Bacon who proudly said, "I have taken all knowledge to be my province." This defect also may account for our ability to control nature but not to achieve mastery over our social organization and progress.

For that matter, we must keep in mind that people, after all, are the crucial elements in our efforts to secure a better life, and technological change is supposed to benefit people. Technology, however, is neutral in the moral sense; it has no social values. These we can provide if we choose to do so.

While we now have an affluent society with large pockets of unemployment, poverty, and deprivation, we can decide to distribute

[5] U. S. Department of Labor, "Manpower: Challenge of the 1960s" (Washington, D. C.: Government Printing Office, 1961). Additional data may be found in the "Manpower Report of the President" (Washington, D. C.: Government Printing Office, 1964).

this affluence more evenly. Most of our population is overfed (or must make conscious efforts to combat obesity), although there are children and adults who go hungry. Most adult Americans, disregarding those who are retired, are working, as homemakers or businessmen or on a payroll, but there are some 5,000,000 others who are unemployed, who have involuntary leisure when they can least afford it. These people tend to be undereducated and unskilled, have obsolete skills, and are ill-prepared to cope with change, adversity, and technology.

This segment of our society is paying a disproportionate share of the cost of automation, especially in human terms. The displaced coal miner, the semi-literate shipping clerk, the Negro migrant, the frustrated dropout from high school—they bear the brunt of technological change. Not that the affluent members of society planned it that way, but rather that the suburban engineer, the professor in the air-conditioned apartment, the businessman in the office building with automated elevators, the myriad beneficiaries of change are most concerned with producing change. Thanks to their ingenuity, to their education, to their initiative and self-confidence—along with luck and fortunate choice of parents—they are reaping the benefits of automation. They are beginning to look nervously over their shoulders to see what inroads automation is making in their profession and in related fields. There may come from this realization a more determined effort to close the gap between our lagging social measures and our dormant humane concerns on the one hand and our deliberate stimulation and exploitation of physical sciences and resources on the other.

Rather briefly, let me recapitulate the educational implications, which sound rather prosaic but are crucial.

There is a need for a broad, general education because there is no room at the bottom for those who are illiterate, unskilled, undereducated, or otherwise unable to become meaningful parts of our society. To the best of our ability, we must cultivate a receptivity to change, for change is certain.

Next, there is a need for all of our citizens to have a better knowledge and understanding of the democratic process, a need for civic competence, as well as an appreciation of human relations. These things, fortunately, can be taught, although the teaching process is not necessarily easy.

Finally, and this is probably the overriding consideration, there is a need for lifelong learning as a means of economic survival. Education is not a pill which can be taken once and which will grant lifelong immunity. This concept is not fully understood by many responsible members of our community because it was possible for so long to acquire a skill and practice it until death. Further, the people who tend to deal with this problem are professionals, and professionals, almost by definition, solve new problems, acquire new knowledge, and are oriented to the idea that the acquisition of knowledge is a good thing. They thus tend to overlook the fact that for many segments of our population the concept of lifelong learning is by no means firmly implanted. That, rather prosaically, is probably the most important educational implication of automation.

It is lifelong learning which gives meaning and content to the human resources of this nation. To use the words of Willard Wirtz, Secretary of Labor, "There is no reason to be afraid of machines. . . . There is great reason, however, to be concerned about how hard it is to get people who are educated and trained to see what machines are doing to people who are not educated and trained."[6]

---

[6] Address by Secretary of Labor W. Willard Wirtz, Fifth Constitutional Convention, AFL-CIO, New York City, Nov. 14, 1963.

5. THE CHALLENGE OF AUTOMATION TO EDUCATION FOR HUMAN VALUES

MARGARET MEAD

TECHNOLOGICAL ADVANCES are themselves neutral. Each technological advance is, therefore, just what the civilization in which it is made can make of it. At present, there is a tendency to treat automation as a devil that is responsible for unemployment at best and for dehumanization of mankind at worst. This attitude is a retreat from the traditional American welcome to technological change. Unlike our European contemporaries, Americans did not conduct vendettas against machines or describe them as soul destroying. Instead, machines that could be substituted for human hands, human legs, or human backs were welcomed. It is worth while asking why we welcomed labor-saving devices and the assembly line that made it possible to mass-produce things that everyone needed, at a price that a majority of the people could afford, and now are balking at devices which save not only heavy physical labor, but mental labor as well. Why are we more concerned with the immediate transitional stage from partly automated to completely automated industry than we are with the ultimate benefits? Why do we not welcome the end of routine factory labor which made no demand for imagination or spontaneity? Why are we not thinking about the other things that people who work can do once some of the tasks they now do have been rendered unnecessary?

There are, I believe, several answers. With the advent of automation we have come face to face with the truth of what social prophets have been predicting for over a quarter of a century—that the problems of a society as productive as ours, with such extensive natural resources and such a large internal market, were bound to become problems of distribution rather than production. While a good part of the rest of the world is struggling with problems of production, we, in the United States, have to face affluence, which means that our task is not to get people to work under threat of starvation, but how to distribute buying power so that the wheels of our highly productive economy can continue to turn productively. Thus, we are facing today a second phase of the moral revolution that began during the Depression, when we abandoned the century-old notion that individuals should be penalized because the industrial society has slowed down. During the Depression we accepted, in practice if not in principle, the idea that society was responsible for the subsistence of all its members and that failure to have a job no longer was to carry with it the penalty of starvation for oneself, one's wife, and one's children. We did not recognize, however, that we would have to disassociate still further the ability to find properly paid work in a free labor market and the right to a decent standard of living. Although it is clear now that this second principle—the right to live well—will have to be accepted also, first in practice and later in principle, we have not yet begun to do so. Welfare still is regarded as a burden carried by society for its improvident and unfortunate members and is kept to minimum standards often well below either health or decency. There is little recognition that the price of preserving our own affluence will be giving up of the old insistence of an industrializing society that in order to share in the society's wealth, one must do productive work.

A second reason why automation is being viewed with suspicion is because the transitional adjustments, which cut down on the labor needed in industry, are being made at the expense of the least well-educated members of the community, and especially of minority groups. Instead of looking ahead to a world in which, with high productivity implemented by machines, we may have enough people at last to care for other people, our imaginations are stymied by the spectacle of the contemporary unemployed, who are pictured as permanently unemployable in a society where only the highly educated will be needed and where there will be a steadily increasing group of unskilled people to be supported.

A third reason lies in the coincidence of automation and the development of a series of technical devices which are pictured as robbing people of privacy, reducing them to cyphers, and subjecting them to decisions made by computers. Automation possibilities and these other developments have coincided and are in many ways interdependent, as when a computer is programmed to invent a better computer than itself, or when the checking of income taxes or registration of university students are said to be "done by a computer." The way in which all of these subjects have been handled in the press has suggested to many people that machines were taking over, Big Brother was equipped with long-distance listening devices, and all individuality was lost. Not nearly enough stress has been put on the importance of the questions that are asked of machines, on the inability of machines to do anything for which they have not received full instructions, and the extent to which all these devices facilitate living in the modern world.

A fourth reason lies in our inability to think of a responsible role in society which is not evaluated as a job, paid for with money, which individuals seek freely, from which they can be fired, and at which they must work or else, if not starve, they will live in humiliation and deprivation. We can look forward to a day in which the privilege of working will be open to all but under no threat of starvation.

We can look forward to a day when all the dull, unrewarding, routine technical tasks can be done by machines, and the human tasks—caring for children, caring for plants and trees and animals, caring for the sick and the aged, the traveler and the stranger—can be done by human beings. We can look forward to a day when we never will ask a human being to do something that a machine can do better, but will reserve for human beings our requests and demands for those things which machines cannot do. Just as jobs multiplied when production and consumption depended upon factory work, we may expect the number of tasks for human beings to perform humanly to multiply once it is recognized that we will need a device by which each member of society can validate his right to share in its productivity. Instead of the old economy of scarcity, in which the product was limited, we will have a new economy which is limited neither by the available workers nor by the available market for the goods produced.

The problem then of putting automation in perspective involves a substitution of long-term goals for concentration on short-term effects, attention to our peculiar American situation of educational contrasts and racial and cultural diversity, and a far better public understanding of the way in which machines can serve human purposes rather than merely create problems.

We then can ask: How will automation permit us to make our society more human? Is it more or less human for mothers and daughters, separated by hundreds of miles, to be able to dial each other cheaply? Is it more or less human to have a machine to help a child review a rote learning lesson, or calculate the milk money, while a trained teacher is free to teach? Is it more or less human to provide a bed-ridden patient with a self-regulating bed? Is a child who can rent earphones in a museum and walk about at his own speed more or less human than one herded in a group of 50? Is it more or less human for a people to be able to share the entire ritual of mourning for a martyred president than for them to read a few short lines in a newspaper printed on a hand press?

Making the post-automation world human will demand new educational measures: an immediate interpretation of the relationship between human instruction and machine execution; new programs which will prepare children for a world in which they will work, not under threat, but as part of their membership in their society; emphasis on human skills rather than upon routine machine tending skills; and greater attention to the development of individual interests and talents to use the greater leisure which everyone may expect to have.

6. AUTOMATION: THE PARADOXES OF ABUNDANCE

CHARLES R. BOWEN

CHARLES DICKENS begins "A Tale of Two Cities" as follows: "It was the best of times, it was the worst of times, it was the age of wisdom, it was the age of foolishness, . . . it was the season of light, it was the season of darkness, it was the spring of hope, it was the winter of despair, we had everything before us, we had nothing before us. . . ." This same sense of paradox prevails today in America about automation and technological change. How incredible it would have seemed even to Dickens that a society could be concerned about the possibility of machine systems taking over production of the necessities of life! America is the richest nation in the history of mankind, and yet one-fifth of us live in poverty. We have a surplus of labor, capital, and in the production ability of both our farms and factories, and yet we have vast unmet needs in our slums and depressed areas, in medical care, educational facilities, and in urban transportation. Today, we are able to control our environment as in no other age before us. Potentially we could be on the verge of a new Golden Age. Pres. Johnson expressed it when he said this generation of Americans in particular faces "the challenge of greatness."

Yet, there are those who say that we are fast approaching a time when 2% of the labor force can produce all we need while the other 98% may be rescued from their workless poverty by Caesars promis-

71

ing bread and circuses. These latter-day Jeremiahs base their predictions on what, to them, seems the logical projection of the growth of machine systems that can replace man's mind as well as his muscles.

Similar predictions were made when steam engines were introduced to power the mills and carriages of the early 19th century. In the early 1930's, the Technocrats cried similar alarms. Prof. Oscar Handlin of Harvard has suggested that the awe-inspiring possibilities of machine systems awaken, at least in Western man, the ancient instinctual fear expressed in the myth of Prometheus—that for so great and useful a gift surely man must pay a price that will "confound the innocent and awe the dumb."

Of opposite opinion are conservative economists who point out that the growth of productivity in the U. S. is only about 3.5% per year and that rising demand, new products, and a flexible fiscal policy should be able to provide adequate jobs for all. The claim is put forth that we are only witnessing a continuation of the first Industrial Revolution. Certainly, without the first Industrial Revolution, what we are witnessing today would not be possible. But the difference in degree in many cases is great enough to become a change in kind. For instance, when the steam locomotive was being introduced in Central Europe, there was debate whether blindness and death might result if the human body was hurtled through space at the unheard of speed of 30 miles per hour. Now those who go to the moon will surpass John Glenn's 18,000 miles per hour. Pascal's adding machine could calculate faster than several men. The new computers calculate faster than tens of thousands of men. In 1800, no machine or single grouping of men or animals could deliver as much as 10 horsepower (10 horses pulling "together" give you considerably less than 10 horsepower). Today, electricity from a central power generating station can run motors delivering several times that horsepower in a million homes. And the largest rockets surpass 1800's record by hundreds of thousands.

"The heart of the matter," according to the Rockefeller Report on Education, "is that we are moving with headlong speed into a new phase of man's long struggle to control his environment, a phase beside which the industrial revolution may appear a modest alteration in human affairs. Nuclear energy, exploration of outer space, revolutionary studies of brain functioning, important new work on the living cell—all point to changes in our lives so startling as to test to the utmost our adaptive capacities, our stability and our wisdom."

Yet, in the midst of these dizzying perspectives there are still with us the old problems of war, poverty, suffering, and ignorance. Although we have achieved Francis Bacon's beliefs that "the goal of the sciences is none other than this: that human life be endowed with new discoveries and powers," our ability to master the world of matter has far outrun our wisdom in coping with social and human problems. We have over 3,500,000 men and women who want work but for whom a society, with vast unmet needs, cannot find a job.

There is no iron law that a high rate of unemployment is the price we must pay for automation. In the 1930's, before true automation—machines controlling machines or themselves—had been devised, we had over 10,000,000 unemployed. Today, many less-developed countries have unemployment rates several times higher than the U. S. Conversely, Western Europe, which is automating some areas of production at a faster pace than the U. S., has a *shortage,* not a surplus of manpower. In fact there is a substantial group of economists and national leaders who fear America may not be automating all sectors of production fast enough to remain competitive in world markets and to retain the high growth rate of recent years. There is no question that either a faster growth rate in the U. S. or a faster pace of automation would create new jobs— as well as displace many old jobs. But there is no guarantee that the displaced men or today's unemployed could qualify for the new jobs.

It is at this point that we can see the critical role education and training must play in determining America's response to automation. But before considering what educational needs are likely to develop, it would be instructive to consider how we arrived at today's situation.

HOW WE GOT WHERE WE ARE

From the beginning, the U. S. had more land than labor. As the continent was developed, Americans outside of the plantation system in the South were looking constantly for labor-saving devices. The 19th century, with its revolution in power and machinery, provided the tools the developing country needed.

The first sector of the American economy to experience a revolution in productivity comparable to today's "automation" was agriculture. In 1800, over 80% of the population lived on farms. Now less than 8% can produce considerably more than our total population of 192,000,000 can consume. The general characteristics of this great change in production are remarkably similar to those which followed in other sectors: larger, more profitable units; higher capital investment per worker; less demand for unskilled labor; higher demand for skilled labor; smaller total employment; and higher pay for those employed.

In American mining the story is much the same. In coal, one-third the number of miners employed in 1947 now produce an equal amount of coal.

In manufacturing the trend is the same. In the 1920's, there were over 50 car manufacturers in the U. S. Today, there are less than 10. And, since 1947, the man-hours required to produce an average car have decreased 50%.

One of the great questions today is whether the service industries can provide the jobs needed to keep our growing labor force gainfully employed. Computer systems are affecting the white-collar sector of employment in much the same manner as past technological change. Less labor is required, but with higher skills and, consequently, better pay. However, we still face sizable shortages in certain service occupations, particularly those requiring higher education or technical competence such as teaching, medicine, science, mathematics, social work, and the technical areas. In addition, other areas of personal service such as resorts, personal care, and the arts do not lend themselves now or in the near future to automation.

Although the "new team" of science linked with technology may surprise us, the only major consumer market comparable to automobiles in the 1920's or television in the 1950's foreseen in the immediate future is the information industry—and more particularly, education. But we face a paradox. Although we are the richest nation in the world, we seem to be unable to find a way to give all sectors of American education adequate financial support. Since 1920, expenditures for technical research and development have increased 200-fold, while those for education only 12-fold. In view of this, it is not surprising that the skill demands of the new technology are out of balance with the skills and education of the labor force. We have several million looking for jobs while many jobs are going begging. Although we have a surplus of labor, we have a shortage of teachers, particularly in areas of expansion and change such as mathematics, science, and the new technical vocations. If, at this early stage in the age of automation, we already suffer from an imbalance between the manpower needs of the new technology and the skills and education of the labor force, what future directions and probabilities are likely to affect this situation?

FUTURE PROBABILITIES

Job opportunities will grow. It is pleasant to speculate that 2% of the labor force could do all the work. Aristotle's dream—when the looms can weave by themselves, then will men be truly free—would be nearly accomplished. If our population and what we presently purchase were to remain constant, then in less than 30 years—barring a cataclysm and projecting today's annual productivity growth rate of 3½%—we all could take it easy. But the birth rate is over 2,000,000 per year and few are the families that have not the imagination to double purchases, given the opportunity.

Although we certainly will see a shortening of the work week and work year, there is a great deal of evidence to indicate that most Americans at this stage of our development prefer increased pay to increased leisure, if given the choice. This has been the case in the New York electrical industry, with its 25-hour week. The men have continued to work their usual hours, but at a much higher rate for the last 15 or 20 hours. The fact that 4,000,000 Americans carry two jobs attests both to our industriousness and to our acquisitiveness. However, whether there will be enough *new* jobs for those entering the labor force as well as those displaced by technological change is one of the major challenges facing the economy. In the 1950's, there was a 7,000,000 increase in the labor force; in the 1960's, there will be a 12,000,000 increase (7 vs. 12). This is particularly serious when we consider two facts: first, that the average *net* increase in new non-farm production jobs, 1958-62, was only 400,000 per year; and second, when we consider the groups hardest hit by technological change—youth (where the growth in the labor force will be) who never are employed, older workers who have the lowest educational attainment level (one-half are high school dropouts) and are the longest out of school, and minority groups, particularly the Negroes, who today have the highest unemployment rate (twice the national average) and the lowest level of educational and skill attainment. Of the two Negro demands, jobs may be much harder to meet than equal rights.

Because of rising productivity plus the growth in the labor force, the U. S. Department of Labor estimates we will need 32,600,000 new job opportunities by 1970 just to remain where we are. Nor is there any guarantee those needing jobs will have the skills or education the new jobs need.

Most of the new jobs will not be created in the private profit sector of the economy. This trend already has begun. Of the *new* jobs created since 1957, less than one-third have been in the private profit sector. This is not so surprising when you consider that education and government service, and much medical and scientific work, occur outside the "for profit" sector which traditionally has been considered the great area of job creation. However, this trend could be reversed if today's defense contractors could be as resourceful in devising ways to apply the systems approach, that has worked so well in meeting defense needs, to urban, medical, educational, and transportation needs. This is not so remote as it might seem. One large West Coast aerospace manufacturer has been using for several years in advanced production work an ingenious work-training system utilizing both audio and video instruction. Such a system, particularly if controlled by a large computer, could have profound implications for general technical education and retraining.

As long as ours remains a flexible and growing society, we will not be content to let resources lie idle in one area while needs pile up in another. To remedy this unique situation, we may see the further emergence of what, for lack of a better word, is called the "mixed enterprise," since it is neither in the private profit sector of the economy nor the public sector. Notable examples of successful mixed enterprises are the turnpike authorities; the Port of New York Authority which builds and operates New York City's bridges, tunnels, and expressways; the Federal Reserve Bank System; and, more recently, the Satellite Corporation which is both private and public.

Certain European and Latin-American countries already are using this type of institutional device much more freely and flexibly than the U. S. Consonant with our ideal of pragmatism, it offers a compromise to accomplish social goals in areas where private profit enterprise is unwilling or not permitted to operate and where pure government enterprise might be unwelcome or unworkable.

The information industry will be the area of greatest growth. Less and less will work center on "things" and more and more will it focus on *symbols* for things. This became true of science a long time ago. It is fast becoming true of production systems. In fact, man's history can be traced in terms of his ability to manipulate his environment through artifacts rather than directly. Great periods of development usually have been marked by advances to new levels of abstraction more effective than the old in managing our environment. Computer-controlled systems of production are one further step in our ability to manipulate things rationally.

The next step in this development will be the decentralization of computer usage. Originally, computers—or information processing systems—were restricted to a few large government laboratories. They were used next in large corporations as well as laboratories supported by the government. Now the more than 15,000 computers installed or on order cover all sizes of businesses (social and educational institutions).

The next generation of computer systems which already are becoming available will allow the individual to have a terminal tailored to his needs that will put the capability of the entire system at his service. The American telephone system is a notable example of a system that can handle spoken information on a continental basis by simply dialing a few numbers.

The generation of power went through a similar decentralization of usage. Many of the first steam engines were enormous giants, inscribed and ornamented, monstrously noisy and completely immobile. Then one system, the railroad, put them on wheels and decentralized them along tracks. But an even more ingenious system used them to generate electricity and, through wires, put the steam engine's power capacity in the form of an electric motor in any home where the need existed.

A series of technological advances in computer systems development at this time hold out prospects for a similar development in information processing. These include small, economically feasible terminals giving access to a system's capabilities to store and process information; and natural means of communicating with the terminals such as typewriters, writing with a light pencil on a display, languages specially designed for a business or an intellectual area with which to communicate with a computer, and the terminals' ability to read even handwriting and possibly to understand the human voice (although the latter two are in the realm of the future). These also include vast memories capable of holding millions and eventually billions of pieces of information.

The effect of this will be to amplify and extend the effectiveness of each individual using such a terminal. The scientist no longer will have to wait hours or days for the answers to complex equations and formulations. And, through terminals hooked together, scientists can collaborate concurrently on experiments across continents. The doctor, lawyer, educator, and administrator will have the ability to retrieve and manipulate incredible amounts of information on a current basis.

It is almost impossible to predict what the limits of such a system will be. On the one hand, there will be economic restraints. On the other, new systems have a way of interacting and compounding one another's development on a vast scale. One hundred years ago, who would have dreamed that over 50,000,000 American homes would have television sets? To make this possible, there had to be a standard of living undreamed of at that time, cheap and widely distributed electricity, the techniques of mass production, as well as the technology of electronic television. I suppose the only disappointment is that taste has not progressed as fast as technology.

But it seems certain that computer usage will be decentralized to the point where terminals will be available to individuals in offices, laboratories, classrooms, and homes where such usage can be economically justified. Whether our standard of living, our technology, and our needs ever would progress to the point where such terminals were as widespread as telephones, it is difficult to predict. It is even more difficult to anticipate what the effect of such a development would be on the way we live and work, but it is conceivable that as information, its processing, and the interactions possible all proliferate, information may do our business traveling for us and the frenetic pace of American commuting may subside.

As man's information processing capabilities stride forward with the speed of seven league boots, knowledge and facts become more important in the context of their system than separately. For instance, when automation was first introduced, the machine's task simply replaced the separate individual's task in the total context of a system that had been designed for human rather than machine capabilities. Now as entire systems are automated, many separate tasks and departments can be collapsed into one, thanks to the vast capabilities of the machine.

The speed with which the U. S. Navy produced the Polaris submarine and its missile system was due in a large measure to the application of a management system called PERT (Program Evaluation and Review Technique) which was computer based. Thanks to the genius of the men who devised the system, the computer was able to retain in its memory and direct far more details than a human mind could store and operate upon concurrently. However, later developments have shown that the computer is not always essential to such systems, but that the advantage lies in the application to a problem of the intellectually disciplined and systematic approach required for literal- and precise-minded computers. We may see this kind of mind-stretching systems approach to problem-solving in many new areas.

FUTURE POSSIBILITIES—PARTICULARLY FOR EDUCATION

We already are in a period when education and the achievements of the intellect will be esteemed and pursued as in no other age. The technological environment is a consequence of the application of intellect to man's environment. It is a result of the spirit of rationalism and scientific inquiry whose flowering is a vital part of Western liberal thought. The Federal government already commits well over a 10th of its total budget to the research and development of new knowledge. The enormous increase in college enrollments as well as the large amounts business now is investing in the continued education and training of all levels of employees attest to the pervasiveness of our race to gain new knowledge.

But, like the sorcerer's apprentice, there is a danger we may drown in our own abundance. Since few, if any of us, can absorb *all* the new advances in knowledge, we have resorted to a narrow and potentially dangerous specialization to try to keep pace with our own sector of the "information explosion." To amplify C. P. Snow's theme, there are not only two, but dozens of different subcultures within the vast edifice known as Western knowledge. We must keep in mind that the various compartments or disciplines into which we arbitrarily have divided knowledge exist neither in the heart of matter nor of man. It is the special responsibility of education in the period ahead to see that we become neither over-specialized mandarins nor generalized ignoramuses.

To paraphrase Robert Oppenheimer, it is true in regard to culture that there are two numbers, but they are one and zero, for unless tomorrow's man is as literate in science as in the humanities—and I believe this is C. P. Snow's essential point—then he can be literate in neither. Unlike our confident forebears in the 19th century whose science conceived the universe to be mechanistic and ultimately knowable (Newton said give me a fulcrum, a lever long enough, and I can move the universe), today's more poetically-based science and mathematics have long since passed beyond the threshold of the finitely knowable into worlds where the scientist's intuitive sense of proportion and simplicity often must serve as his only guide. Perhaps this return to an almost poetic sense of intuition in the most rigorous and disciplined thought may do more to unify the sciences and the humanities than any of us have realized.

A democracy, in particular, faces great risks if, in the age of science, a majority of its citizens are so ignorant of the great processes involved as to look upon science and its practitioners as something akin to black magic. Such a view is antithetic to the goals of education and leaves the door dangerously open to those, like Hitler, who play upon the blind instincts and fears of a people.

Conversely, in terms of public support, particularly at the national level, there is no question but that science has stolen the show. This lack of balance between U. S. support for the humanities and social sciences and that available to support the science-engineering-mathematics constellation unduly limits our flexibility in dealing with the problems posed by technological change. Not that we should decrease our support for science, but increase considerably the amount of financial support and, more important, the *public esteem and attention* devoted to the study of man.

America today has yet to rediscover the full intellectual and emotional meaning of the humanities and of the Western intellectual tradition. Although this will not require billions in national research support, it will require a far greater sense of balance and priorities of value than we have displayed in the fateful days since Hiroshima.

If, in a period when man has so much power to shape his environment, we neglect the study of man, his aspirations, and his tragedies, we are in danger of being dominated by our technology and reshaping man in the image of the apparently flawless machine. Dr. Charles Malik has expressed this consummately:

A world of perfect technicians is the aim, not a world of human beings, let alone of beings devine. A dreary and boring world where there is nothing beyond man and his mastery over nature, including his mastery over other technicians through his scientific management of them. Perfect hierarchy, perfect organization, total efficiency; but no spirit, no freedom, no joy, no humor, and therefore no man.

This is the greatest challenge posed by the new technology with its glittering achievements and even greater promises. And this is the challenge whose profound significance can best be understood— and met—by the community of education.

Since the founding of the Republic, we always have asked more than we had any right to expect legitimately from our great system of public education. Surely this characteristic has been more typical of our dynamic society than any other. Today, although the high school dropout rate has been halved in the last 24 years, the situation that we ourselves have created out of our past successes demands that we increase the holding power of the schools beyond anything now deemed possible.

And, although well over twice as many students now go on to college or advanced technical training, the profile of tomorrow's job opportunities indicates that the rate must increase geometrically rather than arithmetically. The Educational Policies Commission of the National Educational Association certainly is correct in calling for two years of educational opportunity for every American beyond the high school.

To achieve what must be done, we will have to increase the amount we invest in education and training. The foundations and businesses already are doing this at an accelerating pace. We must devise new methods and techniques to increase further the impact of education. The acceptance of research as an ongoing and essential part of all levels of the educational process is a development of the profoundest significance. We have only begun to see the payoff in the use of new learning theory and its application in teaching and in developing new curricula that are in touch with the new knowledge being generated on every side.

But can we go far enough to meet the demands for widespread intelligence, learning ability, and skill generated by the new technological cornucopia? Lest we become discouraged, we should remember how far we have come. In the Middle Ages, it is estimated the vocabulary of the average European was less than 1,000 words. The early results of the application of new educational techniques and learning theories indicate we already may be on our way to a renewal in education as profound as that which is transforming America's capacity to produce.

As we proceed into a time when advancing science and technology demand a more liberal interpretation of "work" as well as a lifetime of continued learning in order to cope with the new kind of "work" so deeply imbedded in understanding and manipulating symbols, there looms on the horizon the intriguing possibility that we may be able to approach the kind of individual development and values for all that have been open only to the aristocracies in the past. To appreciate the value already placed upon human life in America, we have only to look back to 1800 in England when no record was kept of the number of small boys lost in the explosion of steam engines they were tending. However, we must make certain the magnitude of the achievements we surely will witness will not silence our citizens into an awed and amazed compliance with the status quo. As we are better able to organize men and machines for productive purposes, there will be a great temptation to apply breakthroughs in the life and social sciences to make of the citizen a compliant automaton. Never since the American Revolution has dissent and the questioning of orthodoxy been more important to the continued life of the Republic. In a period of such complexity and specialization, it is almost inevitable that the vast majority of dissent will be primarily irrelevant or thoroughly crackpot. But there lives no genius who can discern the tiny fraction which harbors the creative insight necessary to continue reshaping our society and prevent it from becoming frozen or clumsy in adapting to the changes being generated so rapidly. Already in terms of technological and institutional innovations to take advantage of change, countries such as Germany, Sweden, Japan, and France have made significant advances over the U. S. in certain categories.

The leadership of these nations is particularly evident in areas such as the development and utilization of technical manpower. Not only is industry encouraged to locate in depressed areas, but manpower from these areas is assured technical training in skills which are in demand. Of course, the use of an active labor market policy includes many other devices, such as tax incentives, a truly national employment service, etc., but particularly significant for us is the ability of societies with only a fraction of the resources available to America to insure that all those who want training and work shall have it. As we have moved ahead so rapidly in wealth and development, a gap in opportunities as well as aspirations has developed between the two Americas, the one prosperous and moving ahead, the other composed of minorities, youth, and the aged who seem to be forgotten and left behind.

It is significant that Pres. Johnson has coupled his call to greatness with a war on poverty. No society with our values can build the splendid structure now possible upon a foundation of deprivation and hopelessness for a part of its population. Nowhere is the challenge to America, and to education in particular, clearer than in the case of this "other America." Unless we can devise the social institutions and educational means to enable our poor and our disadvantaged to adjust to the opportunities of the new age, we will be unable later to bring the world's billions sunk in this state into the future with us.

The schools cannot be expected to solve the problem of the poor alone. But in combining on a vital and present basis with the other forces responsible for the development and progress of the community, the schools once more can reassert that bond which at its most cohesive has been responsible not only for the success of our schools, but of our society.

Part II

HUMANISTIC
EDUCATION
AND AUTOMATION

7. THE HUMANITIES IN THE SIXTIES

WARNER G. RICE

THE MOST INTERESTING EXAMPLES of the science fiction which has become a part of the intellectual diet of the learned and unlearned alike are found in those books where, having exhausted the marvels of the death ray and atomic propulsion, the authors turn to the problems of the assimilation of science by society. As in so many other matters, the practitioners in this kind of literature have anticipated current problems; they have imagined, often very perceptively, what some of the results of automation and the triumph of the machine might mean for the individual, his politics and morals, his society and culture. As everyone knows, the Aldous Huxleys, George Orwells, and Karl Vonneguts of our time have come to very different conclusions from those reached by the inventors of the earlier utopias, since they uniformly present to our gaze and for our consideration dystopias—places where no one of us wants to be. No doubt there is considerable cause for self-satisfaction in our discovery that we can identify and state the problems of our time and the proximate future. It is a sobering thought that like most academic thinkers we are better at analysis than at invention. We diagnose the disease; we are not yet able to cure it.

We discuss cybernation and automation, the effects of swift and kaleidoscopic change; we confer about technological unemployment, the development of computers, the need for a shift in our outlook on work, labor, and leisure. After we have examined the statistics and contemplated the issues, we still have to ask what is to be done about them—and this is, perhaps, the point at which the humanist is supposed to come in. For, in our time, the humanist and his works—the humanities, humane letters, liberal education—have acquired a kind of talismanic virtue. It is commonly said that the humanities are the repositories and protectors of values, that they teach manners and morals, that they supplement or make meaningful the rest of knowledge; and the humanists, accepting their role as the chief guardians and exponents of our culture, understandably feel that they have cause to complain that they are being neglected at that moment in history when they should be specially cherished, and that the preservation of our society requires that humanistic education should be supported generously by public and private funds. Unfortunately for all concerned, however, humanists are more often emphatic in declaring that they have been forgotten than in explaining why they should be remembered. As they have been warned by such people as Dean Jacques Barzun of Columbia University, who is one of their chief apologists, they must depend for support not upon some reputation which they have acquired, but upon some current demonstration of their utility.

Utility is a word which humanists shun because it suggests to them a Philistine materialism. But utility need not have pejorative connotations; in most cases, worth must be appraised in terms of usefulness. There is a sense, of course, in which the humanist and the humanities should not be used. Milton, in "Areopagitica," tells of the tradesman who, conscious that he would profit by having a reputation for being religious, hires a curate, feeds and lodges him, commits his religion to his care, and then trades all day comfortably without his religion. There are those who would like to consign many heavy responsibilities to the humanist and who, having done so, feel free to go about their business without these cares. The virtue of the humanities, however, lies in their tempering and formative power; they cannot be delegated to some surrogate or given a minor place; they are for everyone; they cannot be left to the humanists so that scientists and technologists will not have to worry about the values with which they are too busy to be concerned.

This is the proper place for a few observations as to what the humanist is and is not. One common misconception is that the humanist is the humanitarian, either of the sentimental or the Baconian variety. The sentimentalist can be dismissed very quickly;

he is the individual who will not number on his list of friends the man who needlessly sets foot upon a worm, the man who meets the problems of life and the "human condition" through feeling and sensibility. It is good to have such people in the world, no doubt, but they are not humanists. The scientific, or Baconian humanists, are a different matter. There has been a long history of efforts to ameliorate the condition of mankind, especially by providing those goods and conveniences which make life easier and less arduous, in order that the world may be a more healthful and comfortable place to dwell in, with good food, good housing, plenty of heat, light, water, and electricity for all. The humanitarian—and one could number here many great names from Bacon to the Huxleys—who seeks these ends is not opposed to the humanist, but he is really striving for somewhat different results. He is inclined to stress overmuch the external and material, to forget the claims of the inner and personal life, and to be a victim of intellectual pride.

The humanist is not simply a person who is professionally concerned with a group of studies called the Humanities—that is, the fine arts, music, literature, history, philosophy. The classicist who gave us the doctrine of the enclitic *de* or showed us what scansion the melic poets used may be only remotely a humanist, and much antiquarian learning may be only remotely humane. The same may be said of the scholar proficient in the use of computer techniques for the compilation of a concordance to the poetry of Longfellow. The man who does this trick—which is being done now every day— may belong to a department of English or a department of American culture; but the activity in which he is engaged when he is making his computer concordance can scarcely be called humane.

What, then, is the humanist? He is a person who studies the thoughts, the creations, the ways of life, the actions, the natures of his predecessors and of mankind around him; but to say only this is not to separate him from the social scientist or from a large body of scientific folk. The differentiating factor must be found, then, in the attitude and purpose—in the temper—of the humanist. What he mainly is interested in doing is to identify those elements in experience and in the world which are regarded as specifically human—that is, which belong to man in contradistinction to the rest of the phenomenal universe. The humanist often has accepted the concept of a great chain of being which leads upward from what he considers the lowest and least sentient until it touches the heavens. It includes all the different orders from the inanimate to the angels, and in this scale he has tried to place man, distinguishing him first of all from the beast.

Now as a matter of fact, this is an extraordinary achievement, since, as the anthropologist has discovered by research, and as any humanist infers from his knowledge of classic myths, it took a very long time for man to regard himself as separated from the animal kingdom. This distinction, made not so very many hundreds of years ago, in its time and place was a most remarkable distinction, for it emphasized a special kind of intelligence, the reasoning intelligence of man; it introduced concepts of will; it introduced the notion of a moral code; it introduced the idea of establishing, through the rule of law, something like justice. And to say this is to say a very great deal, indeed.

Historically, such a concept of humanism is not very old. The word itself is a fairly new one—one finds it in Matthew Arnold, but, with the meaning given it here, not much earlier than that—and it comes into use about the time when modern man began to feel how far his culture was removed from the older—as we now call it, the ancient—world. In the Renaissance and for a century or more beyond it, readers of the classics did not regard them as something that belonged to a very different and remote time. Their importance lay in the fact that they could be read for the most part as though they were contemporary documents. Those writers whom we now call the ancients were accepted as authorities in such matters as cosmology, ethics, history, philosophy, politics, and even practical affairs,.in agriculture and warfare. Treatises like Milton's "Tractate of Education" recommend a study of the writers who used Greek and Latin not because they wrote in the learned languages, and thus provided some kind of philological discipline, but because they were uttering the best that had been thought on many subjects of vital concern.

The humanities, then, might be separated from theology, but they were not separated from science, because the notion of science as something apart from the rest of human activity had not yet arisen. Bacon had some inklings of the distinction, but it was not until the 19th century that an opposition between the humanities and the sciences was brought out—perhaps for the popular mind most clearly in the debates between Thomas Henry Huxley and Matthew Arnold. Huxley, the exponent of science, took a disparaging view of *belles lettres* and equated these with the humanities. Arnold protested, of course, that the humanities were much wider than *belles-lettristic* learning and argued very forcibly that Huxley had quite misunderstood the nature of his claims for humane literature. It may be admitted that Arnold, when he made his rejoinder, was, perhaps, insufficiently aware of the intellectual forces which already were stirring around him and was, moreover, too optimistic in supposing that there was to be an easy assimilation of the then new science by the studies which he defended and advocated. His notion was that science appealed only to one of the great powers of man—that is, the power of intellect and knowledge—while the learning that he called "humane" appealed to other powers—the sense for conduct, the sense for beauty. When he said this, he was not very prescient, perhaps; but as far as his knowledge went, he was right, and his successors, the so-called "new humanists" of the 20th century, constantly insisted upon a distinction between the proper sphere of science, which for them was that of inquiry into the natural phenomena of the external world, and the sphere of man, between the law for man and the law for thing. Famous lines come to mind, of course, in this connection: "Know, man hath all that Nature hath, but more; and in that more lies all his hope of good." For these philosophers, humane knowledge was a growth in experience, a slow growth, through the accumulation of tradition through trials and errors, which had brought about a knowledge in mankind as a whole of a Tao or "way" which constituted the best guide to the good and moral life. Because they saw this Tao taking shape over the centuries, they saw that many contributions from quite different sources and could be assimilated to it. They came to the realization that man's nature has been the same everywhere and always, and concluded that in philosophy, history, and literature, civilization had recorded principles of enduring value —principles which must dominate and overwhelm the monistic naturalism which threatens them.

This case was a good case, but it could not take into account some of the phenomena which we have been considering here, and especially that extraordinary acceleration in the rate of change in human affairs which makes the curve of progress discontinuous. As long as innovation was gradual, as long as great discoveries were infrequent, as long as technologies, customs, and human resources were modified slowly from generation to generation, the past was related intimately to the present, and the necessity for conservation was clearly apparent. But during the last 100 years, this situation has been completely upset by the enormous "explosions" which have occurred in the social and political spheres—and much more significantly in the sciences, both theoretical and applied. We all know the facts: advances in medicine during our generation are greater than all those previously made; seven-eighths of all the scientists who ever have lived are now alive; and so on. Yet, though we are aware that many beliefs long held are now obsolete and that history, in C. S. Lewis's expressive phrase, has turned a corner, we have not yet fully grasped the truth that the consequent redirection of our lives offers not only extraordinary new potentials, but also presents extraordinary new problems. What we have discovered, perhaps to a discouraging degree, is that the ability to adjust to and to control the changes which we are witnessing is by no means easy. We accept, but shrink from, the thought that within a generation we must revise entirely our outlook toward a great many things, or expect to experience the nightmares described by Karl Vonnegut in "Player Piano," or alternatively consent to take refuge in the soma of "Brave New World."

Obviously, under these circumstances, it is not enough to say that we can rely upon tradition and the past, that the philosophy of a Marcus Aurelius or the poetry of Shakespeare will help us to endure the sick hurry and divided aims of modern life. Matthew Arnold could take comfort in the Homeric line which tells us that "an enduring heart have the destinies appointed the children of men," but endurance is not enough and certainly is not in consonance with our temper. We shall seek direct remedies for our ills; we must quickly discover solutions to our problems; and not many of these will be found in the admonition of the Psalms or the Prophets, or the "Ethics" of Aristotle, or the "Republic" of Plato. The societies which produced these noble works are not our society. The outlook which they present is not our outlook. We may listen sympathetically to the laments of poets over the wearisome condition of humanity, but we also must seek to do something about it, and we are encouraged by the knowledge that in many instances we have been able to do a great deal about it. There is at least a reasonable hope that we can succeed in many of our endeavors, for the great fact with which we are faced is that our human capabilities have increased enormously since the fourth century, B.C. Society cannot simply rest, then, upon the assumption that human nature is always the same and that what was good enough for the past is the model for the present.

The results of this new orientation are already manifest, even though they are not always acknowledged. In the first place, there is the radical change in the direction of our studies and researches, a shift away from the historical-genetic axis to the descriptive-statistical. Many of us can remember when history was regarded as a con-

tinuum on which a search for causal relationships was a comparatively simple affair in theory, though, of course, never in practice.
Courses in language, literature, philosophy, the social sciences,
even the earth sciences, biology, and medicine, were presented according to this pattern. But in recent years, following the methods
of the pure sciences, less and less attention has been given to the
developmental or genetic aspects of a subject, while more and more
emphasis has been laid upon accurate description and quantification.
One has only to compare linguistics with the older philology, or the
use of research survey techniques with traditional political science,
to see how this principle applies, and its triumph may be observed
even in the contemporary outlook of historians and philosophers, not
to mention that of students of literature, whose new criticism obviously conforms to the descriptive analytical pattern and whose
method borrows much from the speculations and findings of the
behavioral scientists.

Let us pause on literature for a moment, since it often is considered in academic circles as the firmest center of humanistic discipline. Two points may be made. First, literature used to be accepted
as the most valuable record of man's development, the medium in
which the best that had been said and thought in the world was
enshrined. Second, an acquaintance with literature was thought to
be the best avenue through which the experience of life and its values
in their fullest strength and vigor might be obtained. But the past,
if it becomes irrelevant, is of interest only as an object of antiquarian
curiosity. As for experience, since most of it has become the special
province of the behavioral scientists, it is to these expert folk that
we turn and not to the less well qualified men of letters who are,
after all, only amateur, not scientific, observers.

Since, with the acceleration of change and the decline of history,
the knowledge of the recent, as well as the remote, past no longer
can be assumed, the explication of almost any important book written more than a few years ago requires an immense effort. The main
problem is the establishment of the context, of that social and intellectual order out of which the work emerged. To be sure, Dante's
"Divine Comedy" has long called for elaborate exegesis; but a similar
effort is now necessary if the life of a sailing ship as described by
Conrad or the conventions of a New England household as described
by Henry James are to be understood. And because this process is
time-consuming and difficult for teacher and pupil alike, it is now
common to neglect a study of the environment and to emphasize only

the contemporary. In any case, the student is invited to search for presiding metaphors, or mythic themes, or symbols, or psychological features of the kind identified by Freud and Jung. The inquiry may thus become statistical or analytical, and the poem or novel a case-book to be judged by the authority derived from behavioral science. We are all acquainted with the jargon: return to the womb, frustration, father-image, Christ-figure, the theme of alienation, and so on. The result is often the disintegration of a "literary" work, with a display of ingenuity through an exhibition of "insights" and elaborate disquisitions on "structure."

Some of these endeavors are trivial, misdirected, uninformed by a proper regard for logic and method, and deficient in learning. But the tendency which they illustrate cannot be condemned as wrong. It is inevitable that teachers who are concerned with representations of human activity should try to understand life through the application of those knowledges that are growing up around them. And if the study of the arts is thus redirected, and if the arts, by being anatomized, lose some of their independent status, there is no way of avoiding these developments or of checking them. Critics still are trying to carry out their necessary functions, and if they partially fail, it is largely because the difficulties they face are enormous. They are difficulties which affect the creative artist as well.

Let us consider a few. In the first place, our world society exhibits a cultural leveling. It is increasingly a middle-class society, and a society in which the state dominates the individual. Communications satellites enable widely separated and diverse peoples to share the same news as they now share the same brands of breakfast foods, vacuum sweepers, motor cars, and cosmetics. Scarcely a capital is without its Hilton Hotel. Yet, at the same time, there is a tendency toward tight groupings. Nationalism and racism are by no means extinct. Moreover, there is a good deal of specialization, so that the intellectual community becomes cellular, made up of experts whose efforts can be coordinated but who cannot individually carry out a complex project, *e.g.*, that of designing a highway system or an ICBM. Again, despite the leveling of material culture, the gap between the knowledge and expertise which the specialists possess and the concepts with which the average citizen is equipped widens steadily. Popularizations make us aware that great discoveries are occurring daily, but we feel our incompetence when we try to appraise them analytically or critically. We apparently must be content to accept more and more on the authority of others, and at second or third hand.

In a world of this kind, which is extremely complicated and confusing, the artist finds that he no longer has a public message. Since he cannot compass what is outside, he tends to turn inward and to be immensely concerned with himself and what goes on inside. The artist, in short, is ordinarily not *au courant* with contemporary culture. The confusions which he feels are real, but they are, in a measure, ignorant confusions, partly because he has not yet been properly instructed by the philosopher-critic, whose business it is to take what is known and thought and make it accessible to a public willing to be, and capable of being, informed. The critic, in other words, comes before the artist. The Marxian philosophy comes before the Marxist novel. What we are witnessing now is a kind of lag, the critic being only partly adequate to his task, and the artist contenting himself with half-knowledge. This is precisely one of the problems to which education, if it means what it says, will have to address itself.

The obvious gap between what the best of us—*i.e.*, the best informed—know to be our potential and what most of us accept as our potential, and between the possibility of exploiting this potential and the customs and fashions (on the whole, conservative) which we accept, must be closed. The humanist, because he has been a conservator and a traditionalist, understandably has tended to look back. His danger is that he will continue to look back nostalgically rather than exercise the powers of his imagination to help us realize—that is, to make real—the best that has been and is being thought and said. His great business now is not that of conservation, but of mediation and prophecy; he must fix his attention more largely than before on the present and the future, not allowing it to dwell exclusively on the past.

With what kinds of problems must he reckon? Certainly, he must reckon, first of all, with the problem of knowledge and its assimilation. The humanist used to wish for himself the role of *uomo universale*, that of a man who summed up in himself all knowledges, who, like Bacon, took all knowledge to be his province. This is, of course, now quite impossible. The humanist, like all the rest of us, must rely increasingly upon expert guidance. He must be content with derivative knowledge, and since one of his problems is to criticize as well as to understand, he must make reasonably sure that the knowledge which he is accumulating from the experts is a knowledge which is sound—knowledge on which a judgment can be based. Next, he must be a mediator. We move different parts of our lives into the future at different speeds. This is a very grave problem for most of us; *e.g.*, we know that we accept new technologies quite easily, while in matters of morals we tend to be conservative or fail to acknowledge the changes which actually come into being. The business of the humanist is to help us make the difficult transition from the present to the proximate future, or from the proximate past to the present, or from a remoter past to the present. This is a new and very significant part of his function. For example, we know that traditionally the humanist has been a man who believed in a way of life and thought which emphasized the claims of the individual. But in our age, and to a degree which could not have been imagined a century ago, the role of the individual has changed; in many ways it has diminished, for example, through the creation of a cellular society in which the bonds of cooperation are formed in ways which could not have been possible in the society of our colonial days.

The problem of the one and the many always will be with us— that is, the problem of the individual in society—but it is quite likely that we are going to lose the notion of individualism in the old sense and that man's functions in the 21st century will be quite different from those to which we have become accustomed or which have been passed down to us by tradition. And if our condition is to be changed, it is the enlightened humanist, alert to the nature of man and the world of which he is a part, who must lead in helping us make the adjustment. Instead of falling into an Orwellian pessimism, he will try to work out some means of making the situation not only tolerable, but humanly productive. The humanist, of course, has another problem, and one hitherto, I suppose, undreamed of— *i.e.*, how to extricate man from the machine. This is a more serious problem than even in our darker moments today we seem to have realized. But if the machine threatens to overwhelm us, the humanist must ask how the machine can be adjusted to human life. For the humanist must accept the fact that we always have this pull between our conservative tendency, our delight in "lying in the old straw of our habits," to quote Matthew Arnold again, and the necessities that pull us away from that life and which pull us out of it. This tension never has been, for reasons that we all know, so great and so disturbing as it is today.

Since the humanist has made it his business to know the past, he can estimate the value and nature of the conservative elements derived from it; he can explain, reinforce, cherish these; but he is equally responsible, through his vision of a possible and probable future, to help his fellows shake off the elements which are outmoded, which clog and hinder. This is most important, because we are living in times when wrong decisions are likely to be overwhelmingly disastrous. Never in the history of mankind have we been in a situation where errors in judgment could affect so many in so dreadful a way as we must imagine when we think of the possibility of war or the possibility that the population explosion will not be checked. In the past, the decisions made by a king or council might be disastrous, but generally only to a relatively small group; now, as we know, the fate of whole nations may be determined by a telephone call. And so the humanist, here again in a mediating role, must try to establish some sort of checks and balances. He will recognize, as we all must, that wherever there is a social gain there is likely to be a social loss, and he will try to estimate the loss and gain so that we are aware of both as we move toward our decisions, political or social. This means, of course, that he must have in his mind, and must communicate to others, a philosophic character.

Philosophy is the guide, traditionally, to life, and as man becomes ever more the minister and interpreter of nature, the manipulation of it will require a very significant and purposeful and effective philosophy, indeed. For we must ask again and again where we are going to get the police who can be trusted to watch the policemen. Our society is going to demand this kind of control, and, therefore, we not only must speculate upon the future, but we must add to the speculation what it is the business of the artist and those who study the arts to supply—the quality of imagination. And just here lies the humanist's great challenge. Can the humanities be so directed and disseminated that an informed public, conscious of the possible applications of the best that has and is being thought and said, will exercise the power of imagination which progressively will identify what is desirable in a possible human experience? If this challenge can be met, we have an unprecedented opportunity to experiment with the modification of our lives and of our natures.

As soon as the idea of a purposeful direction toward a generously and wisely imagined future is suggested, many will recoil, for to most of us there is a suggestion here of an authoritarian state dominated by a Big Brother or a panel of social engineers. And there are certainly dangers in trying to imagine the future and in then manipulating affairs so that they will work toward it. But perhaps this danger can be obviated in part by allowing for a considerable variety of experimentation. Of course, we shall have to face many questions—among them, the old utilitarian question, whether it is better to be a pig satisfied or Socrates unsatisfied. (To this kind of question there is no answer in logic, though there is a partial answer in experience!) If we speedily and earnestly can think about our humanity while there is yet time, we can win the race against un-planned catastrophe. What we need, in the light of what we know about the sources of human happiness in the past and in the poten-tial future, is to be bold enough to try to discover probable bases for this happiness. We also must find the sources of strength and the leadership which will make the trial of various systems and societies a possibility.

It is a mistake to think of our time as the twilight of a civiliza-tion. If we live in the twilight, it is the twilight before a new dawn. Humanists, if they are to act a significant role in the new day, must cease to behave as though they inhabited a Laputa where mad sci-entists are trying to extract sunbeams from cucumbers. Scientists are not mad, and their achievements make the dreams of the Laputians seem not vain, but trivial. The humanist, if he is knowledgeable and if he exercises wisely the power of creative imagination, can make the marvels of science produce fruits nobler than those for which Bacon yearned. Like our first parents, we have the world all before us where we can choose our place of rest. It may never be an earthly Paradise, but it can be better than anything that man has known.

8. EDUCATION FOR HUMANE LIVING IN AN AGE OF AUTOMATION

G. BRUCE DEARING

IN MANY of our increasingly anxious discussions of the role of what we traditionally have called "the humanities" in contemporary higher education, our councils have been beclouded and baffled by confusions in definition. "Humanistic Education" is not limited to the standard courses in classical language, literature, the fine arts, and the subjects normally offered in departments or divisions familiarly classified as Arts or Humanities as distinguished from Sciences and Social Sciences. And I do not wish to subsume all knowledge under the rubric of "Liberal Education" and to argue that it is at least as easy to teach Sanitary Engineering humanely and as an humanistic discipline as it is to teach Middle High German. However, it is possible to draw a distinction between general education and specialized education, between education and training, between the liberal and the vocational, and between the humanistic and the technological or technical. I do not aggrandize the one and disparage the other, for each is inescapably necessary to anyone who seeks to be effectively human and humane in our society. We are dealing here not with polar opposites, but with separable, if not wholly discrete elements of the activities which are going forward in our colleges and universities and inside the heads of those who are listening, reading, observing, and reasoning in whatever context. I shall concern myself with those elements of education which I take to be general, liberal, humanistic, and educative.

If I am asked to outline the proper shape of humanistic education for an age of automation, I would begin by quoting the construction arrived at by the hard-working Curriculum Committee of the School of Arts and Science, University of Delaware, after a full year of deliberation and debate. One reason I like it so much is that it turned out to be the statement which I had written for the undergraduate catalogue two years earlier and which the school committee happened upon after being unable to agree on any alternative formulation. Although it sounds a bit ambitious, it still is an earnest essay in expressing what many of us deeply believe about the mission and purpose of higher education:

Courses and programs are designed to help the student to organize his experience meaningfully and to acquire perceptions, skills, and attitudes which will assist him in achieving a full and satisfying life as a contributing member of society. The school seeks to develop in its students a heightened awareness of all aspects of human environment, intellectual curiosity, respect for fact, perception of the complexity of truth, skill in reasoning, and concern for integrity and logical consistency.

Contributions of the humanities include the development and refinement of systems of value, of aesthetic appreciation, and of a viable world view. The humanities should provide, also, an acquaintance with the heritage of both Western and non-Western cultures, and increased skill in communication, both verbal and non-verbal. Contributions of the social sciences include the acquisition of historical perspective; acquaintance with facts and concepts relating to social organization and patterns of inter-action among individual persons and groups; and the development of an informed concern about practical, moral, and ethical issues in the structure and operation of society. Studies in this area aim toward emancipation from provincialism and naive ethnocentrism; refinement of concepts of causality in the social realm; and the development of understanding in the recognition and resolution of intra-personal, inter-personal, intra-group and inter-group conflicts. Offerings in mathematics and the natural sciences are directed at the development of skill in quantitative thinking; acquaintance with the basic facts and concepts relating to the physical universe; comprehension of, and respect for, the approach to knowledge through experimentation; and direct experience with rigor and precision in perception, description, and manipulation.

In the face of the Twentieth Century explosion of knowledge, only that graduate can be considered educated who has developed the tools, techniques, and attitudes for continuing education. In recognition of this fact, a premium is placed on individual initiative and self direction. The University cannot successfully educate students who merely present themselves passively to be *taught;* it can provide an environment in which a well-motivated student may *learn* up to the full limits of his capacity.

Let me expand upon some of the implications of this statement. One of the things anyone who teaches both college-age students and adults in a continuing education program quickly discovers is that older students have more experience, and they organize it differently. But if an education does not immediately and materially assist in the organization and interpretation of life experience, it seems to me to be of questionable value. Moreover, it is by no means enough to acquire information (which, unfortunately, is too often the primary, or even the only, commodity given much attention in the plan of courses of instruction). We need to sharpen all our perceptions, to see, hear, and even to taste, touch, and smell many material and immaterial environments with greater accuracy, precision, and joy or revulsion than those who are only partially educated and, therefore, only partially alive and incompletely human. We need to acquire learned skills not merely to recommend ourselves for gainful employment as typists, draftsmen, or chemists, but to permit us to communicate effectively, to establish acceptable and satisfying social relationships, and to facilitate our continued growth. And too often we overlook the importance of attitudes, whether recognized and consciously evoked or instilled, or developed and communicated without intention or recognition. Consider, for example, the attitude of fear and distaste toward mathematics which is communicated to so large a majority of our elementary school children by teachers who themselves have a fear and distaste for a body of knowledge and for techniques with which they are uncomfortable and uncertain. Or consider the attitudes toward academic honesty which have scandalized so many secondary schools and colleges in these past years and which are properly so grave a concern of the society at large.

We express our concern for alertness and awareness, which is essential if we are to adapt to change, recognize opportunity, respond relevantly to threats and dangers, and experience anything to the fullest. We must be curious if we hope to continue learning. We should respect fact and love truth, recognizing that any truth worth comprehending, like any woman worth knowing, is infinitely various and inexhaustibly complex. We should have learned how to reason and, if possible, how to think, recognizing that there is an important place for the irrational, the intuitive, and the inexplicable in the most penetrating thought, as Jerome Bruner has pointed out so winsomely in his "Essays for the Left Hand." And however unfashionable the idea may be at present of a faculty concerning itself with the personal values of its students, I ally myself with those who believe that both precepts and examples of integrity, consistency, and magnanimity should be available to, and even urged upon, the college student.

I do not claim all the virtues as the exclusive property of the humanities. Such studies are traditionally concerned with preparing a student, in Matthew Arnold's phrase, to "see life steadily and see it whole," or in Gordan Keith Chalmers' phrase, "Not merely to think, but to think in relevant terms about things that matter." However, concepts of the good are as much a property of history or sociology as of philosophy or literature; beauty belongs as much to mathematics as to art history, and truth both transcends and eludes all our formulations and organizational patterns. We do too little and should do more straightway to introduce significant aspects of non-American and non-Western cultures into our curricula, particularly in the humanities and the social sciences. Also, while agreeing with the critics of higher education that our products exhibit too little skill in communication, such as writing and speaking, I earnestly would urge the importance of non-verbal communication—the visual arts, the performing arts, and the language of gesture and of the eloquently unsaid.

The direction which our society appears to be taking with increased interdependence, increased interaction, and, therefore, increased opportunity for choice, conflict, and decision seems to place a premium upon literacy in the sciences of anthropology, sociology, psychology, economics, and politics. Recent events have illustrated dramatically and tragically the residual barbarism in our civilization as well as its potentialities for dignity, nobility, and the rational approach to complex social problems. A world of automation will be a world of groups in any case, whether or not it is possible to preserve the separate, distinct, and distinctive humanity of the individual.

We recently have discovered, to the dismay of some and the delight of others, that mathematics is as basic to the current understanding and development of economics, music, and sociology as it is for physics or engineering. We have begun to tell one another, and at least in part to believe, that scientific illiteracy in our technological age is as indefensible as religious or literary ignorance and indifference have been in former times. Surely, one who expects to live alertly and in a significantly contributing way in an age of automation needs to know something of the physical universe he inhabits and of the techniques of dealing with unyielding and unforgiving reality with rigor, precision, and a healthy respect. One does not have to be an astronaut to get in trouble with a lawful universe if the calculations are off or the reasoning is imprecise. I have heard an astronaut quoted as reflecting in the midst of the pre-launch tensions that everything below him had been provided by a low bidder. Other moments of truth have been and will be approached in analagous ways by managers, political leaders, administrators, and all others with responsibility for action. They should be able to hope that rough approximations, easy generalizations, inviting self deceptions, the almost fine and the nearly true, have little part in the analyses, constructions, and predictions on which they must stake much that they value. We hope and believe that the necessary rigor and precision can be cultivated by a student's experience in quantitative thinking and experimental procedures.

Finally, we feel that higher education is not coextensive with the undergraduate or graduate years and that passive submission to teaching is a poor way to spend those years. It is alleged that most engineers become obsolete in a cycle of from five to 10 years and either must be reeducated continuously or continually if they are to perform their proper functions. I am prepared to assert that both our general and our specialized education are subject to obsolescence if we have not learned how to continue to learn throughout our lives.

One of the most difficult problems is that of determining whether we really are talking about the education of an elite who shall be governors and directors, or undertaking the education of an eligible majority or the whole society. The curricula we cling to were designed originally for governors and professional men. It may be that such curricula are but ill-adapted to the needs of those who shall be making decisions only for themselves and not for others. It may be also that we do a disservice to a man if we educate him for power and authority and he finds not only that he has no one to command or govern, but that he has not even a role in which he can contribute. What Napoleon could ever be happy either in Corsica or on Elba?

We must recognize in ourselves some extraordinarily incongruous and inconsistent attitudes toward work. Most of us are the inheritors of the 19th-century "gospel of work" and have thought with Carlyle that "work is worship." At the same time that we spend many of our days in quiet desperation, we dream of lotus land, plan feverishly for vacations and retirement which seem but rarely to live up to expectations, and recognize, if we do not identify with, Auden's "unimportant clerk" who writes "I do not like my work" on the pink official form.

It has been widely and shrewdly remarked that in our time a traditional pyramid has been overturned. Where once the mass of people toiled that a few might live in ease and luxury, it now appears to be not only possible but probable that a few among the most gifted and able shall work long hours without stint so that their numberless inferiors can vegetate in indolence and ease. The evidence of this shift is everywhere, and it is unmistakable. In many large organizations it appears that overtime work and harassing pressures are not merely the responsibility, but the privilege and the symbol of status of the major executive. Indeed, in many management and administrative circles it appears that a kind of "cult of overwork" is consciously fostered. We all can think of leaders in government, industry, and education who make it a point to arrive early at the office, work beyond regular hours, and regularly take home a briefcase full of work. In an essay in *Vogue* (October, 1963), David Ogilvy chillingly recounts the devices he has employed to pervert the Protestant Ethic and to insure that his subordinates will feel guilty for every moment they are not actively working at their jobs. The implication is that the men who really count will choose to work all the time and that the no-account majority is, by nature, indolent and will work as little as it can get away with.

One of the most striking effects of automation, and of the advanced technology which has made it possible, is the denial of work to the unskilled or semi-skilled majority and at the same time the piling of excessive loads upon the highly skilled minority. I doubt that we really are prepared yet to face the implications of this new situation.

It seems significant that literary artists, for a surprisingly long time, have foreseen and written prophetically about matters which society only recently has begun to take seriously. In the 1860's, Samuel Butler, in his ingenious fable, "Erewhon," described an utopian society which had recognized and met the problems of technological unemployment by the expedient of destroying all the machines and the scientific advances developed in the 271 years preceding the fateful decision. A similar device is employed in Ayn Rand's more recent "Anthem," where a handicraft economy is reinstituted to occupy the time of the society which otherwise would have lost its purpose and its meaning. In the 1920's, Ryunosuke Akutagawa, in the anti-utopian novel, "Kappa," described the direction he felt the industrialization of Japan was taking: "An average of seven or eight hundred new machines are invented every month, and things are produced on a larger and larger scale with less and less labor. The result is forty or fifty thousand more Kappas thrown out of work every month." The solution arrived at in this romance was that of Jonathan Swift's "Modest Proposal." As the spokesman for the society says, " 'We kill all those workers and eat their flesh. Just look at this newspaper here. This month 64,769 workers have been dismissed, and the price of meat has dropped accordingly.' 'Do they meekly consent to be killed?' I asked. 'It's no use making a fuss,' said Pep, who sat frowning by a wild peach in the pot. 'We've got the "workers butchery law." ' " In the late 1920's, the Russian, Eugene Zamiatin, in his satirical anti-utopian novel, "We," described the effects of the mechanization, materialization, and dehumanization of totalitarian Russia. In 1930, Aldous Huxley, in his "Brave New World," developed what is probably the most brilliant and comprehensive analysis of a society in which technology has been carried to its logical conclusion. George Orwell's more recent "1984" owes much to the Russian "We" in its account of a dehumanized totalitarian society.

All of these books are consistent in suggesting that "the most difficult problem that exists today in the civilized world is a problem of the preservation of the independent, original, creative personality," as Gregory Zilboorg said in his 1924 introduction to "We," reiterating in 1959 that "man as an individual, not just as a statistical datum, seems to have lost his value." All postulate the theory that in Zilboorg's words, "most men believe their freedom to be more than a fair exchange for a high level of materialistic happiness. If the present rapid rate of technological development continues, both totalitarian and democratic societies will be involved in this test. As we ourselves pursue even higher goals of materialistic happiness, the complexity of our technological society will increase and exert even more intense pressures for efficiency through the regulation of our lives." The Grand Inquisitor in "The Brothers Karamazov" and the World Controller in "Brave New World" argue persuasively that a regulated, conditioned happiness is the best that can be hoped for by the mass of men in a technological society. The brilliant psychologist, B. F. Skinner, in his novel, "Walden II," seriously proposes the kind of "human engineering" which is anathema to Huxley. Dostoevski, Zamiatin, Akutagawa, Huxley, and Orwell all reveal a passionate commitment to individual human freedom and express hope that somehow humanistic values can prevail in the face of rampant technology and materialism. Have we any reason to hope that their prophetic fears can be prevented from being fulfilled in all their horror?

The area in which we are weakest and least advanced is that of knowledge of the nature of man, and particularly of man in the aggregate rather than as an individual person. We may be horrified at the progress of the development of techniques for brain-washing and for the manipulation of masses of people by totalitarian powers. However, such techniques are far less efficacious, and far less advanced in theoretical explanation, than we have been led to believe. This seems to be the weakest part of the horror stories presented in the anti-utopian novels, like "Brave New World," "We," and "1984." Perhaps I am merely a naive product of a narrowly and optimistically humanistic education, but I prefer to believe that the human animal is more complex and more resistant to conditioning than the gloomier of the prophets of enveloping totalitarianism appear to think.

I prefer to believe that it will be possible to develop and to learn new definitions of and attitudes toward work and to substitute the concept of *relevant and humanly significant activity* for the concept of *productive labor* as the primary basis for human dignity and human satisfaction. This may veer perilously close to social philosophies which are not acceptable to a democratic society. However, I cast my lot with those who are seeking a middle way among the extremes of totally engineered and, therefore, no longer fully human happiness in the manner of the "Brave New World" and "Walden II," the totally engineered misery of "1984" and "We," and a chaotic and demoralized society in which only a minority has a basis for the sense of individual worth and significance which alone can make the human condition a bearable estate. I think that education of the kind I have described has a signal contribution to make to the search for this middle way.

9. EDUCATION, AUTOMATION, AND HUMANISTIC COMPETENCE

PETER E. SIEGLE

I F WE ARE GOING to achieve a society in which change, automation, and situational control by the people are somehow dynamically related, education must look upon its own task as one of establishing a means to mental health. This is what I prefer to call the "therapeutic stance" or, better still, the "prophylactic stance," which we refer to some times in medicine as preventive therapy. I say therapeutic not because I necessarily think everybody is sick. I want it to be prophylactic. I believe there are certain dysfunctions inherent in modern society. There are still large numbers of people in this country who are dysfunctional because they are members of unfortunate disadvantaged groups. They and the society need therapy.

The recurring and very rapid changes in our society do create a rather continuing state of dysfunction. If we are going to deal with this educationally, we have to define the kind of person we wish to produce. This person we call a healthy man, and, in this context, I prefer to define a healthy man as a competent man. That gets tricky because there are at least two kinds of competencies. The first is technical competency. And this requires some competency in the kind of thing that makes people literate in the ways of our society. I refer also to a technical competency, which is reflected not only in a skilled man (which I think is a static term), but a skillful man, and to me that is a distinction. A skillful man is a much more dynamic man who has the capacity for flexibility which our society craves. And I think these are what our educational purposes ought to be. We say we want to "learn him how to learn" (I choose my language carefully here, too, because this implies to me that there is an educable or trainable man); yes, but he is also a man who feels that he can learn. There is a continuing reinforcement necessary which is the continuing province of adult continuing education. A man just cannot learn his competency once. He must be tested constantly and reinforced in this kind of education in order to maintain psychic resiliency.

The second kind of competency is related to feelings. This is what I call personal competency, which refers to how a man feels about uncertainty—his ability to feel intensely without shame, to find joy without guilt, to feel capable of dealing with the unknown and with long periods of non-work, which our society appears to be heading toward.

There are many ways of getting at this goal of competency. Yet, we have looked too much at our own culture and not enough at the whole world. There are very valid educational notions which do exist in other countries. The conflict between specialization and generalization or between rigor and flexibility is really not a great problem if it is approached with the therapeutic stance. For example, we know the Oxonian position; an educated man reads intensely and achieves a considerable competence in something like Greek. This makes him a proper specimen to be a foreign officer in the British Imperial System. This is valid. I do not believe that rigor in one thing necessarily makes a person non-flexible, because rigor is not the same as rigidity. From an educational point of view, we must look to the concept of rigor. In this way we feel our competence and feel a sense of rigorous accomplishment. This gives us the skill that we need in order to deal flexibly with the unknown situations in our society.

There is a new look involved. It seems that the times cry out today for a new look at the meaning of competency, and the relationship between light and heat or thought and feeling with respect to that competency. The new look is a dynamic combination of intellectual and technical skillfulness on the one hand and a healthy psyche which can handle feelings on the other. This may well be the New Humanism which we must look to for our solutions to current problems. The challenge to us educationally is to find the New Humanists to teach the New Humanism.

Where these New Humanists will be found (in what departments and non-departments of universities, in what non-university educational institutions and endeavors) only can be ascertained after a thorough analysis and search in which a clear concept of competency and education is derived.

10. THE EDUCATION OF THE EXECUTIVE AS NEW HUMANIST

C. M. D. PETERS

IT SEEMS LOGICAL that, in the age of automation, the educational priorities should go to the prospective politician, businessmen, and administrator. But what kind of education should they get? As a representative of middle management in a large business concern, I would like to give my personal opinion.

A typical answer to the question is "a broad general education that will make the student well informed about the environment we live in." But, in the perspective of the complex, modern, changing world, this is not enough. What is needed is an education that will refine, sharpen, and develop the faculties for critical appreciation of any aspect of our environment, with a view to wisdom of action. What we are talking about, of course, is a humanist—perhaps a New Humanist. With science and technology and the quantitative concepts of mathematics figuring so largely in the modern world, there must be added to the usual faculties associated with humanism—namely, those of thought and expression in terms of words—the faculties of thought and expression in terms of mathematical symbols. A useful term that is becoming current is "numeracy" as a complement to "literacy."

Actually, the above contains nothing new. From the time of Charlemagne, through the Middle Ages and beyond, the Trivium (grammar, dialectic, and rhetoric) and the Quadrivium (arithmetic, geometry, astronomy, and music) formed a sevenfold requirement for the Master of Arts degree all over Europe. What one is talking about is something akin to the Renaissance man. The vastly expanded storehouse of known facts and the complexity of the modern world do not make him an impracticality. The pruning, garnering, and selection of the essential principles is just a bit harder than it used to be.

Accordingly, I would define the New Humanist as one who *is literate, "numerate," articulate, and human; excels in one or the other of the first two qualities; and has knowledge of a reasonable range of literature, philosophy (including politics and economics), and history in support of the quality to be literate, and of mathematical and scientific theory and practice in support of the quality to be "numerate."*

Some amplification is perhaps worth while. In regard to being both *literate* and *numerate,* rare is the man who can be both a first-class essayist and a first-class mathematician. Words and numbers are different things and a high degree of skill with one appears to require a somewhat different bent of mind than with the other. The pure humanist or "literate" man has been trained to distill verbal judgment as to what is true-false, good-bad, beautiful-ugly, profitable-unprofitable out of the circumstances of human life. Language is the tool and the area of training is literature, philosophy, and history. The pure scientist or "numerate" man has been trained to distill from the massive data of observation in the physical world what is causative, etc., in the relationships of the components. Mathematics, and, to some extent, language, is the tool, and the area of training is physics, chemistry, biology, etc. The crux of the matter is whether in trying to combine both "literacy" and "numeracy" for the New Humanist, one would get a school that is too broad to permit "excellence." The answer is in the selectivity of the subject matter for curriculum.

The New Humanist who is headed for business should aim at being very proficient in numbers. So much of the business world is reduced to numbers. The advent of the computer is more and more translating all his information into mathematical symbols. And it is the products of science and technology that are very largely his stock in trade. By being grounded in the finest techniques of mathematics and in the major laws and principles of science, he should be able to maintain contact with the scientists and technologists, no matter how much these specialized fields may shift or be subject to obsolescence.

In regard to being *articulate* and *human,* there is the danger of being "sicklied o'er with the pale cast of thought." And in these days of the specialist, man is inclined to lose the art of thinking and speaking on his feet. There is inclined to be a loss of confidence in the individual and an unwillingness to speak or act unsupported by specialized assistance. I would like to see the up-and-coming New Humanist a member of the university debating team. Secondly, I would like to see the New Humanist take part in sports—how ever bad his performance.

In regard to *excelling* and *a reasonable range of knowledge,* as indicated above, excellence is incompatible with excessive broadness. And the most that one can expect, therefore, is excellence in limited areas and proficiency in the rest. Furthermore, since the main concern is the development of faculties—the ability to survey an area of experience, dig out the critical details, and form independent judgments, the curriculum need not stress the latest fad or cover a wide range. It should be classical in the sense of first class. It should be concerned with material where the thinking has been tested and acknowledged as first class, and there is no better tester than the passage of time. Furthermore, the prospective New Humanist should receive a plentiful exposure to serious study and creative thought.

The educators still can say that they offer all the subjects, and it is up to the New Humanist to take them and then for business and politics to recognize him. But I think the educator should go further. The definition of the New Humanist offers a certain norm and standard but leaves open a great variety of ways to reach it. No educational institution can excel in everything. But perhaps the curriculum for the New Humanist in each institution can be directed to those subjects where they have the finest experts and teachers. Perhaps, too, admission could be limited to those students who have the potential for reaching the highest standards by confining it to those who have proved themselves in prerequisites of the first two years. Recognition, too, could be advanced if there could be a common name for the school from one institution to another—something like "Humanities Lit. Num."—with a common standard of excellence.

The scientists and technologists inevitably will go on fragmenting the areas of their investigation into smaller and more esoteric units. But if the New Humanist is going to be "numerate," then in the field of education the scientist will have to set out the critical principles in a reasonably tractable form in the same way that the men of literature, philosophy, and history have done. I believe that the new breed of historians of science can help.

The graduate New Humanist will not be at any vocational disadvantage; on the contrary, there will be competition for him. Moreover, there are few starting jobs in business which he would not be able to handle with ease in very short order. Given the appropriate pertinacity and breaks from above, it should not be too long before he will be in some seat of power in some new or expanding institution in politics, business, or administration for which he will have been trained.

11. SOME QUESTIONS CONCERNING HUMANISTIC EDUCATION AND AUTOMATION

EMERY F. BACon

ONE OF THE MISFORTUNES of our modern times is that there are too few humanists in positions of importance in our society having the power to make decisions affecting the destiny of all our people. Not that men in the technical and scientific fields do not have good judgment; I am sure they do. But, by and large, I have been disturbed, as I feel many are, that these men are not completely concerned, nor familiar, with all the problems that involve a very diverse and difficult society. While the problems relating to man have been mounting, adequate solutions have not been forthcoming.

Technology is something that has been with us since the very beginning of time. Man always has been involved, whether he realized it or not, with technology and its influence upon society, culture, civilization, and growth throughout all of human history. Moreover, our present age is dominated not only by technology, but also by highly trained professionals who are deeply immersed in scientific knowledge and its application. There are several good examples of what this combination of men and science has produced in recent times, the foremost of which is the development of the nuclear bomb. The second is the tremendous population explosion which is occurring throughout the world. Research in the scientific and medical

114

fields has reduced the death rate and produced a population which is living longer and multiplying faster than ever before in history.

The world also has shrunk because of the combination of science and technology. Through radio, TV, and other electronic devices, we now have instant world-wide communication. We know immediately what is happening in all parts of the earth; and, when the tragedy happened in Dallas, Tex., there was no country that did not know by radio and TV, within an hour, that the President of the United States had been assassinated. This rapid communicative system works not only for good, but at times it can work for great evil.

Many of the products that we have today, as recently as 10 or 15 years ago, were undreamed of, unheard of, or not needed. Yet, today, they are considered not luxuries, but necessities. And we insist, as consumers, that ever-new products be developed and that new ideas be generated for our own insatiable appetites.

Concurrently, the productivity per man hour has increased prodigiously as a result of applying new knowledge in the physical, chemical, and biological sciences, and still more spectacular achievements undoubtedly lie ahead. The electronic computer and data-processing machines, with their ability for decision-making and production, offer unlimited goods and services in the years ahead. The peaceful use of nuclear energy has been attempted. We have not done too well with it yet, but those who know say that with proper application we will be able to solve many problems of the world, including the production of food and goods, the elimination of disease, and the creation of vibrant economies in many of the underdeveloped areas of this globe.

The de-salting of salt water promises great hope for those parts of the earth which have fertile soil but insufficient rainfall. Genetic improvements of plants and animals portend a life for us and for the plant kingdom which is contrary to anything we have known in the past. We do not know how we are going, we do not know where we are going, and we really do not know what we are going to achieve during our lifetime or that of our children or our grandchildren, but we do know that we are moving ahead with ever-increasing rapidity in the fields of technology and science.

Nevertheless, we, as American people, cannot relax with the pleasures of the world's most affluent society simply because we do not know just where we are going. If neither we nor our institutions are prepared to meet the challenge of change, then we, individually and as a whole people, risk grave economic, social, and political disturbances.

What are the grave problems looming before us today? One of the problems concerns the mounting unemployment in the United States. The Department of Labor reports that unemployment is between 5½ and 6% of the labor force. But a great many economists say that this figure is a fictitious one. The true figure, they charge, is much closer to 10%. In other words, there are a great number of individuals in our society who are unemployed, many unwillingly, simply because the advances made by science and technology have eliminated jobs. We have, simultaneously, in the United States, an increasing number of people of growing affluence. Thus, we have a nation which is literally split in half as to jobs and wealth. On the one hand, we have about 100,000,000 people who live the abundant life as no people ever have lived before. They have satisfied all their wants, they have fulfilled all their needs, and they can do almost anything they wish. On the other hand, we have the gnawing problem of a large number of people—some estimate between 70,000,000- 80,000,000 people—who live in deprivation and poverty in spite of the great wealth of the nation itself. This is a country which has a gross national product approaching $600,000,000,000 and yet has not been able to maintain, through equitable distribution of its goods and services, sufficient income for the lower two-fifths of the nation to provide them with security and with material goods.

There are several questions which trouble us and which we must answer inevitably if we are to solve the dilemma confronting us:

1. How can we reduce personal hardships which seemingly constitute the price of progress enjoyed by our society as a whole?

2. How can we educate and train the millions of displaced workers and the annual crop of new job entrants for those positions and jobs required for the new technology?

3. How can we provide humanly for those who are not needed in the economy and maintain them at appropriate levels of livelihood and conditions of personal dignity and social respect?

4. How can we, as a nation, slowly convert our disintegrating cities into hospitable abodes of a civilized people?

There is no question that technology has done a great deal for us. Technology has made us the leading nation of the world and the acknowledged guardian of Western culture. Other nations look to us and attempt to emulate us because of our material achievements.

Yet, is it possible that some of the questions we have raised either have been ignored or not been answered properly?

Could it be that one of the reasons for this is that we have neglected these areas in the field of the liberal arts so that our leaders today are not prepared adequately to face up to the great social and human problems that beset us? Until they are answered by men of deep understanding and wisdom, our difficulties and our problems will increase rather than diminish.

12. TECHNOLOGICAL CHANGE, HUMANISTIC IMPERATIVES, AND THE TRAGIC SENSE

LUTHER H. HARSHBARGER

HISTORY is our common memory and its heritage comes to us as a repeated summons rather than as a transfer of possessions. One of the ways to see what is at stake in the contemporary technological revolution is to look at the "sweep" of the history of the status of man.

In the classical period, men were equal before their God or gods. In the medieval period, a man was born into his status. He had an inherited position which was good or bad, depending upon how he chose his parents. In the Renaissance and the Reformation, men achieved the right to become conscious thinkers, the right to education. In the modern achievement society, men achieved their basic political freedoms in the West. In the contemporary world, men achieved the right to economic necessity, yea, even abundance. To-day, if we are to understand what is going on in the world, we must see that there is taking place a new revolution—a revolution through which men are achieving for the first time in human history the right to human dignity. The simple phrase, "I want to be treated like a man," is the most powerful force at work in the world today.

That this is not merely a chronological development is clear. These historical revolutions are simultaneous in all societies, including our own. In types of men, Americans are at one and the same time Hebraic, Greek, modern, secular, and Neanderthal. As the masses of men glimpse their dignity, primitive men try to keep them primitive, but the march is on. Future historians will mark the 20th century as the era when men became fully aware of being men.

The "common" man rightly attributes this possibility to the technological revolution. So much does he do so that his image of the scientific technological revolution is almost a caricature. In the popular mind, science is authoritative truth and the promise of salvation. It is the key to affluence, to comfort, to security, to well-being. Science will win wars, help man succeed in business, achieve political office, improve education and morals, purify the health, and correct his complexion. We get on with science! Wisdom is the economic and efficient way of finding out what we want and how to organize our resources to get it. Society is a complex and self-adjusting instrument, and science reveals the shape of the future so that no human decision can change it. Therefore, we need social and human engineers to give us direction.

In more sophisticated language, descriptive norms only are rational. We need no ontology; truth is operational, purpose is an illusion, value judgments are disguises for matters of fact, ought is desire. The formation of policy and the right to organize society is the prerogative of those who know.

Where does wisdom come from? It is knowledge rightly applied. It is the logical extension of technical reason. Through its methodologies, man achieves power and harnesses the universe so that eventually no problem is insoluble.

Admittedly, this is a sad caricature. As one who stands in the Hebraic-Christian tradition, I want to affirm that *esse qua esse bonum est* ("whatever is is good"). Each thing is good in its particularity and all things are good. Therefore, my first response to the world, to science, and to technology in all its materiality is affirmation and appreciation. From my stance, it is this love of the good world which stimulates the scientific and technological responses.

But our response brings certain temptations, like those of spiritual pride and authority once common to the classical priesthood. We may be developing new religious orders in which the theoretical physicist becomes the high priest, the researcher the monastic, and the engineer the secular clergy. These orders are set apart by a discipline (laboratory), a theology (scientific jargon), an attitude (contempt for man and the world), and a church (the scientific community). Should this happen, then we once again would repeat history, for it was in ancient Egypt where the astronomer-priests were the masters of science and the dispensers of its power in society and the harbingers of its omens in politics.

This description may be grossly exaggerated, but I marvel at the extreme confidence society demonstrates in science and technology as means to desired ends. So much is this true in our society that everyone wants to be a scientist. I belong to a society for the scientific study of religion. The theologians want to be scientists. We think of political scientists, philosophers of science, social scientists, and now one can make ethics a science. This is not the fault of the authentic scientist; quite the contrary. Society has erected this idol and expects from it what it cannot and should not do. That the scientific and technological methodologies are enlightening means to truth I never would deny, but they are not the only means. I would want to affirm that it may well be that the authentic humanists of our day are the scientists and technologists. Certainly, they are the advocates of liberal studies very often in opposition to the very narrow and specialized concerns of the humanistic disciplines.

We turn, then, to the task of the humanities. In this new revolution, the dignity of man is at stake—if not humanity itself. In Freudian terms, we are in an "identity crisis," where each man must forge for himself some central perspective and direction, some working unity which accounts for wholeness. We make total demands upon ourselves and our environment; we insist on daily confirming ourselves in either a senseless past or a meaningful future, in virtue or vice, in uniqueness or in self-loss.

The task of the humanities is to elaborate on what we feel profoundly to be true, then translate into significant words and images the exceeding darkness which surrounds man's existence, as well as the light which pervades it beyond all desert or comprehension, and thus come, hopefully, to some understanding of the world and of human existence.

In this setting, there are at least four responsibilities, if not imperatives, which devolve upon the humanistic disciplines:

1. The humanities can help us to see life in its wholeness. They must affirm that not all facts are susceptible to technical reason as the only means of understanding. In a humanistic context, the purpose of learning is to understand the place of man in the vaster design, to provide some abiding place for the mind, some habitation for the spirit. In a humanistic spirit, man must have a view of the

ends to which life should be directed and the principles by which it should be lived. He should be able to see phenomena in context. He has facts, he should have a way of looking at them, and then must be moved to do something about them.

2. It is the responsibility of the humanities to affirm the dignity of man as the apex of creation. Human life must be seen against a cosmic setting, where men are of value to the cosmos, its maker, and to each other. In this cosmos, man has a status by virtue of which he is what he is, an impress of personhood that is "similar" to God. Only then is he actually man.

Shakespeare's description owes much to Psalm 8. He sees man standing beneath "this most excellent canopy, the air, look you, this brave o'erhanging firmament, this majestical roof fretted with golden fire. . . . What a piece of work is man! How noble in reason! How infinite in faculty! In form and moving how express and admirable! In action how like an angel! In apprehension how like a god! The beauty of the world! The paragon of animals!"

No matter how it is with other creatures, man shall not live a dull, unconscious life. He knows what it means to be a creature. This knowledge, this peculiarity, is freedom, and his response to the cosmos is always in the indicative. He affirms, he accepts, he understands, he cultivates, he creates; always he acts on a world unfashioned or in process of being fashioned. He makes things that were not there before—a symphony, a home, or a machine. Man is a mystery to be apprehended in great reverence and humility. Astronomically, to be sure, he is a speck, but also astronomically he is the astrophysicist.

In any proper view of man we will see along with his "grandeur" (Pascal) also the "misery" of man. From Kafka's diary in May 3, 1913, we read: "the terrible uncertainty of my inner existence." In one of Kenneth Rexroth's poems there is the description of a fashion model so exteriorized in the clothes in which she poses that, when she undresses at night, the self she assumed was always there under her clothes is gone. She is forced to wear her clothes in bed in order to keep intact whatever self remains.

This is the irony of man's situation. As someone has said, "man's belief in himself is weakest in the very age when control of his environment is greatest." This ironical dimension has been described by many theologians, not the least of whom has been Reinhold Niebuhr, who describes in moving terms how great and powerful we are, yet how controlled is the scope of our action. We have achieved a standard of unprecedented comfort, yet happiness eludes us. We have a great and useful compendium of scientific knowledge only to run into the larger problems of human destiny. Success hastens the exposure of our limitations. This ironical dimension is heightened by a sense of futility, even despair, so that we are not unlike Sisyphus in the famous myth who was forced to roll the stone up a hill only to be consciously aware of the inevitability of it rolling down again. Sisyphus' fate was to roll it up and up throughout eternity.

3. We must see man as a responsive and a responsible being. He is a moral being who is charged not only with responsibility of assisting in the fashioning of creation and culture, but also being responsive to it. How do we account for the fact of anti-intellectualism in our society, particularly on the part of the alumni of our universities? How could we explain to Comenius and Pestalozzi, the great educationalists of another century, why it is that this century of great power and enlightenment has killed more people in wars than in all the other centuries of the Christian era? Why can Liberace have a piano-shaped swimming pool and a Beethoven die in poverty? Why should a movie star make $100,000 for a five-minute appearance on television and an instructor in the humanities make $5,000 per year after seven years of preparation? How do we exercise our moral responsibility in situations like this?

Man's real values, his ethics and his morals, are articulate in acts of response. As Dostoevski puts it, "the possibility of being able to place the question of right after the meaning of one's existence is the greatest and most ultimate freedom of man."

4. The greatness of man is measured not in the dimensions of power (Marx) or in survival, but in tragedy. Much of the emptiness of our life results from the loss of a clear vision of what man is supposed to be in terms of his sacrificial and eternal significance. If we are stifled by an outlook which makes us cogs in a machine, if we find no vision commensurate with our longing for freedom, it may be due to the loss of touch with suffering and tragedy. I recall reading in a British publication the story of an English officer who met a Korean peasant. He said that he marvelled at the serenity and composure of one from whom war had taken all, and he wrote, "as I talked with him I became aware that my culture was a veneer, my education a gloss, and my standing before him a presumption. In the face of that man who had nothing but God left, I saw myself a spiritual pauper and I loathed what I saw."

In the world we know, is it enough to produce commentators on the passing scene who are like cameras with the shutter always open?

Is it enough to be research specialists or wrecking contractors? Or is it not true that humanity yearns for renewed minds at grips with the staggering facts of existence? The key to man's grandeur is put no better anywhere than in Prokosch's "Age of Thunder": "We spend our lives in chains; but our right to cast off our chains and to learn from our bondage—that is the point. *The right to tragedy* . . . it is the trivial minded mechanical man who is incapable of tragedy— tragedy occurs only to men who live on the crest of life and who refuse to accept regimentation and defeat."

Seldom is it given to a nation to see its history and destiny enacted in one day. It has happened to us in recent events. In the assassination of Pres. Kennedy and the events that followed in rapid fire, 100 years of history passed before our eyes, giving us at the same time sad glimpses of the future. It was out of the absurd, the insane, that our sanity and *raison d'être* were revealed, leaving all men, not just technologists or humanists, with the question whether the human psyche really can take the speed of modern history and technology?

George VI, in his Christmas broadcast in 1946, said that it is "necessary not only to rebuild but to restore the very soul of civilization." This is a task for which the humanities have a major responsibility.

13. THE IMPACT OF TECHNOLOGY AND THE SCIENCES ON HUMAN VALUES

RALPH WENDELL BURHOE

*What will man seek when all that he values is his
by automation?—the Dreams of Joseph and Jacob*

F ROM THE MOST PRIMITIVE human societies until today, technological know-how and tools have increased the productivity, per unit of human effort expended, of the wealth or power to satisfy human needs and desires. The increase of power or wealth available per caput has been greatly accelerated by modern science, and thus, today, our average citizens have more material wealth and power than that possessed by the upper reaches of the nobility only a short time ago. But this gain is trivial compared with the possible gains in the near future from the new scientific understandings underlying automation, cybernation, and related technologies.

While, for millions of years prior to this century, men and their ancestors have had to spend most of their time and energies in finding the food and other environmental conditions necessary for life, modern technology has made it possible to satisfy most of these needs with only a tiny fraction of the effort once needed. It is not consequential for the theme of this chapter whether it will take 20, 200, or 2,000 years before a man need work less than an hour a week to be wealthier than he is now.

Our question is: What activities will or should replace the bulk of the behavior for which human nature has been designated and motivated when that behavior becomes obsolete, meaningless, or dangerous? We might find it difficult to get ready for this even if we had 2,000 years. We had insights more than 2,000 years ago that we should beat our swords into plowshares. We have not yet succeeded. And possibly the technology of the atomic sword already has made our efforts to reform our moral and spiritual values too little and too late. Whether or not we achieve the relatively simple moral reforms proposed so long ago to avoid suicidal war, the deeper and more basic crisis of our values in the leisure that can be produced by automation and cybernation will remain to face us. The hazards of leisure, a period of time during which no serious purpose informs or compels our response, are dramatized in the dream of Joseph.

JOSEPH'S DREAM

In the dream, an angel of the Lord appeared before Joe Doakes and said, "Joe, for your virtues and for your sins, the Lord of History has sent me as a messenger to bring you this magic ring of scientific technology. You have only to rub it three times, utter the name of any goods or services you want, and, lo and behold, you will have them; but never forget that the magic will be lost if your wishes seriously threaten your neighbors.

"You will not need to go to work tomorrow, or the next day, for all the food, clothing, and shelter you and your family may wish will be yours. If you wish, your children may have the best education in the world from highly evolved Skinner boxes which will instruct them more effectively than the mediocre teachers you have known. But such education will not be necessary for your children or for your children's children to earn their bread, for the Lord has commanded me to bring them exact duplicates of this magic ring of scientific technology; and they may command all the goods and services they want by using the ring in the same way.

"Not only will the ring repeal the Lord's former edict that by the sweat of your brow shall you labor all your days to get enough to eat and the other necessities of life, but this ring is at the same time the symbol and agent rescinding nearly all of the Lord's ancient commands, including, for instance, even the one that women shall bring forth her children in labor and pain. Your daughters and sons can have all the fun they want without the risk of pregnancies; and if withal they should still want children, they can be produced in new incubators while mother and daddy are flying around the moon.

"Neither you nor your children need suffer pain of any kind any more, for the magic ring of scientific technology will bring you analgesics and tranquilizers many times more effective than old-fashioned wines. And if it is pleasure you are seeking, you can rub the ring and completely bypass the hitherto required efforts to gain pleasures by means of a short-circuit to the pleasure centers of your lower brain performed by an automated system of neurosurgery and chemistry, which will cause the holding of the ring in your hand to titillate your pleasure centers at any level you may wish from that of a contented cow to a self-consuming orgiastic frenzy.

"Joe, with the Lord's gift of this ring of scientific technology, you will be completely relieved of all duties and responsibilities and labors of any kind, for the magic ring will be able to do all these for you which the Lord formerly required you to do for yourself. You will find it difficult, indeed, to imagine any duties formerly required of you for the support of yourself and your brothers that the magic ring will not be able to do even better. In fact, Joe, nothing further will be required of you. Your family won't need you, your fellow men won't need you, and there is really no cause for you to fiddle around any longer yourself. You may rest in peace." The angel vanished.

INTERPRETATION OF JOSEPH'S DREAM

We may speculate about what Joe may do on awakening from this revelation. It might be that he will rub the ring twice instead of thrice, or it may be that he will threaten his wife or neighbor and break the magic of the ring. While Joe is very likely to mismanage the instructions required for the use of the magic ring, and so delay the effectiveness or consummation of its magic, his revelation tells us that the angel also will give the ring to his children, and we may presume that sooner or later its magic power will be evoked in full.

The fundamental question, therefore, presses upon Joe's children, if not upon Joe: Has scientific knowledge brought us to our end? This is not the finish threatened by the atom bomb, which is only one of the possibilities. The ultimate danger of this technological power is much more subtle and difficult to do anything about. It threatens man's very central sense of his worth, value, meaning, purpose, direction, and will to live. Joe increasingly will worry whether there is anything worth while for him to do.

The avant-garde writers, poets, and dramatists of the past half-century and more have dreamed Joseph's dream; and they have proclaimed man's meaninglessness and the irrationality of life. If the Lord has rescinded the ancient requirements and purposes of man, are there perchance new ones—and if so, what? Who has any message for the meaning and hope of man in an age of automation and cybernation?

In my opinion, the major problem of the educational world today is not the problem of educating enough scientists and engineers to give man the magic ring, which may grind out powers and goods so fast as to overwhelm his moral and spiritual capacities to handle them. The problem of education is to provide the curriculum which interprets to man his meaning, purpose, goals, values. At one time the educers of values in human cultures were called religions. But in those human groups whose reason could not accept the popular myths, both of Greece and Rome as well as of today, the educers of values have been called by such names as philosophies, liberal arts, or humanities. Today, for many a man in the street, as well as for the avant-garde artists, even the classic philosophies and the recent humanities are found to be as empty, vain, and powerless as the religious myths. The contemporary philosophies and arts are more likely to produce a ship of fools and a picture of irrationality and meaninglessness of man rather than an Aeschylus or Epictetus.

The Psalmist of some 2,500 years ago, in contemplating the majesty and power of the world about him, exclaimed, "What is man that thou art mindful of him?" And his colleagues replied that man is a son and servant of the most high, with such and such duties and such and such promises for a better future under a divine program of human destiny. Today, the dramatists, who suppose they are interpreting the contemporary scientific picture of man, are saying he is an accidental and miserable beast in a cosmos that couldn't care less, with no meaningful future. Man is a machine or automaton, operated by forces from a random chemical and social history, and the allegedly divine plan, with its requirements and promises, is only an illusion. The humanist poets and dramatists no longer present us with the fiction of man as an independent and upright soul capable of reasoning his way out of chains and tragedy to freedom and a bright future. This fiction has been destroyed by the same scientific pictures of a random bundle of conditioned reflexes, subconscious irrationalities, and evil wishes, all doomed in a universal heat death.

JACOB'S DREAM

With the ancient myths dead and the contemporary myths dying, what can the educators, in charge of those departments concerned with eliciting or transmitting human values, do?

Jack, the humanist educator visiting University Park, Pa., heard the revelation which had appeared to Joe Doakes in his dream; and Jack, by gum, dared not sleep for fear he, too, would see this angel of the death of humanity. But after much tossing and fretting, he finally did fall asleep, and surely enough an angel of the Lord appeared unto him, and said:

"O, Jack, the Lord thy God hath seen thy distress and heard thy lamentations for thyself and thy brother Joe, and he hath taken pity on thee and hath sent me to comfort you. I bring you a book containing the wisdom of the Lord for man in an age of science. If you will teach from this book, it will deliver thee and thy brother Joe and all thy children from the boredom and the meaninglessness of the day when ancient meanings will be brought to naught by Joe's magic ring of scientific technology. Thou shalt start teaching from this book of wisdom of the Lord even before Joe rubs his ring three times, lest the ignorance of Joe and Joe's wife and Joe's children of the law of the God of life cause him and his wife and his children to freeze into a pillar of salt or, at best, into a herd of cows, all the while they are rubbing the ring for new services and goods."

The humanist educator was overjoyed in his dream and cried out eagerly to the angel, "What marvelous good tidings you bring me! Pray tell me, O Angel, what is this wondrous black book in your hand which you bring unto me? Is it a new Bible? Is it a new Plato?" And Jack eagerly grasped the book from the hand of the angel and threw open the cover to the title page. But his face fell, for there he read: "The Book of the Sciences." Jack woke up in a sweat and vowed never to sleep again.

But poor Jack, of course, was only dreaming that he awoke, for he was destined to wrestle with the angel of the "Book of the Sciences" until the break of the light of a new day. And he dreamed of his awakening in the night as a good humanist should, turning on his bed lamp and reaching for the bedside bookshelf. But each time he reached for one of his familiar favorites, strange things happened. In one, the ink impressions faded slowly away until it made no sense. In another the leaves crumbled. In another the sentences rearranged themselves backwards, confounding paradox with paradox. And thus it came to pass that each book faded, crumbled, or became senseless until there was only one book left. It looked strangely familiar and yet unfamiliar, until he recognized that it must be the book given to him by the angel. Since he must read and there was nothing else left to read, he opened it.

Although the "Book of the Sciences" did not fall apart, it did behave strangely. For as he read an introductory chapter on the history of the sciences, the book grew in size and became heavier; and when he referred back from the history of physics in the 20th century to that of the fifth century, B.C., the pages he previously had read about the fifth century had changed and expanded drastically, although they continued to use some of the same words. Some pages contained future history more accurately than others detailed in the past. But of all the strange characteristics of the "Book of the Sciences," Jack was most electrified when he suddenly felt he was reading the most magnificent dramatic poem of any literature, revealing hitherto hidden but now overarchingly significant values of man and his world. As he skimmed through the augmenting pages, his curiosity grew, and his excitement would not let him lay the book down. Among the titles that intrigued him, then confused him, and then flashed new visions of triumph of man in the midst of the threats of science were:

A history of the emergence of human value patterns during the past billion years relative to the cosmic constants.

The role of the read-out of DNA language information accessioned in chemical libraries in the past 100,000,000 years in the production of the Psalms and Aeschylus.

The relative use of genotypic and cultural libraries by the neurological cybernetic and computer mechanisms involved in the production of human love and self-sacrifice.

The chemical determinants of aesthetic and poetic experience, and the inverse functions of aesthetic and poetic determinants of brain chemistry.

The determinants of man's free will.

The relative importance as sources for self-sacrificial social behavior of the contents of three libraries of imaginative literature: the library of the DNA code of 2,000,000 years ago, the library of the poetry of 2,000 years ago, and the library of the sciences of two years ago.

The operation of cosmic sanctions in establishing the canons of truth, beauty, and goodness in the analogous transformations of genotype, of neural anatomy, and of literature under a common selection pressure.

The evolution of the syllogistic mechanism in the central nervous system during the 100,000,000 years prior to Aristotle.

The flood of new input into human intellectual and aesthetic experience from electronic sensors and analyzers during the quarter-century preceding the year 2000 and its integration with older neurological cybernetic mechanisms—a phenomenon transcending the importance of the neo-pallium in human evolution.

The comparative anatomy and dynamics of emotional disturbances and psychoses in electronic and neurophysiological cybernetic mechanisms.

The year 2000 handbook of the contributions of computers to theology: The unchanging anatomy of God, or the immutable laws which govern human and cybernetic destiny alike.

The higher criticism of moral and aesthetic literature in the light of excavations of libraries of the past 1,000,000,000 years.

And Jack cried out, "O, God, help me! O, Angel of the 'Book of the Sciences,' continue to open my eyes and unstop my ears that I may discern more clearly the human implications of these strange new revelations; and, by the way, bring me a pen for I have a new song on human destiny and meaning."

SOME EARLY
AND RECENT FORMS
OF AUTOMATION

STANLEY LEHRER

[1]   "We're replacing you with an abacus. So sorry."

Drawing by M. Richter; © *1965 The New Yorker Magazine, Inc.*

[2] Tinplating at the turn of the 18th century was a hammered process performed by artisans. This reproduction of a copper plate is from the collection of Denis Diderot, who some 200 years ago created a detailed, illustrated instruction book for French craftsmen.

[3] Modern equipment aids in today's high-speed production of tinplate for metal cans. Operators are watching control panel of electrolytic tinning line at a steel plant where steel receives thin coating of tin.

[4] In the early days of the can manufacturing industry, cans were made by hand. An expert can-maker could turn out as many as five or six cans an hour. It was hard, laborious work and a long way from the most advanced machinery of today which can turn out more than 500 cans a minute. This plant produced cans for the packing of meat.

[5] Syrup used to be added to canned fruit by dipper. Today it is controlled entirely by machinery. Automatic filling guarantees that canned foods will be uniform in quantity as well as quality.

[6] A belt mechanically brought cans to workers in this canning plant at the turn of the century and was indicative of the beginning of the transition to assembly lines and mass production. The workers soldered on the tops of the cans.

[7] In a modern-day plant, metal cans receive double-seamed bottoms and then are subjected to high air pressure for any leaks. Defective cans are rejected automatically.

[8] At the beginning of the 20th century, women in the canning industry applied labels to cans which had been filled, sealed, and cooked. The work was tedious.

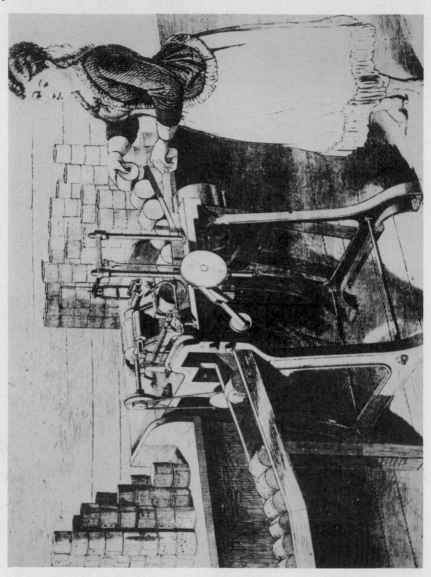

[9]   This is one of the earliest machines that wrapped cans with paper labels. Eventually, lithographic label-ing on metal became a popular method.

[10] Lithography and other modern printing methods
opened new possibilities for sales promotion in metal
can packaging. With the modern equipment below,
labels are being printed directly on metal sheets. Later,
these sheets are turned into cans.

[11] The first commercial telephone was a box, which sometimes was as much as 14 inches long to accommodate a big horseshoe magnet. A person could talk and listen over the same instrument.

[12]   A telephone switchboard in 1878.

[13] The original telephone switch (patented in 1892) was developed by Almon B. Strowger, founder of Automatic Electric Company, now a subsidiary of General Telephone & Electronics. The prototype of this switch was made with an old-fashioned collar box. The Strowger switch was designed to give the caller the desired number.

Photos on this page from Automatic Electric,
subsidiary of General Telephone & Electronics

[14] An improvement of the Strowger switch in 1895. The switch was used two years later in a telephone exchange where it automatically gave the dialer the correct number (see photo on next page).

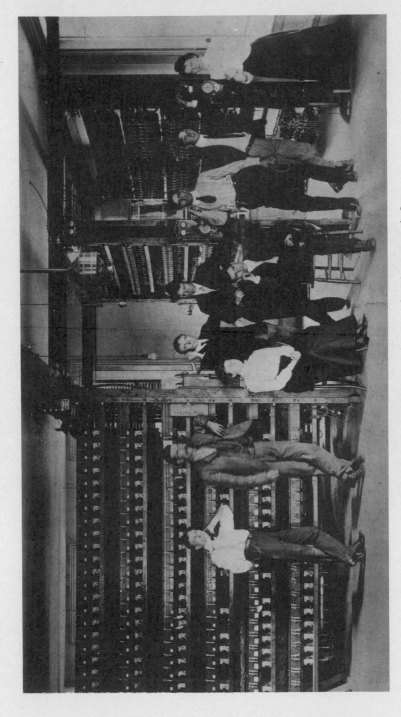

[15] One of the first telephone exchanges using the automatic Strowger switch was installed in Augusta, Ga., in 1897. Note the original dials (large circular discs) on the front of the phones.

Photo from Automatic Electric, subsidiary of General Telephone & Electronics

[16] Automatic Electric Company's first electronic automatic exchange now being tested in Portage, Ind. The
racks are filled with printed circuit cards. This electronic
exchange will offer faster and more sophisticated service.

[17]   General Motors' assembly line in 1910 produced cars without the aid of a mechanical conveyor belt system. After completion of car, human effort was needed to start the motor (note crank below radiator in front of vehicle). In 1912, Charles F. Kettering's self-starter was installed in the Cadillac, thus opening the way for everyone to use an automobile. Previously, cars were limited to those who could wrestle with a crank.

[18] Charles F. Kettering, who developed the first successful electric self-starter, is shown here with a 1913 test Buick at Dayton, Ohio. He later became a General Motors vice-president and head of GM Research Laboratories Division.

[19] This conveyor system, installed in the chassis assembly department of an early Cadillac plant, represented part of an investment of millions of dollars for time-saving machinery.

[20] The unified assembly line of the Buick Motor Company in 1926. These cars were nearing completion. Most operations required individual as well as collective manpower.

[21] In a 1965 Chevrolet plant, speed on the assembly line is essential for mass production. The five nuts holding the wheels go on simultaneously with a compressed-air gang wrench.

[22] Frame is turned over automatically into normal car position and then continues down this modern-day assembly line.

[23] A finished car is ready to leave the assembly line in a 1965 Chevrolet plant. Every 60 minutes, a car's frame starts on the line. In the early days of car manufacturing, production took longer because of the lack or limited amount of automation and other time-saving methods.

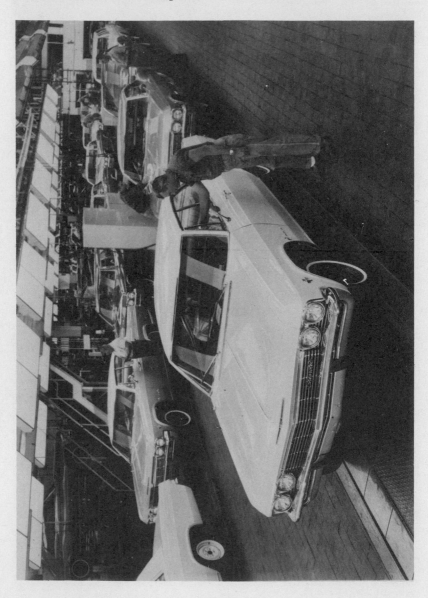

[24] The Skinner Electric Renovator, the first mechanically powered portable vacuum cleaner, was manufactured in 1905 by the Skinner Manufacturing Co., San Francisco, Calif. The cleaner had an electric motor, a brush roll, and two-stage fan that sucked up dust and discharged it into a bag mounted on the handle. The machine is in the Museum of Cleaners of The Hoover Company, North Canton, Ohio.

[25] The first Hoover vacuum cleaner was patented on June 2, 1908 and closely resembled the upright cleaner so familiar today. At that time, only a few portable suction cleaners were available. Women knew of no better cleaning aids than the broom, carpet beater, and carpet sweeper. Cumbersome as it was, this 1908 cleaner was lighter than other portable cleaners and became popular among women who were interested in easing their strenuous cleaning chores. This machine also helped to speed up the cleaning of carpets.

[26] On July 3, 1886, a historic event took place in the composing room of the *New York Tribune*. Ottmar Mergenthaler, seated at the keyboard of his new machine, handed a slug of metal to Whitelaw Reid, editor. Reid exclaimed, "It's a line of type!" Thus was christened the forerunner of today's linecasting machine: the Linotype. Prior to that time, lines of type were set by hand. The Linotype quickened the pace of news reporting and expedited the production of various publications.

Pictures on this page and next by Mergenthaler Linotype Company

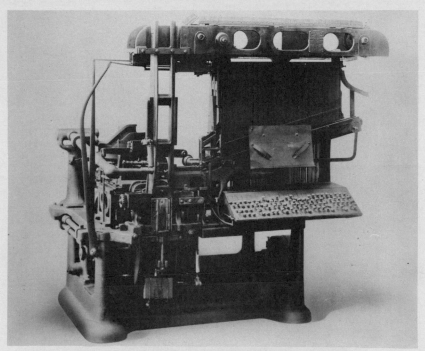

[27]   Ottmar Mergenthaler's original Linotype in 1886.

[28] The Mergen-
thaler Linotype
Company's Elek-
tron, first shown to
newspaper execu-
tives on April 23.
1962, in New York
City, requires no
operator. Perforat-
ed tape sets type
automatically.

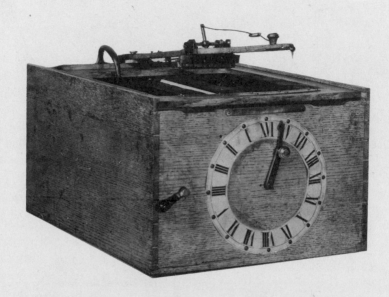

[29] The first American typewriter was invented by William Austin Burt in 1829. Although Burt desired a machine that could write his correspondence quicker than he was able to do by hand, his "typographer," as he called it, turned out to be a slow method of writing. However, his invention did type words clearly, and, in the same year he had developed the "typographer," it was brought to the attention of Pres. Andrew Jackson. The machine used a continuous role of paper, and sheets were torn off when the clock-face indicator showed that the proper length had been reached.

[30] This **IBM** electric typewriter, first manufactured in 1935, was a commercial success. It was the successor to the Electroniatic Electric Typewriter of 1933.

[31] A modern electric typewriter manufactured by the **Royal Type-writer Company.**

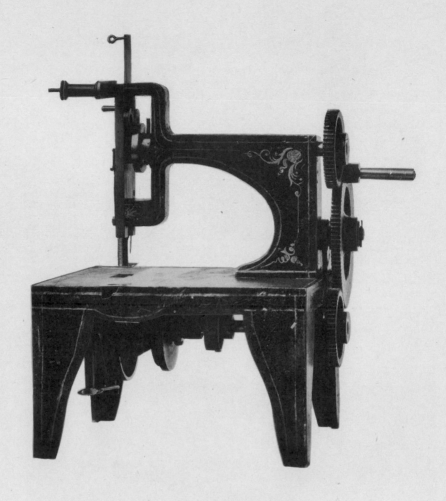

Courtesy of The Singer Company

[32] The sewing machine was the answer to women who desired a faster, more uniform method of sewing. The first practical model (above) was invented by I. M. Singer in 1851. The modern-day sewing machine is more compact than its predecessor, is electrically powered, and provides such services as winding thread automatically and changing from one form of stitch to another to suit the needs of the sewer.

[33] "I see Fenton's is finally automating."

Drawing by D. Fradon; © *1964 The New Yorker Magazine, Inc.*

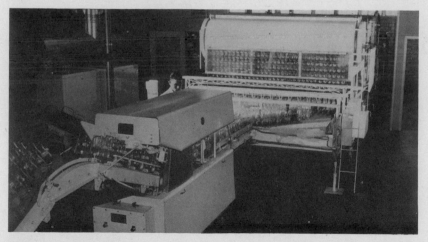

[34] At the Pepsi-Cola Bottling Company of Tulsa, Oklahoma, Inc., bottles are being removed automatically from their cases (at left) and placed on the unscrambling and feed table at the back end of the bottle washer (right). Prior to the advent of the "uncaser," bottles were removed by hand from the cases and then placed on a feed table in back of the bottle washer.

[35] Human labor is not needed to operate this machinery at the Pepsi-Cola Bottling Company of Tulsa, Oklahoma, Inc. Clean bottles are fed by automatic conveyor to the machine (at left) where they are filled with beverage and capped. The filled bottles then are moved by automatic conveyor to a case packer (not shown in the picture).

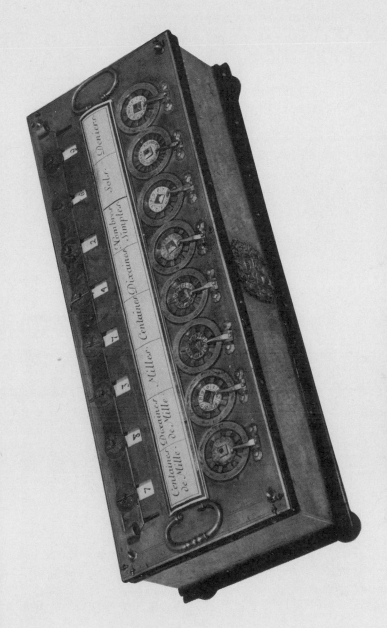

[36] A 17th-century calculator developed by Blaise Pascal, a French religious thinker and writer who devoted much time to mathematics. This marked a major step in the development of automatic computation because it had an automatic "tens carrying" feature.

[38] ENIAC, the world's first automatic electronic computer, was designed and built by J. P. Eckert and John H. Mauchly in the Moore School of Electronic Engineering between 1943 and 1946. It was given to the U. S. Army for the development of firing tables for all types of ordnance equipment.

[39] UNIVAC I was the first *commercial* electronic computer. It was developed by Remington Rand, predecessor of the UNIVAC Division, Sperry Rand Corporation. The first mode was delivered to the U.S. Bureau of the Census. It was retired in 1963 and has been on display in the Smithsonian Institution, Washington, D.C.

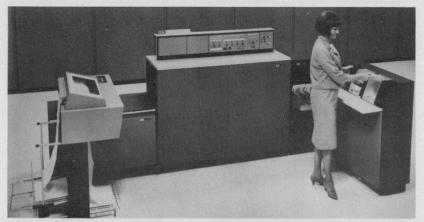

[40] The IBM System/360 computer is designed today to produce accounting reports and payroll checks as well as to serve a variety of other data processing needs of business, science, and government.

[41] This electronic computer is the Radio Corporation of America's newest entry in the electronic data processing field. Above are the main control console and some of the operating equipment of the new Spectra 70, which boasts an advanced "multi-lingual" capability that enables it to "speak" all of the most common programming, data, and communications languages in the computer industry.

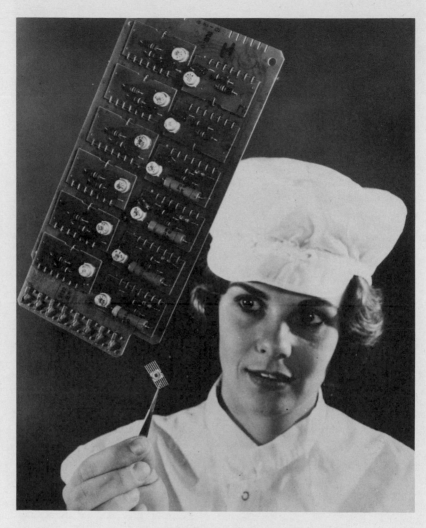

[42]   The two larger computers in the new RCA Spectra
70 Series employ tiny, monolithic, integrated circuits
(the black dot in the center of the unit held by tweez-
ers). Just three of these units perform the same electronic function as the larger circuit board shown, and
they operate at 40 times the speed of this board. The
integrated circuit, called a "flat-pack," holds the equivalent of 15 transistors, 13 resistors, and the necessary
connecting wires. The development of the "flat-pack"
contrasts sharply with the profusion of wiring in the
ENIAC (picture 38).

[43]   This 40-ton D-1000 business computer, the first computer system produced by Honeywell's Electronic Data Processing Division, was retired after six years of service to Michigan Blue Cross-Blue Shield in Detroit. It was replaced by Honeywell's new H-800-III, which is nearly eight times as fast as the retired computer system. The D-1000 was installed in 1958 and had processed more than 420,000 Blue Cross-Blue Shield payments to doctors and hospitals each month.

Courtesy Municipality of Metropolitan Toronto

[44]   Computers now are at work in the field of traffic control. At the Metropolitan Toronto (Canada) Traffic Control Computer Centre, computers automatically control the traffic signals in the metropolitan area and, as a result, have hastened the flow of traffic, particularly during rush-hour.

[45] Each computer-controlled traffic signal is indicated by a small electric light on this large map of metropolitan Toronto. The map is mounted at the Metropolitan Toronto Traffic Control Computer Centre in the Old City Hall, Toronto.

[46] Experiments in the communication of automotive design information between man and computer are being conducted at the General Motors Research Laboratories using the new GM DAC-1 system (Design Augmented by Computers). Here, at the graphic console of DAC-1, a research engineer checks out a computer program that allows him to modify a design. A touch of the electric "pencil" to the face of the tube signals the computer to begin an assigned task where indicated—in this case, "Line Deletion." The drawing also can be altered by pushing control buttons below the screen. The DAC-1 actually helps man to develop workable designs.

[47] Automation helps ships go to sea in the U. S. merchant marine. Aboard one of the ships of the Moore-McCormack Lines, deck officers can control speed by simply moving a throttle located in this control console on the bridge. A similar console is on the bridge of the *S.S. American Racer,* a cargo vessel of the United States Lines. Although such a console permits a ship to be maneuvered from the bridge without assistance from engine-room personnel, a duplicate console is in the engine-room and can control a ship's speed if necessary. Any throttle action is recorded automatically on a chart, and scanning devices monitor all parts of the controlling apparatus for any unusual condition.

[48] The engine-room console aboard a Moore-McCormack cargo-liner now makes it possible for one man to stand watch. The electronic system performs tasks that used to be the responsibility of many seamen.

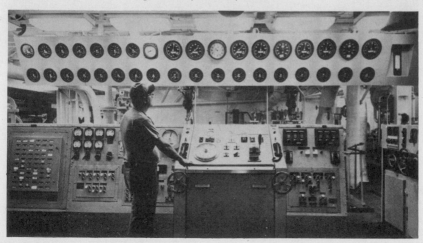

[49] In the engine-room of the *S.S. American Racer*, the most sophisticated automation system at sea (the General Electric Central Operation System)—the same in operation aboard Moore-McCormack cargo-liners—controls and monitors key propulsion equipment. In addition to saving on manpower, this system operates the ship efficiently and thus reduces fuel costs.

[50] The hydraulic hatch covers on the Moore-McCormack cargo-liners open automatically to permit quick and efficient handling of cargo, thus reducing the time that vessels must remain in port.

[51] At Esso Standard Oil Company's Bayway Refinery, Linden, N. J., the control room at No. 6 pipe still receives data on the various temperatures, pressures, and rates required to run the unit efficiently.

[52] At Finney Station, Interstate Oil Pipe Line Company, Shreveport, La., one engineer is in charge of control panel which regulates all operations of the entire station.

[53] A mill operator is at the control panel in the pulpit where he views a large coil that has been reduced in the Gary (Ind.) Sheet and Tin Works of the United States Steel Corporation. The various dials and gauges provide rolling information for the pulpit operator during the cold reducing process.

[54] At the McLouth Steel Coporation, Detroit, Mich., a General Electric computer system controls this six-stand hot-strip mill. The computer actually produces many different grades and sizes of steel with a minimum of waste. The quality of the computer-controlled output of steel is superior to the steel that was turned out before the computer gained acceptance at the corporation.

[55] The computer control panel at McLouth Steel Corporation began operations in 1962.

[56] At the Christian Brothers Data Processing Center, Lewis College, Lockport, Ill., a magnetic tape drive is loaded with a reel containing academic information on thousands of students at Christian Brothers schools throughout a 15-state area of the Midwest. The Center eventually will process and maintain academic and financial data for more than 24,000 students in 45 schools. The Honeywell H-200 computer is expected to save $50,000 annually in record-keeping costs.

[57] Pleased with the speed with which the H-200 computer has turned out the six-week report cards for Christian Brothers schools throughout the Midwest, these Brothers are preparing to store the recorded information until the next grading period. In addition to keeping grades, the computer maintains attendance and financial records, and it eventually will analyze and compare student test data with local and national results and reallocate classroom facilities in 45 schools.

[58] The Bronx (N. Y.) High School of Science, the first high school in the nation to institute a course in computer technology and programming in 1955, installed this IBM 1620 computer in 1962 to help students solve problems in science and mathematics research. The principal of the school watched these two students work a problem on the computer.

[59] Television entered the classroom to help in the teaching process. This picture appeared in *School and Society* in 1956. The students at the University of Minnesota College of Education were observing a master teacher in action in a University High School class in speech.

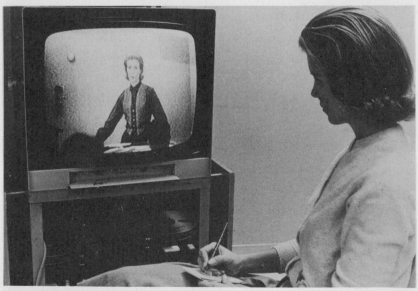

[60] Today's portable TV recorder enables student teachers to evaluate their own performances and progress in classroom situations. The TV tape can be replayed as often as necessary.

[61] Teachers were relieved of study hall duty for the first time in 1956 when this TV camera was trained on students in the New London (Wis.) High School study hall. The closed-circuit television system, installed by General Precision Laboratory of Pleasantville, N. Y., sent the picture of the entire study hall to a monitor set in the school's general office where secretaries could watch the students.

Milwaukee Journal photo

[62] This student was at work on a write-in teaching machine (c. 1957). When a question appeared in the left-hand frame, the student wrote his answer on the strip of paper in the opening at the right. When the window at the left then revealed the correct answer, the student compared it with his response. If his answer matched that of the machine, he moved the lever horizontally and a hole was punched to record his correct answer.

[63] "Talking typewriters" were introduced to kindergarten children in 1963-64 at the Atkinson Elementary School, Freeport, N. Y. This child and others in his group taught themselves to read entirely without formal human instruction in an average of less than 30 hours of instrumented instruction.

[64] The "talking typewriter" is technically called the Edison Responsive Environment instrument (E.R.E.). This computerized typewriter, manufactured by McGraw-Edison Company, reveals a pointer at the top which indicates to a child what letter on the keyboard to press. While it is pointing to a letter to be typed, the E.R.E. pronounces the letter for the pupil and unlocks the proper key to be pressed, thus preventing the child from pressing a wrong key. As soon as the right key is pressed, the letter is typed on a sheet of paper and the pointer moves to the next letter to be typed. If the child does not respond immediately, the E.R.E. repeats the pronunciation of the particular letter to be typed. The instrument also calls out certain words without showing them to the pupil, and the child reveals that he has learned these words by typing them without visual help.

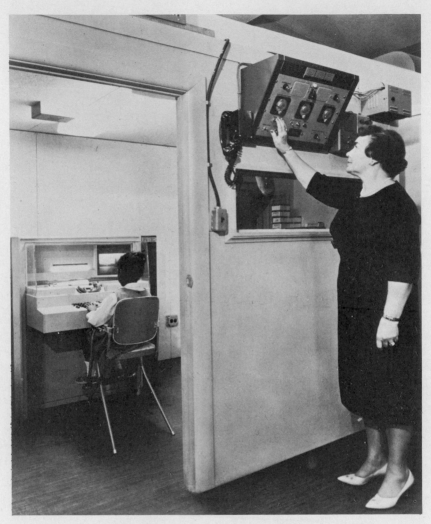

[65] Mrs. Dorothy Johnson, Director of
Primary Reading, Freeport, N. Y., Public Schools, responds to a signal of a
child who is learning to read on the
E.R.E. computerized typewriter. The
door to the booth usually is closed so
that the child is not distracted. The
child's progress is observed through the
one-way viewing mirror.

Drawing by Frank Baginski; courtesy of School and Society

[66] "I wonder if it detects overdue books."

PICTURE CREDITS

The gratitude of the editors is expressed to the following for their help in making this pictorial section possible and for granting permission to publish photographs from various collections, many of them quite rare:

The New Yorker Magazine, Inc.: pictures 1, 33
Can Manufacturers Institute, Washington, D.C.: pictures 2, 3, 4, 5, 6, 7, 8, 9, 10
A.T.&T. Photo Service, New York City: pictures 11, 12
Automatic Electric, a subsidiary of General Telephone & Electronics, Northlake, Ill.: pictures 13, 14, 15, 16
General Motors Corporation, Detroit, Mich.: pictures 17, 18, 19, 20, 21, 22, 23
Museum of Cleaners, The Hoover Company, North Canton, Ohio: picture 24
The Hoover Company, North Canton, Ohio: picture 25
Mergenthaler Linotype Company, Brooklyn, N.Y.: pictures 26, 27, 28
Royal Typewriter Company, New York City: pictures 29, 31
International Business Machines Corporation, Office Products Division, New York City: picture 30
The Singer Company, New York City: picture 32
Pepsi-Cola Company, New York City: pictures 34, 35
International Business Machines Corporation, Data Processing Division, White Plains, N. Y.: pictures

36, 37, 40; Data Processing Division, Chicago, Ill.: picture 46
UNIVAC Division, Sperry Rand Corporation, New York City: pictures 38, 39
Radio Corporation of America, Electronic Data Processing, Camden, N. J.: pictures 41, 42
Honeywell Inc., Electronic Data Processing Division, New York City: pictures 43, 56, 57
Traffic Engineering Department, The Municipality of Metropolitan Toronto, Toronto, Canada: pictures 44, 45
Moore-McCormack Lines, Inc., New York City: pictures 47, 48, 50
United States Lines Company, New York City: picture 49
Standard Oil Company (New Jersey), New York City: pictures 51, 52
United States Steel Corporation, New York City: picture 53
McLouth Steel Corporation, Detroit, Mich.: pictures 54, 55
School and Society, published by the Society for the Advancement of Education, New York City: pictures 58, 66
Neville P. Pearson, College of Education, University of Minnesota, Minneapolis, Minn.: picture 59
Stanford University, Stanford, Calif.: picture 60
Milwaukee Journal, Milwaukee, Wis.: picture 61
Harvard University, Cambridge, Mass.: picture 62
Responsive Environments Corporation, New York City: pictures 63, 64, 65

14. THE SCHOLAR-EDUCATOR AND AUTOMATION

WILLIAM W. BRICKMAN

AUTOMATION involves the application of technological devices and methods to manufacturing or the operation of any process without the direct intervention of the human hand. The principle of automation was a logical outcome of the Industrial Revolution, the Scientific Explosion, and other movements during the past century and a half. Dangers to the human spirit and mind were evident from the writings of sensitive literary men, especially in the 1920's.

What was Karel Čapek's "R.U.R." (1921) if not a potent thrust against robots and robotism? The international success of this play was a warning for the future. Also read, even if not as widely as "R.U.R.," was "Masse Mensch" (1920), a play by Ernst Toller. Here, too, was a reaction against the mechanization of society and culture. Or consider the trilogy by Georg Kaiser: "Die Koralle," "Gas I," and "Gas II" (1917-20). In these plays, the German writer has pointed up the dangers of mechanization and the heartlessness of a machine-made civilization. It may be true that the social criticism of the period has been tinged with anti-capitalist sentiment. Nonetheless, the evils of a cold, machine-dominated society are not the sole property of capitalism; one observes these evils, even in an aggravated form, in the so-called People's Democracies and Republics.

In the English language, too, influential writers have exploited the weakness of an automated atmosphere. Thus, the late Aldous

Huxley, in "Brave New World" (1931), anticipated many if not most of the characteristics of contemporary living, such as communications media as molders of mass opinion, television, and the like. The nature and impact of George Orwell's "1984" (1949) are too familiar to need any comment.

Nor should one overlook the contributions of the motion picture —itself a form of mechanization—to the literature of protest against automation. It is easy to recall the impression made by René Clair's *Le Million* (1931) and by Charlie Chaplin's *Modern Times* (1936), both of which portrayed the eventual defeat of the machine by the innocent men caught in its toils.

As far as automation in education is concerned, it does not appear at first glance that it constitutes the kind of danger that the machine has shown to society at large. In fact, for many years automatic devices, such as films, have been used as aids to instruction in general and as sources of enrichment in the particular areas of geography and art. It should be noted that careful educators always have insisted that such devices were to be considered as auxiliaries only. This is clear when one recalls the uses to which Jan Amos Comenius, in the 17th century, as well as his lesser-known predecessors and successors, put the illustration.

It seems only yesterday that a form of automation has come to education. Recent investigators of the history of the teaching machine have traced the beginning of this movement to an article by Prof. Sidney L. Pressey of the Ohio State University, "A Simple Apparatus Which Gives Tests and Scores—and Teaches" *(School and Society,* 23: 373-376, March 20, 1926). Although some work along these lines was carried on during the next quarter-century or so, it was not until 1954 when the idea seemed to be launched toward future fruition. In that year, Profs. Burrhus F. Skinner and James G. Holland, of the psychology department of Harvard University, set up auto-instructional devices which were based on the principles of conditioning the learner's responses and reinforcing his learning at every point by informing him whether his answers to questions were correct. Since then, the idea has gathered adherents all over the country and even abroad. One indication of the popularity of the movement was the rapid proliferation of publications. In 1960, the Department of Audio-Visual Education of the National Education Association issued "Teaching Machines and Programmed Learning: A Source Book," under the editorship of Arthur A. Lumsdaine and Robert Glaser. This sizable volume contained a compilation of vari-

ous writings as of 1960. The past few years have witnessed the publication of books, articles, bibliographies, newsletters, pamphlets,
and even journals. In short, a movement of magnitudinous proportions is under full steam. Educators and teachers are now firmly situ-
ated on the bandwagon, and the doubters and resisters are on the
defensive as opponents of efficiency and progress.

It appears that the path to the future lies in "Teaching by Machine" (Lawrence M. Stolurow, U. S. Office of Education, 1961) and
"Automatic Teaching" (Eugene Galanter, 1959). The watchword of
the new age undoubtedly will be AID ("Auto-Instructional Devices
for Education and Learning"). Conceding that programmed instruction has some values for the teacher and pupil, it is important to
raise questions. Basically, will the new movement be an *aid* or will
it be regarded and utilized as a major method of learning and teaching? Will it function in such a way as to discourage other types of
instruction? Can men be made by machines? To what extent are
workers in automated teaching convinced of the pronouncement by
Skinner in 1954 that his techniques can "shape the behavior of an
organization almost at will"? Can auto-instructional devices promote
education as they are said to improve learning? No doubt, there are
other pertinent questions, such as: What should be the role of the
scholar-educator in an age of advancing automation?

A scholar-educator, let it be explained, is not a mere technician
or methodologist in education, but, rather, an individual who has a
rich cultural background, a broad grounding in the humanistic-social-
aesthetic subjects, a clear conception of the content and influence of
the account of the march of man from ancient times onward, a thorough preparation in at least one area of subject matter, and a comprehensive knowledge of the theoretical and the practical aspects of
education. It is obvious that there is no surfeit of scholar-educators
in the United States, or probably anywhere else for that matter. The
scholar-educator looks at educational problems and developments
from a variety of viewpoints and in different perspectives. He brings
into play the factors of tradition, logic, values, and other considerations which enable him to regard automated teaching with objec-
tivity. He will refrain, in all likelihood, from full acceptance or
rejection of the new phenomenon in pedagogy. The potential contributions to better learning will be appraised experimentally and
in relation to the values of the other forms of learning and teaching.
He will apply his scholarship and objective thought processes in
order to come to a decision as to the role of the teaching machine

in education. He will not be tempted by extrapolations from inadequate and untested data, by the obliviousness of the past and the foreign experience, and by the passion for novelty.

There is no suggestion here that the scholar-educator inevitably must reject the teaching machine or, at best, consign it grudgingly to a negligible role in the instructional process. From the standpoint of one student of education at least, it is necessary to utter caveats. The nature of automation appears to be antithetical to that of scholarship. While the teaching machine may be helpful in mastering techniques and reinforcing factual details, it is not conceivable that it can function as an essential element in the formation of serious students or scholars.

Scholarship is the product of a constant search for and critical examination of the sources of knowledge. It may be attained through minded men who pool their resources for the commonweal but the expenditure of energy and effort. It must be carried out in the library, laboratory, and field. One might use machines for reproducing documents and specimens, but even here it is unsafe to rely completely upon a mechanical aid. If this is true with regard to aids to scholarship, then it is *a fortiori* true of machines which assist in learning.

The scholar-educator might make a stand in behalf of emphasizing the virtues of labor in the acquisition of knowledge. The machine is likely to encourage speed, superficiality, and sloppiness. Thoroughness requires time, pervasiveness, persistence, and perseverance.

Individuality must be maintained at all costs. The group, in the best sense of the sociological term, is an aggregation of individually whose individual natures are recognizable as the components of a chemical mixture. The machine, it would appear, is not conducive to the formation of the individual thinker and searcher after truth. It minimizes the false or misleading notions; it is not the sure index to total truth. In actual fact, the student or scholar must learn how to extricate himself from error and uncertainty, with the aid of a teacher, of course, but eventually on his own.

The machine has values and uses, but also dangers. In an age of automation, those concerned with the highest standards of learning must protect man from the machine.

15. HUMANISTIC INVENTION IN THE POST-INDUSTRIAL AGE

AUGUST HECKSCHER

WE HAVE MANY PROBLEMS which we as a people have to face up to; but in most of them the objective for which we strive is reasonably clear. This is certainly true in race relations. We know we have a very deep problem, but I think most of us have a clear image of what we would like to see as a result of our strivings and our troubles. In the international field, also, though there may be some division of opinion as to methods, our vision of the world is one which we could state with a fair degree of unanimity.

But, in regard to work and leisure and education and technology, it is not only the means that are difficult and it is not only a question of how we are going to get from here to there; it is a question of where we want to go. It is the very quality of our life that is at issue. We are living, of course, in a time of great change, rapid as perhaps no other age has seen it, accumulative to an extraordinary degree; and the result of this change is that the values are shaken. The norms are dissolved which should guide us in choosing our ends and in moving toward our objectives.

I do not suppose there ever has been a society like ours in which the basic goal of almost everyone in business, science, and government, and all the other groups that make up our society, is to alter the existing facts and arrangements. The amount of money we spend for research and the amount of energy we exert to make things different from what they have been speak for a deep conviction that change is not only inevitable, but probably good.

In a period such as this, I do not need to specify or enlarge upon the crises developing throughout our national and social life. There is a crisis in education, although we sometimes speak as if it were only a matter of more classrooms or higher paid teachers. We do need these things, but that, surely, is not the heart of the matter. The heart of the crisis in education is the difficulty in transmitting the values of one generation to another generation which is not quite sure that those values have much meaning or make much sense. I remember a few years ago dedicating a college library. After the speaker had said the things that the older generation always says on an occasion like this—that the library is the center of the university, and so on—one of the students came to me and said, "That's fine, but I don't think the library is the center of the university." I asked why not, and he said, "Because the library represents stored-up wisdom, the kind of wisdom which is very often meaningless in our generation." I asked what, then, was his concept of the center of the university. He thought for a minute and answered rather acutely: "The center of the university is the Student Union, because it's only there where we who are young get together and where, through the long hours of the night, we work out our problems among ourselves— where we begin to get near some kind of truth which we deem to have relevance."

If this crisis exists in education, it certainly exists also in the field of art. It is disturbing to realize that ages when art flourished and when the greatest geniuses arose in Western civilization have been times when the foundations of things were reasonably secure. The artist was able to innovate and experiment within a fixed frame of values. He knew pretty much what he was expected to paint, and innovation consisted of finding new ways of making the thing itself more beautiful. If a crisis thus exists in art—and we see it, I think, among the artists who are confused by the degree of freedom which has been offered them, dazzled by the wide option of choice which confronts them—it exists also in our politics, in our whole social life.

We speak of the present age as a consequence of the "Industrial Revolution," but surely that describes imperfectly and partially what is the truth of our present situation. We live not in the 19th century, but in the 20th century. We live—if we could pick a neutral term to describe where we are—in a "Post-Industrial Age." Many of the outward forms continue to be the same. That always is true when men

move through historical transformations and revolutions. The outward forms exist, but the inner spirit is altered almost unrecognizably.
We have passed from a period which might be characterized as one
of scarcity to a period of plenty; we have passed from a period dominated by the needs and problems of production to a period dominated by the needs of consumption or dissemination; we have passed
from a period where the prevailing ethic was based on authority
within the family to a period where the prevailing ethic seems to be
permissiveness. In all these ways, subtly and sometimes without being
aware of it, we have passed out of one age into another—from the
Industrial Age itself into the Post-Industrial Age.

Many horrors have been outlived. One cannot look back on
industrialism without being shocked by many of its manifestations,
by many of the things we put up with. One thinks of darkened cities,
of the burdens that lay upon men, of the exploitation of children,
and the way women were kept in subjection. In comparing all that
with today, one feels, in spite of our shortcomings, a kind of ease, a
sort of general good taste, even a kind of public happiness. At the
same time, partly because we are in a world we do not yet really
know, filled with possibilities we never yet have been able to unravel,
there is a sense of nervousness and apprehension. People feel that if
they only could have a little more leisure, they would be rested—and
then they discover that it is not work alone that wearies, but that
leisure brings its own choices which make them even more tired than
they were in the first place. People feel saddled with obligations and
necessities, with things and commitments. They feel that if they only
could break away from this and have a little more freedom, they
would have the kind of peace which they lack. Yet, when they do
break away, they find that they are dazzled by the very absoluteness
of the freedom, by the lack of structure and discipline which formerly
characterized their lives.

The main characteristics of the Post-Industrial Age can be defined
fairly simply. We live, first of all and overwhelmingly, in an urban
age. In the United States, we have awakened only recently to the
fact that we are a very great urban civilization. Long after we lived
predominantly in cities, we persisted in the belief that we were really
a rural folk and that very probably we would go back to the farm
as soon as we were released from the necessities which compelled us
to live and work away from it. The result has been that our cities
became places of frenzied ugliness. They were ugly because we
thought that all beauty remained in the countryside, all grace on the

farm. When some students and scholars at Harvard did a study of American urban civilization, they said that "a faint feeling of civic nausea" was characteristic of all those who lived in the modern city. But I think we have escaped from that. We finally have recognized that if we are going to find the good life at all in the second half of the 20th century, we are going to find it in the city and not on the farm. We finally are getting away from the Jeffersonian myth—from the idea that virtue resides in the countryside, evil in the town. The symptoms of this change are all about us. We at last are facing up to the problems of city life. We are recognizing the possibilities for beauty, for the arts, for a genuinely habitable existence in the midst of the great metropolis.

As we have become more urban, we also have found the life of the farm becoming more and more residual. One of our gnawing political problems is that so many people no longer are needed on the farm; and yet, if we were only a little more free in our spirit, we would look upon this as one of the liberating factors in our civilization. One thinks of the men who have been dragged down all the centuries of civilization by an effort to bring from the soil enough food to maintain them. One thinks of today's underdeveloped countries where 75% of the people are condemned to this single end alone and where the possibilities of turning energies into other ways of life seem like the open door to greater progress and greater happiness.

In the Soviet Union, 45% of the people, I believe, still are on the farms. Think what the Soviet people would feel in the way of freedom and the possibilities of an ampler life if they could reach a situation such as ours, where less than 10%—perhaps only 8%—of the people are working on the farms, and yet where these are supplying an abundance of food which provides not only for ourselves, but for other parts of the world as well.

The character of work has changed greatly as a result of urban existence, as a result of the science and technology which underlie urbanism. The kind of toil which men do has been radically altered. In up-state New York where I had my farm, I went back recently to see a man who had been working in one of the welding shops in town. I had known him some three or four years ago, and I asked him how things were going now. He said, "Oh, they are going fine. I am doing very well, but I'm not working any more." I asked, "What do you mean? What's happening?" He said, "I am over in Syracuse, in one of the electronics plants. It really isn't work at all. I drive over there in the morning, I put on a white coat, and I just walk around the factory and watch the machines."

What had happened to him was that he had entered into "transformed work" which becomes more and more characteristic of our society, and he was finding the change, at least in the beginning, entirely enjoyable.

Free time, meanwhile, has increased and will increase enormously. At the Twentieth Century Fund, we are rather cautious in our projections as to the amount of free time that will be available. We have been struck by the cleverness of men and women in using up the time which the machine is ready to grant them, the ways they have of distracting themselves and taking on new and sometimes unnecessary burdens—anything to escape the challenge which leisure offers. In spite of such delays which we are able to interpose, it is certainly clear that in the years ahead men and women will enter later into the working force. They will retire earlier. They will live longer, and they will have lots of time in the midst of their working careers comparable to sabbaticals. In all these ways there will be open vistas where men can choose, and, indeed, will have to choose, what they are going to do and what they are going to find worth while.

In the midst of this change, there is another fundamental transformation occurring—a transformation of our understanding of the function of education. It will seem incredible not so very long from now that we should have thought of education as belonging exclusively or even predominantly to the period of youth. Education will become a lifelong pursuit in many areas. We do not realize today how much education does go on outside of the formal institutions of education and after formal schooling is completed. Men and women will return all through their lives to sources of knowledge, to places where they can achieve new skills and new experiences, and where they also can have those basic delights of the liberal arts without which work and leisure both can be vain.

In looking forward to the kinds of problems that confront us, I have decided to focus on a single problem—the problem of unemployment in our society. The more you think of it, the more you see that it is a key to the way we solve all our problems, the more it seems to open up the choice of values and ends which is so important for us to face.

Unemployment is, perhaps, the great central dilemma of our advancing technology. It is striking that we have had unemployment during a period when our production was so rapidly increasing, and it is striking that we have had unemployment close to the intolerable figure of 6% while our economy was being sustained by the massive economic pump-priming of our space and defense program. We used to think that if we produced more, we would solve the problem of unemployment; we used to think that the machine would create more jobs than it displaced; we used to think that, as a result of the machine, there would be sufficient new demands and products to keep people constantly employed. All these assumptions are being re-examined today.

In the 19th century, John Stuart Mill, with some surprise, looked upon the early development of the Industrial Revolution and remarked, "We have all these labor-saving devices, and still labor has not really been saved." There is still a relatively constant amount of work within our society, and it is true that in the period since Mill's little joke, we have found all sorts of means for complicating our desires, for enlarging our interests, for developing goods which are more complex and require a higher number of man-hours to manufacture. The victrola was a startling invention, although a comparatively simple device; the radio was more complicated, and television more complicated still. We move constantly into an area where the complexity and the novelty of things seems to take up some of the slack which the machine otherwise would provide. And yet, in the long run, the inventions created to save man from toil surely will have that effect. We have arrived at a period where we have not merely increased the quantity of things we can produce in a given hour, but we radically have transformed the nature of production so that we will find we can meet our needs without being able, under existing ideas and concepts, to provide employment for all our population.

We are attempting to solve the immediate crisis of unemployment by means of education. It is a very good way to begin and a necessary thing to do. It is felt by large numbers of people that the jobs exist and we can train people so as to be capable of doing them. A massive and pointed use of education can break up existing blocks of poverty and unemployability. Nothing is more disturbing than what is known as inherited poverty or inherited lack of employment. People are on relief whose fathers and even grandfathers have been on relief. But I am not convinced that education by itself is the long-range answer to our problem. In the South we must train the Negroes to take on jobs which they now are barred from by ignorance or lack of skills. But if we rely upon training and education alone, I do not think we are going to solve the problem of discrimination and unemployment. And so, five or 10 years from now, what may be called the second crisis in unemployment will occur. Only then, I think, will we meet the growing threat by trying to deal on a large scale with the social needs which so obviously are lying all around us and which, to so large a degree, have been neglected.

We then, and only then, shall begin really to evolve systems of mass transportation which will take care of the needs of our social order. We will begin seriously to reconstruct our cities. We will begin to take measures to avoid contamination in our streams and rivers. People will be very excited. They will rush about and create all sorts of wonderful programs. No doubt a great deal of good will be done, but the spectre still faces the prospect of finding that, despite all we do and because of the new technology in which we do it, we will have a great number of unemployed remaining. Indeed, in the General Motor's exhibit at the World's Fair there is the model of a single great machine which moves a distance of a certain number of miles per day, actually chewing up the trees, leveling the land, and laying the cement as it moves along. The great machine casts doubts on the whole picture of being able to employ large numbers of people by building roads or even rebuilding cities. It tends to look as if this machine might be very good for the road and very good for the cities, but not necessarily a solution for the problem of unemployment.

So finally we will come to a third stage in dealing with this endemic crisis in our social order. At that time we will begin seriously to question the very idea of full employment. We will ask if it is a valid concept in a technological society such as ours to keep everybody busy all the time. Instead of trying to keep more and more people active doing things which we want or do not want—as the case may be—we will begin to ask whether it is possible to make people productive and creative. When we come to this period, we will begin to attend seriously to the need of rearranging the careers of men and women, of apportioning time in wholly new ways so as to allow people the chance for more fruitful individual lives.

There are two patterns for the revised use of time which are fairly obvious, and both of them are at work already within our society. One is toward shorter working days; the other, toward radically shortened working weeks. It is unlikely that either will be permanently acceptable. They are illusory in the short run because no one seems really to want them. Even the shorter working week is not very attractive, either to the family or to the unions, so far as we have been able to observe. An experiment carried out in California provided one of the airplane factories with a three-day weekend. Evaluators went about asking people how they liked it. One of the workers said that he did not like it so much; in fact, he called that extra day his "Honey-Do Day." When asked why, he said, "Well, from morning until night, it was 'Honey, do this!' and 'Honey, do that!' " The time created in this way is "left-over time"; it is time at the end of the working day or at the end of a working week when people do not really have a chance to embark upon a separate kind of existence. It is impossible for men to undertake a genuinely new enterprise when they still are dominated by the rhythm of the working day and the whole psychology of the industrial order.

Indeed, much of the popular interest in art today, which we are inclined rightly to encourage and consider one of the bright spots in our present cultural scene, is disturbing, nevertheless, because it represents the kinds of things that people do in their "left-over time" at the end of the working day or week. The kind of work which then is done is done as a hobby. It also may have secondary purposes: to keep people busy, to keep them occupied, to help "pass time" or "kill time." Sometimes it is done for therapeutic purposes. Or it may be done because people want to get away from the family room and work in the comparative quietness of the cellar.

A second device which we see already employed within our society is to allow a smaller and smaller part of the population to labor and, meanwhile, to increase spare time quite dramatically for the rest. Every time I speak about leisure and free time, somebody gets up in the audience and says, "Well, that's all fine and good, but I'm a doctor, and I never have any free time!" or "I'm a teacher and I never have any free time!" Who, then, are all these people who have free time which we speak of? The answer is, of course, that the people with the free time are the very ones who, in the 19th century, were working 16 to 18 hours a day—namely, those engaged in the production of goods. Those who followed what were essentially the liberal pursuits or who completed the lighter tasks are those who, today, work virtually full-time. And so it might be that we will come into a civilization where small parts of the population take upon themselves the challenge, the thrill, and the burden of working to their full capacities, while the great mass work very little and amuse themselves as best they can.

I would not praise either of these developments, although, to some degree, both of them certainly will occur. There will be shorter working hours. There will be very intense work on the part of the creative individuals paralleled by a much slacker existence on the part of those who man the industrial machines.

There is a third path indicated presently by certain somewhat prevalent and dramatic careers—the careers, for example, of policemen or army officers, who retire after 20 or 25 years of service. These people do not really retire at all, in the ordinary sense; they take up a second career. Aided by their pension, they are able to move freely and to begin something which they would have liked to have begun earlier except that it would not have paid enough without their pension to support their family or themselves. They may operate a small shop or manage a counseling service; they may become experts in travel or craftsmen and artists. In these careers we see an example of what might come about for a considerable part of the population.

The pension system is basically a way of paying our industrial workers deferred wages. Under this system you say to the people: You work now, but we will continue your wages later on—through this other form. That pay, added to what the individual would make in some area of the economy where high productivity does not exist— such as income from a small store—then would enable him to continue in a second career which, amply supported, would release his energies and fulfill his desires.

Thus, I can foresee growing up, side by side in a country like ours, essentially two economies—the economy of abundance and the economy of scarcity. I can foresee growing up here, side by side, the economy of the great machine and the economy of the craft—each supporting and sustaining or inspiring the other.

It is interesting that this type of solution is what Edward Bellamy proposed in his "Looking Backwards"—a book published in the 1880's, one of the crucial volumes which influenced, much more than Marx, a whole generation of American thinkers such as John Dewey and Thorstein Veblen. Edward Bellamy made exactly this point: that people would serve the industrial machine by working in a sort of industrial army for 20 years and then would be liberated for other, more humane pursuits. In one of the dialogues, the 19th century man, cast forward by dreams or visions into a new world, is protesting this arrangement. He maintains that men at 40 are not superannuated and should not be put on the shelf. Dr. Leete, the 20th-century scientist, replies, "My dear sir, child of our race and yet of an age long past, don't you realize that these people are not going to be put on the shelf? They are really going to enter into the best part of their lives." He goes on to say that if a man at 20 achieves his majority, then at 40, under this new system, he will be liberated and will be ready to achieve his true manhood.

It seems fanciful to talk in these terms, and yet, when one looks about, he cannot help being amazed by the different kinds of work and forms of employment which once occupied the whole working lives of men or of women but which now have become largely residual. Once, for example, all the manpower of society was engaged in hunting; today hunting is a hobby—a memory we preserve. At certain periods, the whole male population was engaged in preserving the integrity of the borders within which they lived. Wars had to be stopped temporarily so that they could sow and reap. The central objective of their life was something which is now accomplished in three years or less by our young men. Indeed, I have no doubt that when our grandchildren look back upon this period, it will seem to them extraordinary that we should have wanted to spend virtually all our lives doing something so simple as producing the goods we consumed.

In our own time, we have seen people pushed constantly out of one sphere of employment by the whip of automation and new technological means into areas where technology had not been introduced rapidly and decisively. We have seen them move out of manufacturing into the services. We convinced ourselves for a while that services could not easily be automated, but it is evident that they can be. Service in shops, telephone service, and transportation of all kinds indicate that people are being forced out of these areas by automation. The question is: "Where are they going?" One might be tempted to say they are going into the armed services, but even there one discovers that manpower is no longer the decisive national weight on the world-wide balance of political power. I suppose that the final answer must be that we will pass into some new sphere of freedom and art. But I would like to suggest one further possibility.

I am constanly struck by the number of needs we seem to have while jobs seem so comparatively difficult to provide. There is need for better cities, better transportation, and a more beautiful landscape. These needs certainly can provide jobs if we are willing to spend the money which is necessary, if we are willing to create the institutions which make the accomplishment of a great public work possible. But there are also many individual and personal needs, lying quite deep within us, which strangely enough do not result in jobs. We need, for example, gardeners, cooks, nurses, and musicians; we need all kinds of people who enhance life, who refine its pleasures and develop its rewards. And yet, our economic system does not provide the adequate compensation or suitable conditions necessary to fulfill many of these needs. Thus, one way of looking at this entire problem is to ask the question, "How can these social needs be converted into economic jobs?"

Our problem is that we have many simple human needs, but we cannot pay the nurse or the gardener the kind of wages which we have come to think of as reasonable. One solution suggested informally by a leading economist is to lower the minimum wage. This expert argued that there are numerous things that young people, coming out of our schools today, are able and are ready to do, but the prevailing wage is set at a level which prospective employers cannot afford to meet. When I asked if it were possible, at a time when we are fighting poverty, to talk about reducing the minimum wage and lowering the individual income, it was argued that there is no reason why the lower wage which is paid by the private employer could not be supplemented by a subsidy from other revenues. One can conceive, for example, of nurses who are paid at a rate which the average patient can afford and whose salary then is supplemented, as other social services are, by the state or the community.

Secondly, to convert needs into jobs, we could do something that is being done all around us already, and that is to take unpleasant jobs now done unprofitably by the individual and organize them so that they can be done as a profession. One no longer hires a man to clean his windows; one hires a window-cleaning service. One used to hire a cook who would come in and busy himself in the kitchen; today, more and more, one hires a catering service. In this way the individual, engaged in such work, increases his productivity; in this way his wages are increased and a job is created where it seemed that none existed.

Finally, there is a vast area in our society where we simply have to recognize that a need and a value exist, where we have to lift our eyes and raise our spirits to the point where we recognize that the services which answer these needs must be provided. School teaching, for example, was in danger of becoming a need that we could not pay for adequately. When we realized that teaching lies at the very heart of our society and civilization, we found the means to raise the teacher's salary substantially. In the same way, the musicians in symphony orchestras are beginning at last to receive an adequate wage. We believed just a few years ago that we could not afford to pay our musicians. But we are discovering that the resources exist, if we have the will and the desire to organize them and to draw upon them.

The same thing is happening in the theater, where previously there were few stable careers or jobs. Actors would get a little work now and then, and the rest of the time they either starved or filled in. As repertory theaters develop in communities throughout the country, we may make it possible for young actors and actresses to enter upon this career, creating jobs to sustain them in a continuing and dignified way.

Underneath this waterfall of suggestions, I have intended to stress the idea that what we really need, in looking at our society and trying to cope with the great problem of technology, is the capacity to be socially inventive as well as scientifically and technologically inventive. We need to see the machine as a means of liberation and not as something which imposes its necessity upon us from without. What we are witnessing is not simply a scientific revolution. We are witnessing a deep transformation, and the need is for new approaches to the concept of work, to forms of education—indeed, to the whole social order.

Any solution to the problems of technology must be, above all, compatible with the real needs of men and women. Does it give them a sense of fulfillment? Does it give them a sense of participation in something worth while, of belonging to the community? The question which must be asked about each proposed solution is whether it ultimately enhances the value and dignity of the individual.

Man is not placed on this planet to be merely comfortable, but to strive and to seek. The challenge of this generation, when we have settled such radical matters as the creation of a better international order and the establishment of a larger social justice, is to find the purpose that will give meaning to life and then to fulfill that purpose within the framework of a sound economic system. But let us never forget that the economic system and the technology upon which it is based were created to serve man. They were not created before him; they were not a condition that was given for living upon this earth. We made them and we shall remake them. So let us move forward with the idea not of creating a system which is more perfect and logical, but of making a world which is a little nearer to the heart's desire.

Part III

EDUCATION
AND TECHNOLOGY:
VARIED ASPECTS

16. EDUCATION, TECHNOLOGICAL CHANGE, AND THE NEW SOCIETY

ROY C. BUCK

PEOPLE AT ALL TIMES AND PLACES have described themselves as at the end of one era and at the beginning of another. Presently, a literature is accumulating on the major shifts and mutations occurring in technology dealing also with its organization and impact on society; and the burden of this literature is that ours is such a great divide between one era and another. This chapter is in that vein. It proposes to evaluate the significance of an aspect of epoch-changing technological change and its transformational impact on educational organization. A second goal is to suggest how these changes may contribute to achieving some measure of greatness and realization for the contemporary community as it moves into the new era.

Man, as a highly developed animal, has brought himself to the threshold of this new era. This "New Time"—and that is precisely what it is—marks the beginning of the *human community*. It is a time of new presuppositions about human order. Nature will provide few useful guides. Society and culture would seem to be passing out of the period of nature and into the primeval period of humanity. In this new period, man no longer sees himself as lord of the jungle

EDITORS' NOTE: Dr. Buck wishes to acknowledge the gracious, yet thorough, critical review and editorial suggestions from his colleague and friend, Prof. Maxwell H. Goldberg.

—first among many—but uniquely endowed to live, though still in nature, yet not wholly by nature's laws. Just as early man began civilization with the crudest tools and thought forms, so the new human being tumbles with technology and social systems growing out of this new awareness.

As one reflects on the significance of this mutational turn of events, he is struck by the stark irrelevance of so much of the traditional wisdom regarding man's relationship to man and to nature. Education, the institutionalized means by which we traditionally have equipped ourselves for the encounter with the future, preoccupies our thoughts. We have misgivings: will the traditional lore, customarily transmitted by conventional education, be relevant to our needs for coping with the new epoch? If not, will formal education be able to make adaptive and innovational changes and serve as a major agent of such change?

THE EDUCATIONAL PROBLEM

In the Western world, specialization of work and compartmentalization of knowledge have been the classic means for organizing the economy and developing systems of education. This atomistic bent has produced a highly intricate complex of mechanical know-how, intellectual content, and community organization. This is held together by an elaborate network of interlinking hardware and an elaborate bureaucracy of men trained specialistically for linking the bits and pieces into workable systems of economic production and human-need satisfaction.

There is no more convenient exhibit of the consequences of this specialization and fragmentation of work and knowledge that marks this elaborate aggregation of bits and pieces than the catalogues of courses and curricula offered at colleges and universities. Here, capsulated in outline form, are the institutionalized and officially approved, proliferated residues of academic polities and exchange systems. Responsible academic freedom in too many cases seems to have been eroded by the free-enterprising entrepreneurship of professors eager to stake out specialities on the landscape of truth.

While campuses are defined as wellsprings of reason, rational behavior, and change, there are myriad impacted values bordering on the sacred and eternal associated with much of the paraphernalia of the higher learning. Probably in no other sector of society are the traditional values of a specializing, fragmentizing laissez-faire philosophy more entrenched than in the intellectual. Unbridled competition, duplication of effort, and fragmentation of disciplines have been condoned so the individual has freedom to pursue his interest wherever it may drift. The highly specialized scholar, staking his claim on a facet of thought and building it into a little intellectual empire, is a common phenomenon. It is held that only in this approach can academic mysteries be dissolved. It is believed that, in the give-and-take of the intellectual marketplace, those who attain recognition as specialists are, by definition, working in the "proper way" and toward the common good. This tradition has deep philosophic and, indeed, religious roots. It powerfully reinforces the specialistic set of our higher education.

Another symbol associated with specialization of interest is the naive scholar. It is believed that scholarship must carry with it a certain "divine naiveness" in order for it to be productive. It is held that the intellectual who is too aware of the world beyond his immediate concern becomes muddled in his thinking. But one is reminded of the prehistoric, highly specialized dinosaurs who nibbled in the tree tops unmindful of other specialized little animals nibbling away at their feet and body. The little specialized brains in the tree tops geared to nibbling leaves to feed the vast and slow-moving hulks could not get the message down to the feet fast enough to escape. Dinosaurs perished. Specialization of function has its limitations. The so-called lower animals are designed to do a few things and do them rather well. But their adaptive and integrative powers, their non-animal qualities, are limited. Their "natural naiveness" limits them and destroys them. There is a lesson in this for our academic "naive specialists" as we are propelled into a new era. They, too, may find that they naively have specialized themselves into extinction.

The traditional approach in learning likewise adds impetus to specialization and fragmentation. This approach is to raise a difficult and complicated question and proceed to break it down into what appears to be its logical components. The components are linked to relevant technical and intellectual disciplines for analysis. There emerges a vast amount of information. One gets the image of the exploded drawing of a power lawnmower in the little envelope attached to the handle at the time of purchase. The drawing, the analysis, makes the parts visible, but it is the synthesis of the parts that produces the power and the manicured lawn. The bill of materials for a house is a limited definition of a house. It is the relationship of the parts that solves the problem of shelter. Traditional academic specialization often fails to achieve such synthesis; it fails to put Humpty Dumpty together again.

The tendency toward analysis, coupled with the growth of specialistic knowledge around involved components, leads the learner to simplicity of thought and a specialized mentality. Thorstein Veblen, a generation and a half ago, named this condition "trained incapacity." Sometimes we say that people "paint themselves into a corner." Recently, a colleague remarked, after listening to a paper in which the reader pursued not one, but several specialized lines of thought as they bore on his problem, "He has painted himself into the middle of the room." Whether specialization leads to the corner or the middle of the field of truth, the problem remains the same: education and the intellectual vocations, patterning themselves after the technological content of the culture, have adopted the format of specialization and division of labor to a remarkable degree. As technology moves on to another—and generalistic—order of integration, and thus helps usher in a new era, education—specialistically honeycombed—is faced with the possibility of obsolescence of such dimension that it, too, literally stands at the threshold of a new intellectual epoch.

Without realizing the precise nature of this new epoch, everywhere educators are in an experimental and inventive mood. Educational journalism is in full production turning out analyses, criticisms, and recommendations designed to fix education as the fulcrum about which popular adjustment to the new demands of advanced technological and bureaucratic development can be attained; but, thus far, there seems to be little awareness that the new demands may mark the end of the reign of exclusivist specialization, inaugurating a new reign of generalism.

Throughout the educational establishment there is enjoyed a feeling of being the center of attention. This comes, in part, from renewed public and private support and sympathy for the educational worker. Through education, it is alleged, we can come to terms with the world of people, things, and ideas. Education is eagerly looked to as the transformational deliverer of humane society in an epoch of advanced and meteorically advancing technology.

The reflective observer only can be mildly optimistic. While great educational programs are under way, one is faced with the stark realities of institutional specialistic and segmented encrustment, the growing sense of peace between the campus and the habitually segmented thinking of main street, and the burgeoning popular demand for specialistically "schooled" replacements to man the increasingly bureaucratized economy and its supporting community. The great public expectations and demands placed upon the educational establishments do encourage, in the professor, attitudes and values antagonistic to the traditional academic norms which guaranteed a certain maverick vitality as a counterpoise to routine academic conformity with specialistic pressures.

Actually, the variety of vested interests in the status quo presents strong arguments for education to play not an expansive, progressive role, but a restrictive, conservative role in adjustment to change. Thus, education, pictured often as an innovative institution, may be faced increasingly with pressure to guarantee trained specialistic replacements for economic and social systems faced with increasing obsolesence as they are propelled powerfully into the post-specialistic era of an advanced technological impact.

The creative contribution of education can become rather "academic" in a society faced with heavy investment in specialistically rationalized industrial hardware and community institutions from which decreasing returns are realized. This sunk capital, both real as well as psychic and imagined, is not easily written off. Every effort will be made to salvage the last bit of income. And education will be looked to as a prime agent in the salvage operation rather than as agent of adaptive or innovative change.

In a word, what we are asserting is something often overlooked when education is presented as a prime mover of cultural and societal change on a grand scale. The demands of the present have to be met first; and these are dominantly conservational. Then, if there are resources and energy left for creative movement into the future, all well and good. But first things first. And what is first is the structure of immediate sunk assets and how to salvage as much return as possible. This means: how do we extract conventionally specialistic returns from costly specialistic assets, accumulated over decades?

It would be irresponsible to be completely pessimistic. As a nation, we are beginning to see the wisdom of protecting not only our present investments, but also the value of planned anticipation of the future. But before we outline what seems to be the prerequisite for the new and post-specialistic education, we shall attempt a summary of the major changes in other segments of society producing what we referred to earlier as the beginning of a New Time. For it is in accordance with these societal changes that we must project the potentials and the problems of the new education for the New Time.

THE NEW TECHNOLOGY

Technological advancement is no longer simply that of increasing productivity of machines. Contemporary machine design is based upon wholly new concepts and presuppositions. The new machines retain the "tireless" quality of their ancestors. But they no longer are single-purpose, specialized systems. They are taking on a certain universal character. They no longer simply reproduce and speed up motor skills of human labor. There are the additional human qualities of decision and control, and a limited morality frequently is built in. The new machines are not only extensions of man's muscle power, but also of his nervous system and his decision-making capacity—and to make decisions is to moralize.

An obvious example of mechanized computation skill that carries an ethical component is the "guaranteed honesty" coupled with the automatic change maker connected to cash registers. The little metal trough with its opened palm offers the customer the correct change every time. The register's innards record everything required to keep the exchange between customer and firm accurate and honest. Operators of the new registers are really programmers. Once the exchange relationship is set up and the button pushed, the machinery takes over. An error in programming, of course, causes a great deal of "anxiety" in the operator as well as the machine. The error usually has to be corrected by hand. This is a far cry from the old change drawer underneath the counter, open to all and subject to the calculating skill and moral fiber of the clerk.

As the slave was dehumanized into an obedient biological system of motor skills, with only those human attributes retained which guaranteed obedience and the most elementary decision-making, so we humanize the machine into something approximating the slave.

The new slave machines do not trouble us in the way human slaves did. Man, first among the animals, has achieved a level of creativity where he dares to humanize the product of his skill and to share a little of his uniqueness with it. As a slave-man economy required a minimum labor force of whole men, so also will the slave-machine economy. Now, of course, we are a long way from the slave-machine way of life. But it is not too early to reflect on it. Significant cues to the new life can be envisaged by careful review of classical slave-man cultures of the ancient world. We shall not review slave culture here. Suffice it to say that it freed the favored few for development into wholly human beings. Now, however, we shall be faced with the potential for total human development as a mass phenomenon rather than as a quality reserved for an elite minority. The pursuit of beauty, dignity, and grace, coupled with a sense of composure, but at the same time motivated by the enlarged principles of respect for people, ideas, and things, is on the verge of becoming a live option for the many. Perhaps, within the present generation, millions will find what it means to be intellectually and spiritually alive and free and will discover new dimensions of political freedom heretofore never envisioned. We may be, indeed, on the threshold of a new era of such magnitude and impact as to stagger the most willing imagination.

What will the slave machines be like? Only a cursory view is possible at this time. Once machines were massive. Early industry was characterized by a certain heaviness. Big, grunting, groaning, belching mills and presses, powered by giant engines and motors, once symbolized the Industrial Revolution. The newest machines have grace, lightness, elegance, and a parsimony of movement. Smallness is the premium quality of the new technology. Little elegant systems, performing great feats of production, are replacing the iron leviathans of the early 20th century.

Plans for activating mechanical systems by use of brain waves are on the drawing boards. Some crude experiments have been successful. The kind of mentality that this break-through suggests and, indeed, will demand sends one reeling. Thought, as a source of machine control, opens dimensions of human development heretofore reserved for science fiction.

One wonders. Man, of his own will and design, passes over the threshold into a truly New Time. Labor, once believed to be a curse on man, and later a kind of penance and character builder, is destined for marked decline. New machines will require human attention, but of a wholly different order than that presently employed. Traditional human contact with machines is that of operator. The biologically alive hand, eye, and brain guide machines as they weld, sew, stamp, turn, mill, press, and so on. The operator's mind guides hands and feet as they connect and give meaning to the mechanism. New machines with operator skills and low-level judgment built in will continue to demand attention—yet with a marked difference. The new relationship will not be simply physical and routine control. It will be highly administrative and technical in character. Consequently, the labor force as we presently know it will change. There will be a relatively small group of highly trained maintenance engineers and others devoting full-time to general surveillance or "machine sitting."

Removed from immediate contact with production will be the truly new workers. These are the programmers, or those who "wire in" the operative skill traditionally embodied in the laborer. And behind them will be a burgeoning bureaucracy working out "wiring" policy. These "masters" of the new slave machines appear in greater numbers every year. We are not able as yet to generalize their position in society. Certainly they are of a different mold than traditional plant managers, foremen, or operators. The traditional relationship between men and machines was such that human skill was of utmost importance. For example, no matter how well designed and crafted a metal lathe might have been, it required a skilled craftsman, guiding the cutter over a bar of brass, to produce a candlestick. The candlestick emerged under the skillful eye and hand of the operator. It was his.

Once the crew foreman moved among his workers, criticizing, reassuring, correcting, listening, joking, complaining, and helping. He was a source of inspiration, morale, and, for some workers, trouble. The new machines do not require this middleman, this carrier of company policy and worker grievance. The new machines, with their orders programmed, are instances of total recall and obedience. With no concern other than meeting production schedules, the "new master" throws the switch and we witness, if we are sensitive people, a virtual miracle of human intelligence and ingenuity. Before our eyes, shapeless raw materials take on form, design, color, utility.

What are the demands on education of this new technology? Before we address ourselves to this question, let us first consider another. What are the demands on the community of this new technology? To what extent will our traditional cultural heritage, supported as it is with values that assume human life to be a pilgrimage of hope, inform the new society being born around these new machines that represent a measure of hope realized?

THE NEW SOCIETY

These questions are not empty rhetoric. We assume a posture of realization of large potentials and of greatness. Everywhere there is a sense of achieving, winning, and attaining on the grand scale. There is eagerness to enjoy and even to revel in a vast world brought to heel at man's command. The remaining pockets of human frailty are popularly viewed as dust to be swept under the national rug. Generally, things are good. The remaining problems are a kind of clean-up operation around the fringes of a Great Society.

The position seems to be one of "Why wait?" One is reminded of a news commentator's parting phrase in the days of full-time radio. He signed off with, "Take it easy, but take it." The American Dream, the Great Society, is something to be involved with now. The tactic, however, is not one of populist movement and personal direction by the masses. Rather, there is an air of cool-headedness, professional expertise, and calculated corporate love. The New Society is ushered in by a new elite—a technological and bureaucratic elite—disinterested, impersonally efficacious—and closely linked with advancing technological change.

The community is increasingly rationalized and instrumental in its pattern of social action. Personal civic concern, once a prerequisite for responsible community life, is passing from the public scene. It is being replaced by a comprehensive and compassionate well-trained civil bureaucracy. The heartlessness predicted by the early 20th-century social critics has not materialized. Depersonalized compassion and good taste are the distinguishing features of contemporary planning. The faithful individual, the man who personally cared and who regarded himself as personally responsible, is being replaced by the faithful caring agency and board. The private sector of society has been quick to respond and, indeed, to compete with the public sector in demonstrating a corporate humanitarianism of considerably more than traditional Scattergood Baines dimension. Private foundations and trusts compete for status in promoting a corporate image of brotherly love and concern, such image expressing itself through the application of the new technologies to comforts, conveniences, and pleasures of the many.

Ultimate concern, that idea recently given fresh currency by existentialist theologians such as Tillich, once believed to be a matter of private faith and personal conviction, is secularized and transferred from man to his corporate attachments, with its technological implementations. Modern man finds less and less need to be concerned ultimately about anything. He permits himself to be "stirred up" at seminars, study groups, and in the privacy of his patio and study; but to the public he presents a posture of detachment, perspective, and relativistic tolerance. For him the sense of responsibility is widely and vaguely diffused. The new man avoids situations requiring clearcut choice and significant commitment. This analytic bent, inculcated in his education, keeps him so preoccupied with the search for relevant facts that conclusions are likely to be substituted for decisions; and, as John Henry Newman once observed, "No man will die for a conclusion"! Decision-making, especially in matters concerning the commonweal, is drifting toward professionalization and collectivized responsibility. The traditional responsibilities of citizens are undergoing bureaucratization everywhere. A pattern of remote control through voting on a widening variety of issues and an ever more comprehensive tax responsibility remain as the major outlets for personal popular involvement in public affairs.

Man, experiencing freedom from responsibility for fostering the daily nurture of his way of life, needs new ways of relating himself in authentic fashion to the burgeoning civil bureaucracy which is linked so closely with advancing technology. As an era of active citizenship passes where what one did was often more valued than what one thought, a new form of responsible citizen is called for. He will be judged on the basis of reasoning and philosophic skill as he joins with others in evaluating various professionally devised policies and programs to be implemented through the instrumentalities of advanced technological change.

Questions pertaining to community goals are destined to become more important than formerly, because, among other things, thanks to advancing technological change, the chances of attaining them are greater. The tremendous increase in civic competence because of the productivity of the social and engineering sciences—because of the instrumentalities of technological change—takes goals and objectives out of the arm chair and ivory tower context. They become appropriate to "realistic, down-to-earth" discussion.

A deep and profound change in the way a community organizes its affairs is making itself felt. The tendency to utilize the fruitful achievements of technological change as useful analogies and projective models for social change is marked. It is commonly understood that progress in industry and technology means reduced direct contact between men and machines. Automation places the worker in a role of guardian, checker, reader of dials, sampler, and so on. The tendency to transfer automation theory into new designs of community organizations seems to be gathering momentum. In the civic process, citizens find themselves to be more and more in the role of the worker in an automated industry. The new citizen demands are those of careful policy review and evaluation, intelligent voting on a widening spectrum of referenda, and, of course, continued fiscal responsibility.

As we continue to staff communities with full-time civic experts and further automate the means of production, wholly new patterns of life will develop. A central question in this new age of civic responsibility and industrial production by remote control is how to infuse it with grace and dignity and at the same time continue the traditional values associated with responsible citizenship and also continue the human values that make for the dignity of the individual.

Planners and other civic technicians are quick to support and encourage citizen guidance and review of their studies and proposals. But this requires a level of sophistication beyond that attained through casual observation and experience. A knowledgeable citizenry is today, more than ever, prerequisite to a continued flourishing of a highly developed democratic system—a system stressing the human values that make for the dignity of the individual in an epoch of breathtaking technological change.

THE NEW EDUCATION

We have argued that technological advance, coupled with increasingly comprehensive bureaucratic organization, has brought us to the threshold of a new era. It has been pointed out that this turn of events has education caught on the horns of an embarrassing dilemma. While traditional wisdom claims that through education societies find ways to *new* levels of attainment, there is reason to believe that in times of rapid change education—viewed as agent of the established order—is called on to brake, buffer, and contain the thrust of change in the interest of continued stability.

Education not only informs, but is informed by its supporting society. The two-way relationship takes on qualitatively different attributes, depending upon the stage of advance of a given social and cultural situation. Where mass education and its support by the public sector are high priority values, it is not surprising to find educational institutions mirroring prevailing mass norms. This is especially true of publicly supported higher education. Subject to review by laymen as well as professionals, public colleges and universities are especially sensitive to being responsible agents in the service of the present social and economic order and also wellsprings of people, ideas, and things shaping the emerging community. This duality of function frequently is the center of political debate, campus investigations, and pressure-group concern. While compromises frequently find a policy congenial to both points of view, there remains the need to be continually aware of a moving emphasis.

The educational establishment now feverishly works at servicing the high demand for trained personnel to man the new society and technology previously outlined. At the same time it is expected to function responsibly in the salvage and containment programs occasioned by rapid change. In these contexts, little may be expected from the establishment in the way of leadership toward creative confrontation with the new society. The establishment is preoccupied with orderly and humane transition. In the long view, however, one can only be optimistic. As time goes on, people, their ideas, and hardware wear out. Elbow room to exercise its developmental and innovative responsibilities will accrue to education as the last evidences of "lever, wheel, and axle society" are phased out.

We do not wish to imply that attention is not being given to internal adjustments in educational institutions as they look to the future. But what is going on is frequently less visible and less a part of official operating policy. As it is sometimes useful to refer to the visible and invisible church, so it may be practical to differentiate between that which is sanctioned officially and institutionalized in the educational establishments—the visible—and that which is in the confines of the institution but not wholly of it—the invisible.

In almost every major educational enterprise there is evidence of new educational forms and processes nurtured by people who have decided to go beyond the official, prescribed, and codified offerings, and accept the challenges to creative adaptation made necessary by advancing technological change. Here we find experimental work not only in methods of knowledge storage and transmission, but concerning the very problem of how knowledge itself is developed. This sort of experimental effort most intimately comes to grips with the latest developments of technological change—as, for example, the computer.

General education, already a part of the establishment in many instances, was an early attempt at creative encounter with the new time and the New Society being evoked, in considerable part, by advancing technology. In theory, general education was revolutionary. It was to be a forthright attack on vocationalism and overspecialization in higher education—both of these induced, partly, by the advances of the "older" technologies. In practice, it was faced frequently with the choice of which end of a specialized study track it wanted to pick up the student. It either could be a foundation from which students graduate to clearcut speciality; or it could be a kind of cushion into which they fell at the end of a specialized intellectual trek. In either instance, the students frequently experienced anxiety and frustration. In the first instance, if they were serious, they were likely to ask the wrong questions of their specialized instructors. In the latter case, they merely related to the general educational experience as if it were another specialized course.

Instructors in either situation paid a price. If they were honest, they lost their departmental "homes" on the campus. Many tried to be all things to all people and, by effecting a "now I am a generalist, now I am a specialist" way of life, became academic schizophrenics. The problem was that general education was likely to be seen by universities as an extra added attraction and not integral to a course of study. General education, like the new technology which, in part, has produced it, challenges vast "fixed capital investments" in both material and non-material culture. It challenges the division of labor and specialization themes. It would appear, however, that it was captured by the forces of salvage and containment to polish encrusted courses of specialistic study. In almost desperate eagerness to redress the criticisms heaped on education—especially higher education—in the post-Sputnick years, general education was incorporated eagerly as visible evidence of universities being responsive to long-run generalistic educational needs.

Originally conceived as a new direction, general education, with notable exceptions, is a series of courses, guided by committees, and taught by short-term recruits from the traditional disciplines. In academic polity, general education can provide a notable example common in political circles of appearing to be a major innovative thrust when it may be only a technique to guarantee a certain quiescence and the status quo. What we have said should not be taken as a general criticism. We point out what happens to academic innovations when, perhaps too soon, they are incorporated officially into ongoing programmed activity, all too frequently geared to short-range tactical goals.

Adult study was mentioned earlier as an integral part of the emerging community of the new age of advanced technology. The relationship of the educational establishment to adult study suggests an hypothesis and an emphasis worthy of some consideration. A possibly unpopular hypothesis is advanced: educational innovation happens and makes an impact in areas where there is least institutional commitment. It is suggested that adult study is where one must look to find timely, creative attacks on the adjustment problems occasioned by the new technology and the new society.

Always something of an unwelcome intruder in academia, or at best a dignified public relations program, adult education traditionally has been the arena of trial-and-error instruction. Because there is believed to be less at stake, workers in adult study frequently have been less liable to the establishment. This, of course, has had obvious disadvantages, but the great advantage is that educational innovation has been possible without the slow machinery of approval that legitimizes credit courses in resident and graduate study.

Many of the traditional weaknesses of adult education are being corrected. More competent personnel are attracted to it. Traditionally defined as a kind of public relations activity, adult study presently attracts the attention of resident and research faculty as responsible academic endeavor. Not only is the campus climate improved regarding adult study; increased interest and demand are also building up in the community. For years the educational establishment claimed that the local community did not appreciate the need for continued deliberate learning in a free society. Local citizens were charged with being "alimony supporters" of adult education. They were willing to pay a reasonable price for its support but especially did not care to live with it.

In this respect, the situation is fast changing. There is a great surge of public appetite for adult learning. Book clubs prosper. The paperback industry flourishes. Study groups are in. Homes, churches, club rooms, schools, and newly assigned "cultural space" in banks, department stores, city halls, and factories are the scenes of seminars, discussions, symposia, and lectures.

A number of causes contribute to this upsurge of public appetite for adult learning. For one thing, because of world-wide tensions and marked social and economic dislocations at home, there is evidence of an increased demand for study on the part of the adult community. A special instance, and one which deserves careful nurture, is the increase in study of public affairs. Study groups and seminars in a wide spectrum of academic concern for community development are an integral part of day-to-day living for an enlarging proportion of the population. Cynics are prone to brush aside this sort of adult study as a respectable substitute for action and often assert that the understanding gained is useless in relation to community progress. Adult study is sometimes described as a kind of doll-play approach to citizenship in the professionalized public bureaucracy of an age of advanced technology. On the other hand, it also must be said that study—significant, challenging, illuminating study—of man's attempt to construct a good society is looked to by many as a great resource for infusing the new society with modes of life and thought congenial to its demands.

In the past, continuing education after completion of formal schooling often was economically motivated. "They help a person get ahead" was a common judgment on the worth of evening schools and correspondence courses. Whether one was on the executive track, professional and technical career line, or the skilled labor ladder, education was evaluated in terms of its contributions to raising incomes, status, and prestige. The appeal was to the immediate vocational-social utility interest of the adult learner.

But a new emphasis was to develop. Shortly after World War II, when advanced science and technology were beginning to make themselves felt on a mass scale, it became obvious that the traditional appeal often was ill-advised. The newer industries required more than an updated technician or an evening-class retrained craftsman. New workers, with not only new skills, but wholly new presuppositions about themselves in relationship to the new machines, were required. This, of course, demanded an education that combined skill training with exposure to the humanistic and liberal education disciplines. Just as Renaissance man was an archetype distinctly different from the Medieval sage, so the new man (no convenient rubric is as yet appropriate), combining marketable skills with an appreciation of how he relates to his world, is a departure from the traditional man who labored in order that some day he might live. The new man takes life and work to be integral, emergent, and tentative. Machines and people intertwine in the new society. The clearcut divisions will diminish and man will seek to find a new unity between himself, society, and culture. Continuing liberal studies for adults, often outside the routine credit and degree curriculum, will be one of the prime instrumentalities for this search and its fulfillment.

As the demand for adult study, regardless of emphases, is met, there will be the inevitable tendency to institutionalize the relationship between the university and the adult learner. This, as suggested earlier, commits not only material resources, but attitudes and beliefs. The tactics of academic polities surrounding adult study will shift from aggressive encounter to defense. Innovation will be less expected, and set patterns will be encouraged. This seems to be the path of an idea as it rises in the eyes of an established social system —be this education, industry, family, or church. Popular demand, coupled with official response to meet it, requires scheduled, routinized, "sure-fire" procedures. The risks of innovation, of trial-and-error programs, of experimentation are not likely to be countenanced. There will be polite evaluation, but here again our hypothesis of quiescence is likely to be operative.

Well, then, what should be done? Obviously time is running out in one of the few areas left where there is significant room for creative encounter between education and the new community developing through technological change. For too long, leaders in adult study suffered all the negative symptoms of being alone and unnoticed in the larger educational establishments. They developed, on the one hand, a set of tactics guaranteeing their continued marginal relationship, but unfortunately for the wrong reason. On the other hand, every attempt was made to be on the "inside"—to be like everyone else. In many instances, even now it is too late to talk practically about fresh new looks in adult study. There is too much commitment, too much vested interest.

What is needed is the recognition of the unique opportunity an uninstitutionalized program has. This is appreciated more and more in research. New research units deliberately are set up to be in universities to encourage workers to make their way somewhat out of step with the great institutionalized "drum beat" of the establishment.

But we are not going to close on a gloomy note. Great institutions have tremendous survival value. Like the mythical Phoenix, while the old is destroyed and enshrined, the new is born—born sometimes unnoticed, sometimes screaming and dragging its feet, and sometimes like a brilliant creative work of art.

The new education is being born both in and around the educational establishment and in the scores of other agencies and organizations that see education as a responsibility. We need to be sensitive to the quality to be found in the less official, sometimes outside, developments. In the new society, the boundaries of function will be less clear because specialization itself will become passé. Members of the educational establishment now need to be aware of a not too distant future where they shall have less of a corner on the education market. In the new society, education will be diffused among a variety of agencies and organizations. Education will be less a nucleated, place-centered activity, and more a feature of life itself. It will be less scheduled and more available.

The dropout problem will decline as dropping out of school is redefined as natural for many people. Getting back into school will have to become more natural than at present. The future probably will see a decline in the idea that every phase of life should have an introductory, an advanced, and a graduate course attached to it. As specialization ceases to be less of a model for understanding, courses of study will be less crowded, more field-oriented, and will provide a better fit between the student as a whole human being and the world of scholarship. Finally, we must learn to look again at little children. In their movements, their ability to shift interest, their capacity for inventiveness and unimpassioned discard of the outmoded, their wonder at a caterpillar, and their welcoming of the new experience, we see qualities that will have to be nurtured to meet the challenge of the new technology and the new society. Nursery school and kindergarten education have been traditional foci of sophisticated and imaginative research and innovation. Let this literature, this experience, be examined for continuing relevance to education and to the community.

A classic position in the social sciences is that technology is the "bellwether" of social change, pushing ahead while society follows. The consumption of automobiles outruns readiness to provide highways and parking. Industries automate faster than obsolescent workers can be reabsorbed into the labor force, *e.g.*, coal mining. Advanced communication technology reduces the world's size to where practically every location is within commuting distance. Yet, some continue to harbor attitudes of provincialism, look with reserve on cosmopolitan values, and are quick to judge the "outsider" by the most archaic Yankee qualities.

It is not too much of an error to say that once "necessity was the mother of invention, but today invention is the mother of necessity." Laboratories and drawing boards spawn hardware of every sort at an increasing rate. Research and technological development are major industries. This surge toward control of nature and to divine her secrets has placed tremendous strain on traditional norms which frequently were based on "changeless" laws of nature. But as we wipe away error in understanding the natural order, we find distinct obstacles to correcting error in human community organization. There are, however, signs of a new integration, a new equilibrium, being established. While it would be naive and perhaps incorrect to look for a time when social institutions and technology would be in harmony, there is increasing support for the relationship to be susceptible to management for optimum human goals.

Certainly in this view there is sufficient cause for hope in the power of man to project and realize the timeless human qualities of wisdom, dignity, and grace as characteristics not reserved for the few but common to the many. Technological advance, releasing man from dehumanizing labor and at the same time reassociating him with humanizing work, is the heart of the educational problem in technologically advanced societies. Education, emphasizing what once was considered the less practical arts and sciences, will become increasingly popular. Already it makes itself felt in the burgeoning enrollment in the liberal arts and sciences and the corresponding difficulty of maintaining undergraduate interest in the agricultural and mechanical arts. The new education, then, is the process of becoming. It has to be searched out in what now may seem to be strange and irrelevant places. But such has been the story of change. The trinkets and toys of one period are likely to be the very basis of life for another.

17. THE IMPACT OF TECHNOLOGY AND THE NEED FOR A DIALOGUE

LAWRENCE K. WILLIAMS

A VERY ANXIOUS SOCIETY seems to have selected technological change, and particularly automation, as developments to be
feared. Distinct from anxiety, fear has a particular reference object.
So, instead of just feeling uncomfortable and anxious, we find a
degree of comfort in knowing that we may be able to do something
about those objects that we fear. To be sure, our fears about technological change may be well grounded. There is a distinct possibility, however, that technology and technological change such as automation have been put in the roles of "scapegoats." Rightly or wrong-
ly, automation has been linked with nearly every social problem, and
the fear with regard to automation is spawning an increasing number
of contemporary Luddites.* One way of conquering a fear is to fight
back, but fighting back blindly may lead only to more frustration
and anxiety.

Blaming technology will not make it go away. Indeed, impeding
technological growth may make the problem at hand worse rather
than better. Technology may be the cause of all our problems or it
may be mainly emphasizing old problems for which the suggested
remedies should be quite different. It is obvious that good programs
of action will come from understanding technology, not from blam-

---

* Luddites were 19th-century workmen who banded together to cause riots for
the purpose of destroying machines.—EDITORS' NOTE

ing it. It is certainly reasonable to suggest that technology has, is, and will continue to create problems of an extreme magnitude for those who are concerned with human values. But the technologist and the non-technologist often do not understand each other; certainly in the past they have tended to ignore each other. A continued and widening dialogue between the parties has become an imperative of our time. The following is offered as a prospectus for this dialogue.

THE NEED FOR A DIALOGUE

It already has been stated that the humanist must take steps toward greater comprehension of technology and that the technologist must become much more aware of the implications of technological change. These cannot be independent activities, but must come about through the process of interaction. It is asking too much of the technologist to ask him to describe the total impact of technology on society. Perhaps the best we can hope for in this case is that the technologist becomes aware that the "hardware" he creates or introduces will have an impact on society and its value and that inquiry into the impact is a legitimate and necessary exploration. It is also rather ridiculous to expect that the humanist will come to comprehend technology completely; even if he did, the understanding of technology on its own terms is not adequate. The language of technology is completely divorced from the language and concern of those who would worry about its impact. The best available technical description of the computer, for example, does not allow one to anticipate the problems of displaced older workers, unemployed youth, an increasing need for education of minority groups, or other problems that currently are being discussed—problems that have been accentuated or caused by the installation of this form of technology. Lacking a theory or science of technological impact, we must depend upon dialogue if we are to predict, for it is prediction, not description, that will keep us out of trouble. At present, there is no science which can substitute for confrontation of the technologist and the non-technologist in anticipating the future.

There is very little comfort to be taken in one of the popular alternatives to understanding technology—the enumeration process. In this case, instead of getting to understand the enemy, one merely counts and tries to estimate the size of the regiment. But counting the number of pieces of hardware or gadgets produced is usually of limited utility until much too late. Counting computers is of no more advantage than counting gumball machines, unless there is an awareness that computers will create problems of a given nature and that gumball machines will not.

Another alternative to participating in the dialogue has been the use of historical analogy. A very rosy future has been predicted by those who pointed to a history of technological change that created more jobs than it destroyed and numerous technological changes which have created wondrous job opportunities. Current problems suggest the weakness of this historical analogy. Many forms of technological change are quite unlike their predecessors. For example, one must consider the tempo of change and its implication for occupation and work. In the past, while technological change did create and destroy jobs, the problem of adjustment was left to succeeding generations. A man usually could continue in his career or occupation even though his son might have to change. The current rapid introduction of technology, which finds whole industries existing on the basis of a discovery that is less than a decade old, creates severe disruptions during a single work life and predicts a future with two or more changes in a man's occupation. History also has failed to inform us that the jobs created by technological change cannot necessarily be performed by the same individuals whose jobs were destroyed by it.

A look at our immediate past, or even a consideration of the present, also results in imperfect predictions. One problem lies in the fact that non-technologists have lumped too many processes under the same label. While, to some in our society, automation is a new word, others are suggesting new words like cybernation in order to draw distinctions which are more than academic. A real confusion of terms is involved in trying to identify mechanization, automation, or cybernation. What some refer to as assembly-line automation, or perhaps, more properly, mechanization, is really a symbol of the past rather than the future. Here automation was conceived of as a highly rigid system and a process which broke skilled crafts down into menial jobs. Such a view of automation rightly caused the humanist to be concerned about the dignity of work and the imposition of the technocrat's values on consumer preferences and choices. But the humanist must be concerned now with a new phenomenon distinctly different from the previous view of automation. Automation now means flexibility rather than rigidity and complex rather than menial tasks. Automation affects the white-collar as well as the blue-collar world. In other words, the symbol of technological change in the form of automation is not one that affects only the man on the assembly line in the factory, nor is it necessarily a symbol of boredom and monotony. Automation now means constant change and, as a consequence, necessitates a continued dialogue.

WHAT CAN BE EXPECTED

Even if we are convinced of the need for a dialogue and accept the idea that society must be able to predict part of the impact of technology, it is still legitimate to ask what can be expected of the dialogue. To a certain degree, the ability to predict the impact of technology on society rests upon the ability to predict what will happen to technology. While some meaningful forecasting probably can be made in terms of the rate of introduction of current forms of technology, it seems difficult, if not quite impossible, to make any good long-range predictions about new forms of technology. New technological forms increasingly depend upon theory rather than invention, and theoretical breakthroughs have proven to be more revolutionary in their impact on technology than has been the impact of any single invention.

There are some forms of technological change in the foreseeable future to which more attention should be paid. In a recent conference which stressed education for the future, representatives of education and of many business firms agreed that we should spend considerable energy producing key-punchers. While there are doubtless important questions to be raised about specific training to begin with, the technologist had a most telling point when he informed the audience that the key-punching activity was the weakest link in information processing and that a considerable amount of money now was being spent to develop optical scanning devices and other implements that would *eliminate* the key-punching activity. It is still possible that a number of institutions finally will become equipped to produce a generation of highly accomplished key-punchers for a labor market that no longer requires them.

A similar example comes from a conference which discussed the shortage of automobile mechanics. It was noted by the technologist that if automobile mechanics were taught on a strictly "how-to-do-it" basis, then they would be ill-equipped to handle the problems of the turbine engine which might be just around the corner. This problem of training is not restricted to non-professional activities; in fact, there is a real problem in training people for the professions in an age of technology. This is most notable in the business world. Again, it is quite possible that individuals who are highly trained to step into certain accounting functions and other areas of the business world might find that they are outdated or that their knowledge is very nearly useless in the face of the growing utilization of such forms of technology as the computer in the office operation.

Other than predicting some immediate changes in technology, it is perhaps possible to describe in more gross terms the forms of technology in the future. As has been stated, participants in a current dialogue can learn that automation is best characterized by the term flexibility rather than rigidity. As a consequence, it seemingly dictates a flexible society. The implication for the educational process, given the imperfect predictions, is an educational process which allows for maximum flexibility. For vocational education, this probably means a greater focus on the "why" rather than on the "how-to-do." The mechanic who knows why a spark plug works, as well as how to change it, undoubtedly will be a more valuable employee in the future. The problem is more than theory versus application. In many cases, we probably have underestimated the capacity to learn of those who receive the more applied forms of education. A rather vicious cycle has been started by underestimating capacity and reducing the attempts to impart the most meaningful education, thereby leading to a less responsive audience and to a further underestimation of capacity. Society seems to reward those who impart theory and abstract knowledge to people far in excess of the reward it offers those who instruct in the more applied areas. Education and training often are considered to be mutually exclusive terms.

If more attention were given to the problem of offering a rich education to those who now study a rather cut-and-dried curriculum, we might benefit by having a society with a more flexible work force. One might even advance the notion that it is not the knowledge that is important, but rather the attitude toward learning which may result. One of the greatest problems confronting retraining efforts is the large segment of our society which literally is afraid of the process of learning. Too many individuals have seen themselves as second-class citizens in our current educational process, and a natural response is the belief that they are incapable of learning anything meaningful. This very often is masked by distaining the whole process of learning. A requirement of our time is the creation of a more positive attitude toward learning. Unable to predict the exact requirements and knowledge required in the future, a great need in our educational process is for the individual to be prepared for a lifetime of learning and re-education. Only when we have an educational process that is geared to individual capacity, which makes the process of learning exciting, or one which at least leaves the individual confident in his capacity to learn will something have been done to effect the kind of flexible society that is required. This kind of an objective seems to be in keeping with the values of the humanist but, at the same time, helps realize the objective of the most pragmatic individual who only may be concerned with the utility of resources.

Impossible as it is to anticipate all of the consequences and findings of a continued dialogue, it at least seems reasonable to forecast that, as a result of technological change, man will have more free time in the future. He may take this in terms of hours in the day, work weeks in a year, work years in his life, or some combination of these. A humanistic imperative is a consideration of free time and leisure. Leisure connotes something more than non-work time and implies constructive or creative use of one's time. The unemployed already have more free time than they know what to do with. The values system of the humanist can become a model for the future, and it is still possible to hope that crash programs will not be required to deal with free time. Nearly all of us were told, a long time ago, that technological change would mean the destruction of menial jobs, with their accompanying drudgery and boredom, and that this would be a benefit to society. Unfortunately, a large segment of society seems to be prepared only for such jobs, and this benefit has become a hardship. With or without a dialogue, we must concern ourselves with the problem of free time and constructive leisure before another supposed benefit turns out to be the cause of a social disaster.

18. AUTOMATION AND EDUCATION: REFLECTIONS ON THE INVOLVEMENT OF GOVERNMENT

JAMES A. DONOVAN, JR.

"**T**HE MACHINE must not be worshipped as god or devil, nor must it be damned, save when it is misused as in the deadly instruments of war. The poet must accept it as part of his world in the way the author of John Brown's Body has urged."

> Out of John Brown's strong sinews the tall skyscrapers grow,
> Out of his heart the chanting buildings rise,
> Rivet and girder, motor and dynamo,
> Pillar of smoke by day and fire by night,
> The steel-faced cities reaching at the skies,
> The whole enormous and rotating cage
> Hung with hard jewels of electric light. . . .
> If you at last must have a word to say,
> Say neither, in their way,
> "It is a deadly magic and accursed,"
> Nor "It is blest," but only, "It is here."

The first paragraph above was written, and the poem was quoted, by Paul Engle in 1937 in "Poetry in a Machine Age." While Engle was commenting upon the fact that poets now must take their figures of speech and draw their pictures from machines as well as from nature, there is something interestingly quaint about the notion expressed less than a human generation ago that one can, or even should, simply accept the machines as being there.

Perhaps one of the most disturbing things about our increasing dependence on machines is that the experts themselves are uneasy about the use to which these robots will be put by persons who necessarily must use them to keep up with control of an increasingly complex society—a control which must include the manipulation of human beings. This unease has been expressed recently in a review in the *New York Times Book Review* by John Pfeiffer of Norbert Wiener's book, "Cybernetics: Or Control and Communications in the Animal and the Machine." Pfeiffer writes, apropos of Wiener, "The story is not entirely a happy one, however, because he did not trust robots. More precisely he did not trust men of affairs to use robots, or their fellow human beings for that matter, with either constraint or compassion."

Such a statement about Norbert Wiener's book, which first was published in 1948, a scant *half* generation ago, is mild compared to the genuine concern which more and more persons—social scientists, government officials, humanists, and even scientists themselves—are expressing about the possible "manipulation" of human beings for even good purposes. It is certainly true that those who must have the most knowledge at their disposal will be those who control the vast computers and the correlations of facts, which can be made by the computers once basic information has been fed into their voracious maws.

But enough has been written and spoken about the possible consequences of automation on society in general to permit us to pass to another aspect of automation—namely, the changing pattern of employment in the Federal government and hence, soon, in state, county, and local governments as well. It is important that the private citizen and the average government employee develop a clear view of this pattern, of the picture in the mosaic, and the variation in the picture as piece by piece it quickly changes. To give some notion of what these changes amount to, let us first cite briefly an article entitled "The Changing Federal Service," by Robert E. Hampton, a member of the Civil Service Commission, published in the *Civil Service Journal* for April-June, 1964.

Commissioner Hampton makes a number of interesting observations. If one were to assume, he says, as once was the case, that the Federal service is "an army of clerks," one would further assume that out of 2,489,000 Federal employees, at least 1,000,000 must be general clerks at the bottom of the pay scale. He then points out the truth of the matter: the latest survey of the Federal government's white-collar employees (1961) shows that there were only about 28,000 general clerical employees in grades GS-1 through GS-4 (GS—General Schedule). But, he goes on, there were more employees in physical science occupations and nearly four times as many in engineering as in general clerical positions. Part of the reason for this, of course, is that whereas, in 1947, there were approximately 14,000 employees whose work involved the operation of bookkeeping machines, calculating machines, and card-punch, sorting, and tabulating machines, today this number has increased approximately to 22,000 and on top of that a new dimension—the computer—has been added, the Commissioner pointed out.

Since 1951, when the first computer, UNIVAC I, was installed in the Bureau of the Census, the Federal government has become the nation's prime user of automatic data processing (ADP) equipment. There are, indeed, 10,300 computer employees, and many of the 22,000 machine-operating employees mentioned above now work in direct support (in care and feeding) of the government's ADP and computer systems.

The use of these machines presumably has put a number of persons out of work. These are the sub-professional mathematical and statistical employees, of whom there are now 32% fewer than there were when the first computer was obtained. But the professional mathematicians have doubled in number since 1951, totaling 2,532, and professional statisticians have increased nearly 13%, totaling 2,569.

All such figures demonstrate, of course, the increasing dependence of the Federal government upon machines for information and knowledge, on the basis of which important decisions must be made in a number of new fields such as space technology, the anti-poverty program, and so on. Indeed, in science and engineering, the changes have been particularly dramatic. The number of employees in the physical sciences has jumped 21% since 1957 to 34,320; employees in physics are up 60%; in chemistry, 29%. In the biological sciences the increase is 28%—this group now totaling 36,917.

The rate of change of employees in engineering is even greater than in the pure sciences, with 116,854 persons working (1964) for the government in engineering. These represent an increase of 67% since 1957. Moreover, there are more technicians, although not many more, than typists in the government—78,326 of the former and 78,105 of the latter.

Obviously, more highly educated persons are needed to take care of the machine work. There are increasing numbers of white-collar, and fewer blue-collar, workers. What is more, the government's grade structure generally has shifted upward or, as the phrase goes these

days, it has "escalated." Many jobs are necessarily being filled at a
higher level for the simple reason that the government is able to
recruit and must recruit higher quality and more fully trained persons. Thus, the Congress has provided legislative authority to hire
these skills at the GS-7 level instead of at GS-5, a raise in salary for
these entering employees of approximately $2,000.

There are ever larger numbers of persons in the higher grades,
GS-11 through 15, than there used to be, and a good part of the
reason for this happy (for them) situation is that persons more educated are being paid more. The Federal government keeps up with
the general society and economy and is increasing the proportion of
its professional employees. These increased 40% between 1954 and
1962, while other occupations increased only 17% during the same
period.

All of the above, of course, has many and numerous ramifications
and implications for the kinds of persons the government is seeking
to employ, to train after employment, and also to promote. But
before we get into the educational aspects of government employment, let us look at another Civil Service Commission report.

Important to keep in mind from this report is the fact that employment by state, county, and local government is increasing far
faster than Federal employment. And the employees tend to be more
and more professional. So even in the larger cities there will be centers of power—meaning centers of knowledge—available to persons
who have the machines at their disposal and know how to use them.
This will tend, over the next generation, to create even further and
deeper gaps between the understanding of the average citizen and
his traditional view of what the government is to do for him and
what he is to do for the government, whether state, local, or Federal.

The Civil Service Commission staff has some even more interesting figures and statistics having to do with the prospects for the
Federal work-force through fiscal 1968 *(i.e.,* June 30, 1968).* It should
be noted at the outset that these particular estimates are conservative
and the changes in the Federal work-force herein outlined are those
which are *minimum* changes likely to occur between the end of fiscal
1964 and fiscal 1968.

Before we discuss employment in the Federal government and the
role of automation in the changing and evolving pattern of Federal
employment, let us take a quick look at government employment

---

* "Federal Workforce Outlook, Fiscal Years, 1965-1968" (Washington, D. C.:
U. S. Civil Service Commission, 1964).

altogether—that is, in Federal, state, county, and local government.

First of all, from fiscal 1953 to 1963, total employment in the economy of the United States went from an annual average of 50,232,000 jobs to 57,175,000. The increase was about 6,943,000 jobs. The increase in government employment during this period (Federal, state, county, and local) accounted for 2,890,000. Thus, it appears that, for the 10-year period, "government" has accounted for fully 41% of the total increase in employment in the U. S. Of this increase in government employment, the Federal share amounted to 1.9%, or 53,000, whereas the increase in state, county, and local governments accounted for 98.1%, a total of 2,837,000 persons.

This means that at the end of the period for which the Civil Service projects its figures—from 1964 through 1968—the employees of state and local governments will outnumber Federal employees by more than 8,500,000, or by almost 4 to 1. At the same time, though the rate of population growth is estimated to be 6.1% from 1964 through 1968, state and local employees will increase 20.5% and Federal employees by only 2.7%.

For the administrator in the Federal government, these figures having to do with the ratio of Federal to state and local employees have three important consequences. First of all, it will be important that the Federal service intensify its recruitment programs in order to hold its own against the increasing competition for better trained persons who wish to work for government. Second, despite the fact that the number of employees in the government sector of the economy is increasing, the work force per 1,000 persons in the population will be declining as regards its availability to Federal administrators. Thus, it will be absolutely essential that improvements in productivity be made if the present levels of public services are to be maintained and improved (and here we hit upon, for the first time in the recital of all these statistics, the notion that automation in government, great as it already is, has got to be increased). Third, state and local governments will tend to attract a growing share of promising administrative and technical talent, particularly as state and local organizations become competitive with similar Federal units in salary scales and employee benefits, professional career prospects, and opportunities for major public service. Yet, the supplies of such talent are expected to continue to be limited, especially in the age group between 35 to 45.

To make these figures even more significant, it should be pointed out that despite the fact that the rise in the Federal employee population has been slow as compared to the total rise of the whole population and as compared to the rise in local and state government employment, the pattern and structure of the Federal work-force is changing significantly. There are strong currents of evolutionary change, as the Civil Service Commission puts it, in the composition of the work-force. The main point here is that between the end of fiscal 1964 and the end of fiscal 1968, the white-collar worker will have increased in number from 1,275,000 to 1,398,000, for a total increase of 123,000. In the same period, blue-collar workers will decrease by 76,000 from a total in 1964 of 641,000 to a total in 1968 of 565,000. A slight increase of 21,000 is expected among the postal workers, bringing a total of 590,000 to 611,000 during the same four-year period. We wonder, however, after reading these statistics from the Commission, whether the increased automation in the Post Office Department, despite the increasing population of the country as a whole, will not keep down the figure of 21,000.

A very important fact is that, although employment in the white-collar sector of the Federal work-force is growing faster than employment in the Post Office Department, and although blue-collar employment is decreasing, Federal white-collar employment is growing with far less rapidity than is white-collar employment in the national work-force as a whole. This fact is not the result of below-average growth in Federal professional, administrative, or technical employment—that is, in the so-called high-graded occupations. It is, rather, the result of the slow rate of growth of the lower-graded sector of the Federal work-force. And it is this extraordinary low growth rate in clerical occupations which holds the total Federal white-collar growth rate below the national average.

The figures show, however, that between fiscal 1964 and 1968, the higher-graded occupations will increase by 112,000 and the lower-graded ones by 12,600. While many developments may occur in this four-year period to change significantly this expected 10 to 1 ratio in growth as between higher-graded and lower-graded occupations, it is difficult for the layman to avoid the conclusion that somehow or other this is a reflection of increased uses of automation. In any case, the upshot of these figures is a change in relative employment "mix" of higher- and lower-graded occupations, which, in turn, is probably the predominant cause of the escalation of average grades in the Federal white-collar work-force that appears to raise so many questions in Congressional committees concerned with Federal employment.

One last set of statistics to show the change in the "mix" is to be found in the four years referred to above that will result in a 17.4% increase in major professional positions in government, whereas there will be only a 2.7% increase in clerical and kindred occupations. Thus, it is expected that mathematicians will be increased by 58.4%; educationists, by 30.4%; physical scientists, by 25.3%; and engineers, by 21.0%—all by the end of fiscal 1968. As for specialized clerical personnel, while those in personnel and supply occupations will go up 11.2% and 2.4%, respectively, clerks working on statistics will decrease by 9.5%; on accounting, by 12.4%; and correspondence clerks will decrease by 24.1%, leading to a total decrease in specialized clerks of 2.6%. However, buried in the statistics given in the Civil Service Commission report on the Federal work-force is this sentence: "To what extent this extremely low clerical growth rate is due to the Federal government's acknowledged leadership in the automation of routine workload, or to what extent it is attributable to other causes, is not known.

To a government employee who has not been directly concerned with personnel matters as they occupy the Civil Service Commission or the personnel departments of the huge agencies, such a statement is striking enough. But what is perhaps more striking is that neither does the world of business know what effect automation has had on employment, nor, indeed, the effect on unemployment. Thomas J. Watson, chairman of the board and chief executive officer of International Business Machines Corporation of New York, was quoted, for example, in a *New York Times* article, March 14, 1965, as saying that no one knows the real effects of labor-saving machines in coal mines, auto factories, and oil refineries in regard to employment. In fact, during a national automation conference sponsored by the American Bankers Association, at which Watson spoke, the *Times* reported that there was one group of experts numbering the jobs destroyed by automation in the millions, while another argued that many industries that have automated the most also had expanded the most in employment. It thus became evident during the conference that no one knows which of these views is correct. The only fact all could agree on as the result of such differences of opinion was that far more study was essential.

One gets the impression, nevertheless, that there is no change likely to take place in the next generation which will cause more consternation in government and among educators and businessmen than the fact that the country is increasingly going to be dependent on machines for vast amounts of data and reports.

To jump quickly from some of the facts about the changing pattern of employment in the Federal government (in part, one assumes, because of automation), let me cite one similar pattern which necessarily will involve changes in types of employees, in the education of employees, and in their training and retraining in Alexandria, Va., a city with which I happen to be familiar because I have lived there for 19 years. It has received much publicity recently because it has automated a large part of the information in its files in order to get at it quickly. One of the great advantages of the use of a computer for the retrieval of such information is that one can find out what a situation is *now*. The progressive city manager of Alexandria, Albert M. Hair, Jr., stated his belief that all cities, moderate and large in size, will have to record information on school children, police departments, zoning, sanitation, fire hydrants, square footage of sidewalks, and thousands of other items for rapid retrieval.

In some ways, the use of such information is almost more vital to a city government than to the Federal government, which is operating huge projects that frequently take such a long time, *e.g.*, the construction of instruments to get a man to the moon. What a city needs information for, and frequently at once, is to make decisions as to the location of a firehouse. Data, provided on all the buildings in the square blocks, intersections, traffic patterns, previous experience with fires, and so on, are fed into a computer and rapidly show in some cases that a new firehouse should be located in that part of the city where there are buildings that are least fireproof and most likely to be the ones to burn.

Of course, one might find segments of society or branches of the government, even within as small a city as Alexandria (115,000), vying for the use of the information and arguing as to its interpretation. This is most likely to develop, although it certainly has not done so yet, as between the largely autonomous school board in any city and the rest of the city government, both of which must work together. One has, however, an uneasy vision of the city government itself controlling the magnetic tapes on which the data are stored, renting a computer to pull out certain information and certain correlations regarding parts of this information and then having the same thing done over by the school board for its own reinterpretation. This illustrates how important it is that we develop institutions through which the citizens (voters) and groups of citizens (advisory boards, planning commissions, traffic committees) can get at the information in such data banks of a city, or county, or state.

The question arises, Who is to feed what information into the data banks in the first place? One cannot correlate facts and figures which are not there. Even so, if all agree that what is there is what should be there, from what funds should what group of citizens pay for the rental of what magnetic tapes to produce what correlations?

Now, we come, as always, to the importance of the education of these citizens who will be concerned increasingly with the control of the machines. Here one is impressed with the everlasting need for persons in and out of government who will meditate on the effects on the human spirit of the rapid evolution of the machines. Figures which show that persons in the middle grades—that is, technicians, data processors, and others—can expect to require retraining two or three times within their working lives are not as important (although they are significant and portend fantastic changes in the patterns of vocational and semi-professional education) as the genuine education of the persons who will put significant information into the machines and know the questions to be asked. Since education will remain in the hands of private citizens, even though government (Federal, state, local) contributes more and more money, control being exercised through school boards, boards of regents, trustees, and the like, it is through these bodies that the crucial question of quality and content of education must be settled.

Since education is, itself, an abstraction, there being no such thing in reality, but only more or less educated persons, we are confronted by the question of what education is for and what government is for. Endless books have been written on this since Aristotle stated that man is a political animal. But no one has expressed more pointedly than Walt Whitman, in his poem, "By Blue Ontario's Shore," what the U. S. government is for, even though opinions may differ as to the purposes of government in general. Whitman wrote:

> Underneath all, individuals,
> I swear nothing is good to me now that ignores individuals,
> The American compact is altogether with individuals,
> The only government is that which makes minute of individuals,
> The whole theory of the universe is directed unerringly to
>   one single individual—namely to You.

Thus, if the use of machines by the government does not result in the improvement of the whole man as well as the improvement of the physical lot of the individual, government in the U. S. will have lost its way.

The education of the whole man will have to come ultimately from the inside out as more and more thousands of people are faced with the frightening prospect of increased leisure. The prospect is frightening because the persons best able to use it will have the least leisure and those least able to use it will have the most. Indeed, one wonders if there is not something Mephistophelean in the lure of leisure as increasing numbers of persons struggle their way into boredom through fruitless pursuits, waiting always for the perfect moment to come.

But a more important aspect of the devil in the machines, and a more optimistic view as well, is to be found in Mephistopheles' statement to Faust—that he is

> *Ein Teil von jener Kraft,*
> *Die stets das Boese will und stets das Gute schafft.*

19. A LABOR VIEW OF THE SOCIAL AND EDUCATIONAL IMPLICATIONS OF TECHNOLOGICAL CHANGE

WALTER DAVIS

I F ASKED TO EVALUATE the national mood today in relation to automation and human values in the community, I would reply that despair outweighed the hope. However, a change in the mood of our thinking is on its way. As wisdom overcomes our pessimistic foolishness, there will be a change toward hope. Perhaps I am unduly impressed by the fact that the nation seems to be making a public decision that the real root of our social problems is poverty, not race. It may be illogical to assume that one sound decision will be followed by another. Nevertheless, the one sound decision provides ground for hope.

In sounding this note of hope, however, I keep in mind the real gravity of the situation and the outlook. By way of reminder of this gravity, I cite a story which may or may not really have happened. If it did not, it should have, for it effectively dramatizes a basic confrontation, in the world of reality, of the sort for which myths have to be created or invented when history itself defaults.

The story has to do with the first really well publicized automated line in the auto industry that opened in Cleveland, Ohio, in 1955 as as part of the Ford No. 2 Engine Plant. As indicative of the terrific speed-up in the rate of technological change, this operation is now completely passé. When started, however, it was regarded as a demonstration of the spectacular impact of technological change upon industry. It was inevitable, therefore, that the Ford people would invite the president of the United Auto Workers to visit the plant and see this marvel at work.

As the story goes, a Ford vice-president took Walter Reuther on a personal tour of the automated line. The Ford official could hardly wait for the tour to be over because he had a gem he wanted to unload on Mr. Reuther. The moment finally came, and with a note of triumph in his voice, he pointed to the machine and said, "Okay, Walter, how are you going to collect dues from that machine?" Reuther's reply was instantaneous: "How are you going to sell it a Ford automobile?"

A moral to the story may be that the fear engendered by technological change is not a one-way street. It is everybody's business. Fear and its companion, panic, are the greatest single roadblocks which face us. The American worker looks around him and sees all sorts of changes taking place. These changes generally are lumped into a single category of "automation." Actually, continuing mechanization of our society is one of the things that disturbs the worker, but he does not really differentiate. "Automation," therefore, has become an ugly word. The more awe-inspiring word, "cybernation," is not really in popular circulation as yet.

Whether the great fear of automation that exists among workers is justified is not really important. The fact is that the fear is very real — whether caused by automation, cybernation, technological change, or other factors.

There is very great argument and loud disagreement as to how imminent is automation or cybernation, which completely will revolutionize our society. In reading only a fraction of the literature on the subject, I have changed my views considerably. I am forced to agree that there will be a real limitation because of the vast amounts of capital needed to convert to either automation or cybernation. What is important is that the revolution is coming, and the key is: how are we going to handle it?

Like many people, I have taken refuge in the notion that the advance of technology always provides more jobs than are eliminated. However, I simply do not believe that any more. And it is interesting to note that John I. Snyder, Jr., president of U.S. Industries, which produces automated equipment, agrees that this notion is archaic. In fact, he lists five fallacies that have concealed the shattering impact of automation.

Fallacy Number One: Automation is not really going to eliminate many jobs. *Fact*: Already it is gobbling them up at the rate of 40,000 per week. (This is a high figure; the variation is from 20,000 to 40,000 per week.)

Fallacy Number Two: Automation will create new jobs in the building, running, and maintenance of new machines. *Fact:* In the building of them, maybe. But if it took a big battery of men to run and maintain them, why automate?

Fallacy Number Three: Those displaced can be retrained rapidly and immediately replaced in other jobs. *Fact:* By present techniques, many workers simply are not retrainable.

Fallacy Number Four: Workers displaced in one area can be assimilated easily somewhere else. *Fact:* Those who lose their jobs are usually the ones least able to move in the first place.

Fallacy Number Five: There is no relationship between the automation revolution and the Negro revolution. *Fact:* Actually, the technological upheaval has intensified the drive for civil rights because the Negro, always the last hired and first fired, is suffering the most from unemployment.

Against this background, time becomes a desperately important factor. How fast are all of these vast changes likely to take place? J. Robert Oppenheimer judges that our scientific knowledge doubles approximately every eight years. Gerard Piel, the publisher of *Scientific American,* points out that "the displacement of workers in both white-collar and blue-collar functions is proceeding at an exponential rate, that is, proceeding as the square of time."

The real test, then, is how fast our economic, social, and educational complexes can face up to the infinite changes posed by automation and cybernation. We must decide whether we are willing to abandon the pious platitude that, if a man wants to work, he always can find work. It seems to me that this notion played a rather central role in the Presidential election of 1964. The other alternative is a position enunciated by Mr. Piel, who says, "The human muscle began to be disengaged from the productive process at least a hundred years ago. Now the human nervous system is being disengaged." Many of us shudder at the notion that machines can make more sensible decisions than human beings. The notion is so awesome for many people that they simply reject it totally.

Economist Robert Theobald sums up the nature of the problem in this simple prose:

The difference between the industrial age of the nineteenth and the first half of the 20th centuries and the cybernated age today is that the first combined human skill and machine skill and the second combines machine skill and machine power. The human being has been pushed right out of the productive process. It is a question of how long it will take us to realize he has been pushed out.

In the face of this statement, I am reminded of a little speech that I made while serving as president of the Cleveland, Ohio, School Board several years ago. These pearls of wisdom were dropped at commencements, open houses, and various other events. The speech concluded with the observation that many of our youngsters somehow never had learned the infinite joy and reward of hard work. This one-liner used to get very enthusiastic applause from parents and teachers, who apparently agreed with me that we were the only ones who ever had worked hard. This was a demonstration of our adulation of the notion of hard work somehow ennobling the human spirit. Now we are talking about a workless society. In such a society, what happens to the "Ethic of Work" as central to the human values that make for the dignity of the individual?

How is the labor movement facing up to the question of technological change in terms of the human values that make for the dignity of the individual and his community? In an effort to ease the impact, a number of devices are being used. Up to this point, collective bargaining agreements usually called for advance notice of a layoff or a shutdown, but often this was no longer than a week. Automation is inspiring provisions requiring several months' notice. Other approaches include the avoidance of layoffs through attrition, early retirement, work-spreading, retraining, transfer, and relocation. Cushioning actual layoffs are such devices as severance pay, vesting of pension rights, aid in retraining and placement elsewhere, and supplemental jobless benefits. To help towards new employment, approaches are being made that include compilation of worker profiles, systematic industry surveys, more effective education and training programs, and elimination of racial discrimination.

Labor points to three programs which have resulted from collective bargaining and which have had some favorable effect on the changes caused by automation and cybernation. In West Coast longshoring, the union agreed to accept all forms of automation if jobs were guaranteed for all those presently employed. Kaiser Steel established the Long Range Committee, which devised a profit-sharing plan. Under this plan, workers are to receive about one-third of savings in materials and savings resulting from increased labor output, and there are guarantees against reductions in income or employment as a result of technological change. In the case of the

Armour Meat Packing Company, under the terms of a contract worked out with two unions, a fund of $500,000 was set aside by the company to assist workers who had been displaced in a modernization program which resulted in the closing of a number of obsolete plants throughout the country. This was a very disillusioning experience. It proved that people resist relocation and retraining and that age and race are pivotal factors in finding new employment.

We should note that, in instances where collective bargaining agreements have helped to cushion the effects of technological change, these advantages have accrued only to those covered by the contract. Only a fraction of the work-force can enjoy such protection. The worker without a union to protect his interests is virtually helpless.

It is a hard fact of life that labor and management alone, at the plant level, cannot solve broad national social problems. Federal government efforts — nationwide programs — are needed. Here are some of the suggestions labor makes to meet the challenge. To the extent that private businesses do not create enough job opportunities, the government must expand its job-creating public works program. The Federal minimum wage law should be extended to millions of low-wage workers, and the minimum should be raised above $1.25 an hour to strengthen consumer markets and enhance the sale of the growing volume of goods and services that can be produced. The work week should be reduced immediately to 35 hours. We should modernize our woefully inadequate programs of assistance to the unemployed, the aged, and the disabled, and we must develop an effective social system to meet the costs of proper medical care. But, even with all of these suggestions, we would be using only a small fraction of the social inventiveness that will be required to survive the monumental impact of cybernation. We have to build a new society (if not a great society, then surely a better one) with an entirely different functional pattern of values.

Simple standards of current "creature comfort" and "fun morality" materialism will not do. The Judeo-Christian ethic of an outgoing concern for the welfare of our fellow man is a pretty fair base on which to start. A simple and clear sense of responsibility for society must be the key. What a difficult switch this will be. The society of scarcity has demanded that one man's well-being could be increased only at the expense of the other man. In the society of abundance which cybernation will produce, the well-being of all is the key to human relationships powered by justice and compassion.

In 1963, I was host in Cleveland to the International Labor Press of America. As I worked with the committee that was developing plans for the convention, there was great insistence on a visit to the Ford No. 2 Engine Plant so that these professional labor editors could see automation in action. The trip was in two parts. First, we were shown the automated line that machined the engine blocks. This was about a city-block long, and there were various panels on which lights blinked on and off. In all, I counted only four men watching this operation. Then, we were taken over to another part of the plant, where Ford engines actually were being assembled. As the conveyor belt moved along, thousands of men performed individual tasks. These were repetitive—over and over and over again, eight hours a day, five days a week. After the editors left the plant, we assembled outside to talk things over. If we had taken a poll, the vote would have been 100% for automation over the agonizing stultification of the assembly line. As one of my colleagues put it: "My God, we have finally found a way to free the human spirit."

I agree. In the cybernated state, man will have the opportunity to realize his potential to a greater degree than at any time in history. The possibilities are limited only by our feeble imaginations.

However, it will not just happen. We have to plan it that way; and this means that we have to plan different types of education to help make good these plans. In shaping the new education — both for youngsters and for adults — we will have to be flexible, imaginative, and bold. True, we should hold fast to the traditional ethic as our moral base. Yet, we will have to invent new means of making these traditional, ethical powers freshly functional for our radically altered, and even more radically altering, industrial and social situation — both as it confronts the individual and as it confronts the community.

For this great task of inventive inter-meshing, we will need all the creative enterprise we can muster. We need to give our professional educators intelligent and informed support as they address themselves to these complex problems. Also, the laymen — whether in the labor movement or outside it — must give their best creative thinking to devising ways to make the universal ethical and social imperatives freshly functional in an epoch of pervasive technological change, advanced industrialization, and the submerging of the individual by floods of statistics.

20. AUTOMATION AND SOME NEGLECTED ASPECTS OF SOCIETY AND EDUCATION

LUTHER H. EVANS

ONE OF THE MAIN THINGS wrong with our country is that our dispositions of power are not adequate to provide the solution of our problems. Technology is talked of as though it were a disembodied force that opposes man and is a friend of man, perhaps in equal parts. It is obvious, when we stop to think about it, that technology is utilized in our society only because somebody gets some good out of it. The people who control technology are largely the entrepreneurs, and they use technology if they can make a profit, and they do not use it if it does not help them to make a profit. What is happening today is that they are taking too much of the profit from automation for themselves. With the decline in wages relative to the total product of automation, consumer purchasing power is being reduced, relatively speaking. Hence, the greatest change we need today is a readjustment in the distribution of the product that now is being created and may be created by automation. And the potentiality is much, much greater, as we all know, than the actuality.

Why cannot government deal with this problem adequately? One of the main reasons is that we do not have an adequate democracy in this country. We are on the way to solving that problem because the Supreme Court recently has said that the rural minority cannot dominate life in this country anymore, that we have to have the urban people, who represent 70% of the nation, in control of the government by redistributing the elected positions in our government among the population on a fair basis. Until this happens, the rural minority will be running this government to an undue extent. This minority does not live in the real world in which the country finds itself as much as the urban people do. When the urban people get greater control, it will be easier to deal with the purchasing power problem, and we will achieve a better distribution of the products of our economy. It ought to be clear to anyone who studies the problem carefully that the present administration not only is not radical, it is hardly liberal in this important respect. Compared to what was done under Roosevelt, it looks more like a Harding type of administration.

I think we are in for a much more regulated life — but regulation is not necessarily the opposite of freedom. It is the opposite of freedom for some of those who have power now, but it is not the opposite of freedom for the great majority of people. We must have a great deal more planning. Life must be much more regulated, but I think this should and can produce greater freedom in the areas where freedom counts most.

Besides the control of the southerners in the committees of Congress, we also have a great imbalance of power in the control of the means of communication. We cannot have a fully developed democracy in this country as long as the press and other means of communications are so tightly controlled by a small wealthy minority. It is very difficult in this country for some of the great ideas to have a hearing.

A remark about the unemployed. I am not nearly so concerned about retraining the unemployed as I am about preventing the increase of the pool of unemployed through lack of the education of young people. I think our money would be far better invested in preventing high school dropouts and in helping them to go on to college than in trying to retrain the unemployed coal miners. Since we are not likely to find ways to re-employ a large proportion of these people, perhaps we ought to find ways of using their presence among us to develop imaginative ways of enjoying leisure to greater advantage. The main difference between unemployment and leisure lies in the attitude taken toward being not-gainfully employed. Let us encourage the unemployed to develop a new attitude and become a leisure class rather than an unemployed group. We have to take care of their needs better than we do now by increasing unemployment benefits, redistributing our income to some extent. Self-improvement should be one of the things that occupies the vacuum, but, in addition, one of the most crying needs of our society is for more attention to the duties of citizenship, including volunteer activities to improve the lives of other people. If we would set ourselves the goal of achieving the brotherhood of man, we would have a new religion that would motivate all of us; and the present unemployed millions could be a great asset in the achievement of this purpose.

21. EDUCATION: THE CENTRAL NEED OF 20TH-CENTURY AMERICA

HUBERT H. HUMPHREY

RECENTLY, IN MINNEAPOLIS, I participated in a television program. As I spoke, my voice and my image were transmitted simultaneously to living rooms of men and women on the European continent. There was a time-lag of only a split-second in that communication.

In March, 1965, at Cape Kennedy, I watched as two men left earth in a space capsule. They knew their course and their destination far better—and were, I might add, in less danger—than Columbus and his men when they ventured west a relatively short time before in history. And, on that occasion at Cape Kennedy, I observed, too, that Wilbur and Orville Wright had kept their 170-pound aircraft aloft for 12 seconds over a distance of 120 feet.

Read the advertising headlines: "Language Barriers Are No Longer a Business Problem." "New Capabilities To Make You Forget the Old Ones." "Cut Seat Reservation Time from 2 Minutes to 34 Seconds." "Never Before So Many Instant Answers Available to So Many." "Is Man Obsolete?" And only 30 years ago the most exciting of human experiences was described by Carl Sandburg:

. . . riding on a limited express, one of the crack trains of the nation . . . hurtling across the prairie into blue haze and dark air go fifteen all-steel coaches holding a thousand people.

. . . I ask a man in the smoker where he is going and he answers "Omaha."

Thirty years ago man's aspiration was Omaha. Today it is the moon.

I have heard it said that the everyday life of the average man has changed more in the last 65 years than in the 2,000 years before. If one examines these changes, it becomes clear that they rest on new transportation and communication, sources of power, new knowledge —almost all connected with the growth of modern technology.

There are more scientists and engineers alive today than all previous scientists and engineers taken together. And, in this technological society, we almost have invented the technique of invention. Today, being able to state clearly a technological problem or define a technological need is almost tantamount to a solution to that problem or that need.

The fact is that our knowledge is becoming so extensive that its very size and complexity can cause problems. We almost know too much. In some fields today it is easier to rediscover something than to search existing literature to find it.

Americans of all people are known for their technological efficiency. In fact, we often are criticized as being so materialistic that we spend all our time and energy in the pursuit and manufacture of objects.

I think the great part of that criticism is unjustified. But, in the midst of our technological progress, we must ask questions: Is technology desirable for its own sake? What changes is it creating in our society? How do we harness it? As the advertising headline says, "Is Man Obsolete?" I personally have no intention whatever of becoming obsolete.

Technology has brought us tremendous good. It has made life longer and better for millions of men and women. But, in recognizing technology's benefits, we must not allow it to become our master. We must recognize technology's effect on our society and insure that it continues to serve us, and not itself.

There is only one certain way we can achieve this. It is through education. Technology has made education the central need of 20th-century America.

Curricula have changed from grade school through graduate school. Changing technology, in fact, has made it a necessity that all of us make education a lifelong activity. What was true yesterday may not be true tomorrow.

This Administration has recognized the necessity for educational excellence. And this Congress is passing historic legislation which makes long-range investments in that excellence.

But no amount of government investment will be enough if all of us as citizens do not recognize our responsibility to make education—in our own homes, in our children's schools, in our libraries—our first priority.

In this age, what kind of education shall it be?

First of all, there is, of course, the need to educate people to utilize and develop technology *per se*. It is a reality that, if we expect to benefit from technology, there must be those who can operate it. In the past 10 years, for instance, a new industry has come into being in the United States: the computer industry. This industry requires those who can design, develop, manufacture, maintain, and use its products. Over 20,000 general-purpose computers now are installed in the United States alone. By 1970, another 500,000 additional computer programmers will be needed in this country. That number will multiply many times over during our lifetimes. Computers are multiplying and so is the need for people trained to use them.

Secondly, we must educate people so that they may find useful work in life. It is quite apparent that, in this age of technology, the man with little skill has difficulty finding a job. Only 5% of the entire American labor force is unskilled. But even 5% is too much. Today, one out of every three unemployed never went beyond grade school. Two out of three unemployed do not have a high school diploma. Jobs for the unskilled are disappearing. They will continue to disappear.

Then, we must recognize that technology—beyond reducing the need for the unskilled worker—has made basic changes in our patterns of employment. Today, workers in the service-producing industries number 10,000,000 more than workers producing goods. And the white-collar worker is far more numerous than the blue-collar worker. This pattern will perpetuate itself.

In the future it will not be enough, then, even to possess a skill —if that skill is not needed in great number. There were thousands of bankrupt carriage shops and unemployed blacksmiths when we entered the automobile age.

Yes, we need education to provide the people who can operate the instruments of technology. We also need education to prepare people for the changing occupational patterns which technology has thrust upon us.

But finally—and most importantly—we need men and women who can look beyond technology. We need education to produce those who, indeed, can see more than the pursuit and manufacture of goods and objects.

There are those today who worry because many of our schools and universities still carry such a high percentage of liberal arts in their curricula. Why, they say, study literature or language? Why study ancient history? Why a major in the theater arts? Haven't you heard, this is the new technological world? It is the world of plastics, heat-shields, solid-state, and the Great God Transistor.

To these, I give my answer: Let us not confuse means and ends.

What do we seek for man on this planet? Human dignity. Personal expression and fulfillment. Freedom. Justice. Technology in itself is not the end of our aspirations.

No, I am not among the Luddites — those who, in past times, destroyed technology so as to remove a threat they did not understand. I believe that we, as a nation, must continue to develop a technology second to none in the world. We must offer the best possible education in technology and for technology. But those who lead technology are the first to say that it is no more than a tool. The value of that tool depends on the intelligence, judgment, and creativity of man himself. The value of that tool depends on the resources of intellect and spirit of our nation and its citizens. These resources only can be developed by education which involves man in ideas as well as things, in ethics as well as engineering.

Technology, despite its achievements, is only coming today into early maturity. If we are prepared to engage it wisely, it, indeed, can help us toward our ultimate ends.

Physical well-being will not make all men philosopher kings. More rapid communication will not make men more wisely communicate. But these things someday can ease man's everyday burden so that he may lift himself beyond his search for food, shelter, and material comfort.

John Stuart Mill said the worth of a nation "is the worth of the individuals composing it." Let us then, in this generation, produce men and women who, as individuals, will build a society of compassion as well as comfort, of humanism as well as hardware, of freedom as well as Frigidaire.

22. THE TECHNOLOGICAL REVOLUTION AND EDUCATION

ANTHONY J. CELEBREZZE

THE REVOLUTION IN TECHNOLOGY, which has so radically transformed our society in so many ways, is making its impact also in the field of education. Educational television is only one of its manifestations and an important and dramatic one. But there are others we can point to.

There is the changing curriculum in mathematics and science, which some of us encounter when we try, often vainly, to help our children with their homework. There are changed techniques in teaching: the team approach, for example, which makes room for the specialist now at all levels of education. And there is education's whole new array of tools: the TV sets and teaching machines, projectors and tape recorders, and, in the larger school systems and universities, the talented and versatile computer.

Impressive and extensive as all these changes may be, they do not constitute any radical change in the substance or aims of education. They are essentially the products of our response to the quantitative demands of today's technology: teaching more people more facts more efficiently.

EDITORS' NOTE: At the time this chapter was written, the Hon. Anthony J. Celebrezze was Secretary of Health, Education, and Welfare. In July, 1965, he was appointed a Federal Judge, U.S. Court of Appeals for the Sixth Circuit, Cincinnati, Ohio.

The question that education has not yet answered is the question that technology poses for our entire society — the question of its mastery for human aims and human uses rather than for its own sake. We need to ask ourselves: Are we controlling technology? Or is it leading us? Are we bending it to our own aims and uses? Or have we become its slaves? We are not opposed to the idea of change. Progress is change. Its movement cannot be halted. And we know that the forces of technology which we have set in motion will continue now to move with even greater momentum. We cannot stop them, and we do not want to stop them. Yet, we must control change if we are to preserve our freedom as individuals and as a nation.

Pres. Johnson struck this theme in his Inaugural Address. Liberty, he said, was an America "where each man could be proud to be himself: stretching his talents, rejoicing in his work, important in the life of his neighbors and his nation." And this, he acknowledged, "has become more difficult in a world where change and growth seem to tower beyond the control and even the judgment of men."

Looking at our society today, we can see where change has gotten out of hand. The baneful effects of technology are evident all around us — in polluted rivers and lakes; in the smog-laden air; in the decaying hearts of cities where the "other Americans" have lived too long in dismal, unchanging poverty. We can read the painful story of technological change in the faces of the men and women whose jobs are threatened by or lost to automation. We can see the hardship of change among those older citizens who lack the means to enjoy their lengthened life span and also among the young ones—the children of the poor—who lack the opportunity to build the needed foundations for a good and abundant life.

We look around us, and we cannot be satisfied with the quality of life that today's technology has brought us. And so the question becomes even more pressing than before: What are the human uses of change, and how can we best achieve them?

More and more people feel that they are being swept along in the stream of change, helpless to guide themselves. Take the case of those whose jobs are taken over by computers. What choices, what alternatives are open to them? How can they retain their economic independence—and their sense of dignity and human worth? Our first, immediate, instinctive reaction has been to turn to education which *can* open up new paths and which *can* provide alternatives.

We have moved quickly to provide broad opportunities for retraining in currently needed skills for young people who have failed to acquire useful skills, as well as for older workers displaced by the new technology. The manpower development and training program alone has enrolled 175,000 during 1962-64, and 73% of those retrained have been placed in new jobs. A number of private industries have developed their own retraining programs, particularly for workers with easily transferable skills.

Already many Americans have realized that riding the waves of automation might require training and retraining three or four times within a working lifetime as the level of skill of machines increases. In the professional fields, the rapid obsolescence of knowledge creates similar problems. The professional engineer today, for example, has what is called a "half life" of only 10 years which is to say that half of what an engineer has learned when he receives his degree will be obsolete within 10 years. Engineers must study or perish, occupationally speaking. Physicians and other professionals must do the same.

The impact of change and the knowledge explosion are not limited, of course, to the professions, but are setting off shock waves that are being felt in varying degrees in virtually every form of human endeavor. It is a compelling fact of life that we must commit ourselves to being students all our lives. A continuing education — training and retraining—is our primary response to the challenges of automation and technological change. Yet, the pressures will doubtless mount for other measures to make room for both man and his servant machines: a shorter workweek, longer vacations, and a lowered retirement age. A shorter workweek, longer vacations, and added years of retirement offer both an opportunity and a challenge. They offer an added educational opportunity to individuals to advance their skills and knowledge. They offer a challenge to education to stimulate and equip those who have increased free time to use it for a fuller and more satisfying life.

I would like to think that human beings with less time required for their work would welcome the opportunity to explore the world of ideas, to travel, to savor the arts, to join volunteer efforts to build a healthy community environment, and to help their fellow men at home or abroad.

This is an ideal of the Great Society—an ideal which is attainable, though its perfection always will elude our grasp. Education bears a heavy responsibility to lead the way and to keep us moving toward that elusive goal.

Diogenes attributed to Aristotle the observation that "education is an ornament in prosperity and a refuge in adversity." Education indeed has been both in the history of our nation, but we now have come to a realization that it is much more than either an ornament or a refuge.

Education is basic and central to our personal, community, and national well-being. It is fiber that gives both strength and beauty to the fabric of our society. It shapes our daily existence and gives form and substance to our aspirations.

Pres. Johnson has said that education is the first work of society. And this conviction is amply illustrated by his program to strengthen education.

Our democracy always has needed educated citizens. It needs them more than ever today.

We need wisdom. We need judgment. We need competence—a competence that combines technical skills with a deep appreciation of human values. Without this kind of competence, I believe we will become victims, rather than the beneficiaries, of technology.

It is education that prevents the erosion of individual liberties. It is education that teaches human worth. It is education that multiplies our choices and makes us free men.

How can we as a nation meet this vast need for education? Granting this boundless need for knowledge, how do we provide it in the face of rising educational costs and inadequate resources? We have struggled with this question for some years now, while the disparities in education—from state to state and from school district to school district within the states—have grown larger and more damaging to the nation as a whole.

The fact is very plain today that many communities simply do not have the money to support good schools. The great tragedy is that these poverty-stricken schools serve the nation's poverty-stricken children who are most urgently in need of the very best that education can provide.

It also has been plain to many citizens that the national government, with its broad tax base and its responsibility for the well-being of all the people, has both the means and the duty to help shoulder the costs of education. During the last few years, and most notably in the 88th Congress, our national commitment to education has been clearly acknowledged and Federal support has been provided in a number of crucial areas: in college construction, in vocational training for young people and adults, in expanded programs to upgrade the proficiency of teachers, in training special teachers for the mentally and physically handicapped, and in helping meet our pressing needs for additional manpower in the health professions. The list is far from complete.

On one crucial point, however, we floundered repeatedly, and that is on how to strengthen the very foundation of education — the elementary and secondary schools. In the past, proposals for Federal aid to elementary and secondary schools sought to provide financial support for the entire public school system. The President's program would concentrate funds on the educational needs of the children of the poor — on all of them in both public and private schools. The purse strings would not be held in Washington. They would be in the hands of the states, which would receive Federal aid according to their need — on the basis of the number of school-age children from families with an income of less than $2,000 per year. Additionally, the states would receive funds for school library and instructional materials — and they would select those materials, just as they do today.

The President's program would help communities to establish education centers and special services for both children and adults. It challenges the imagination and ingenuity of every citizen to devise new, more effective approaches to meet our vast need for continuing education. It does not tell any state or community how to meet that need. It says merely that the national government recognizes the needs of education — and the vital importance of education in this age of change — and that it has responsibilities to support the costs of education, which are essentially the costs of freedom and safety and progress.

A good example of how the national government can and does help local communities is provided by the new educational television station, WVIZ, in Cleveland, Ohio. As much as $250,000 of Federal money has gone into the establishment of this broadcasting station — about one-forth of the amount necessary to put the station on the air. This is really only seed money — a stimulus to further growth. The responsibility for that growth, for direction of this station, for the content and quality of its programs, and for services that it will or will not perform all remain with the citizens of Cleveland. Those educational television services which are provided will not only be an invaluable new asset for Cleveland's schools, but will offer new stimulation and opportunity for a lifelong commitment to education throughout the community.

23. AUTOMATION: BOON OR BANE FOR EDUCATION?

FRANCIS KEPPEL

THE PROCESS OF CHANGE in society is continual. There are few times when we can mark the beginning of an era. At some point in these past few years, our nation entered into a new age. This is the Age of Automation, an era when fewer hands can produce more goods, when muscle is being replaced by machines. The growth of technology is not new, but what is new is the sweeping pace at which this change is taking place

As a layman peering into the new world on which science is raising the curtain, I find myself duly and properly amazed. I find totally fascinating some of the concepts which the scientists and engineers take so easily in stride. In Washington, a computer created only recently is already preserved at the Smithsonian Institution as a historical relic. It was just over a decade ago that the computer was introduced commercially. Today, thousands are in use and thousands more on order. Changes come rapidly and each day brings some new discovery. At the current rate, creative thought and invention will lead to a world 50 years from now as different from ours as the present is different from the world at the start of this century

There are those who look toward this new era with fear and foreboding. I agree that we should have a healthy respect for the perils ahead, that we should be alert to dangers. Every breakthrough in science generates still another series of discoveries. And, as each of these is put to practical use, our society is required to adjust itself accordingly.

We are at a stage in our history when the complex of technology called automation demands that we re-examine many basic assumptions. The rise of automation comes at a time when unprecedented millions of young people are entering the labor force. Many problems are raised by the computer and its family of complex machines. But surely, as Pres. Johnson recently declared, "If we have the brainpower to invent these machines, we have the brainpower to make certain that they are a boon and not a bane to humanity."

The rush of automation forces us to look back critically, to look clearly at the present, and to look prudently ahead. The world of work has changed and our society must keep pace. Whatever moves we make to adjust to the future, it is clear that education will play a major role. Our system of education is called on to transmit knowledge of the past, to help us make transitions from the past to the present, and to create and contribute new ideas to the future.

Today, as never before, education is summoned everywhere to service — summoned, in fact, to a growing variety of services — to meet the challenges of poverty and ignorance, to supply the skills needed in this increasingly interdependent world, and to prepare America for a time in which the only constant appears to be change itself.

Education has not always been so highly regarded in our land, nor has so much been expected of it and in such short order. In these days, it sometimes seems that even the word "education" has taken on overtones of magic, as if it were an incantation which suddenly would exorcise all evil spirits if only we repeated the word enough.

In this same sense, "automation" also has become a magical word. Like "education," it, too, has become supercharged with strange meaning. If education is sometimes mistakenly seen as a sudden cure for every evil, automation often is seen blindly as a sudden source of malevolence.

We can perform a public service by bringing education and automation into rational speaking distance of each other and by addressing ourselves to the reality of what we might reasonably expect of both forces within our society.

As an educator, seeking to measure the task ahead, I view this new world of expanding technology as the greatest challenge in our educational history — and as our greatest educational opportunity.

The truth is that today, in education as in other fields, if we merely keep our present pace, we will be moving backwards. The old ways simply will not serve our needs.

I welcome automation as a force to liberate us for more efficient use of the human mind and to free us from the bonds of mindless toil. In the very threat of automation to the unlearned and the unskilled is the opportunity to justify our faith in a free society of educated citizens. Automation summons us to a breakthrough in education.

There was a time when a young person entering the labor force without a skill and with little education had a fair chance to achieve an adequate economic life. Today the odds are against him. As the President pointed out in his "Manpower Report," "Occupationally, unskilled jobs are declining in importance. Demand is expanding most in professional and technical, clerical, and service occupations. Requirements for education and training for employment are increasing steadily."

At the same time, despite a rising economy, unemployment went up in 1963 as fast as the increase in the teen-age labor force, and almost one teen-ager in six who seeks work today can find no one to employ him. Two-thirds of our unemployed have less than a high school education; one out of every 12 workers with only an elementary education is unemployed, compared with one out of 70 college graduates.

There is no denying that in education there has been progress and achievement in which we can justly take pride. America's educational system for generations has raised our general level of learning and continues to do so. But let us be honest and admit that we have failed to meet our responsibility to educate all Americans. We believe that the punishment should fit the crime. What crime have millions of our citizens committed that they must suffer the life-long punishment of poverty and ignorance? These Americans lack the fundamentals of education that would give them a decent chance for economic survival. Of what comfort is it to these millions to point to high over-all levels of education and general prosperity?

Unemployment and the demands of technology have drawn increased attention to our system of vocational education. The examination has exposed serious flaws. We find vocational and general education to be far too often separate streams in the development of secondary education. Vocational schools have been considered too long a "dumping ground" for the poor, who often have difficulty in academic learning. This is a double-edged slur. It is a slur against

modern vocational training, which increasingly requires basic academic skills for any hope of success. And it is a slur against the
poor, who deserve more than detours from education.

Fortunately, we now have at hand the opportunity to build a
truly modern system of technical education. The Vocational Education Act of 1963 — a landmark in our history of vocational training —
calls for a sharp break with the past. Under this law, Federal funds
to strengthen and expand vocational education can be more than
quadrupled. Congress has authorized an increase in appropriations
from some $57,000,000 a year to an additional $731,000,000 over
four years (1965-69).

Equally important, in view of the demands of automation, the
law gives educators greater flexibility than ever before. It can help to
fashion the kind of vocational education system we need — one that is
responsive to labor market trends and free from the rigid categories of
previous occupational programs. It allows money to be spent where
it is needed — to prepare workers for occupations where needs exist.
As the labor market changes, so can the emphasis in training be
shifted.

With this kind of flexibility, we can build a technical training
system able to fulfill the basic requirements of the policy described
by Pres. Johnson in his "Manpower Report." The President called
for new attitudes and efforts geared to three functional goals: to
develop the abilities of Americans, to create jobs to make the most
of these abilities, and to link the first two — to match people and
jobs. This undertaking can succeed only with the able planning, the
support, and the enterprise of the states and communities which
recognize the economic needs of their own regions. It can succeed
only with the active cooperation and support of leaders of industry
and labor who can help us be sure that vocational training is in the
mainstream of this age of automation, that it is truly responsive to
the economic realities of today, and that it will be responsive to the
coming realities of tomorrow.

We have mentioned vocational schooling, but we would make
a grave error to set it apart from the basic fabric of education. Our
time demands that we raise the broad educational level of all our
people, that we deny to no one education's passport to the future.
General education is the foundation of all learning. It can be
neglected only at our peril.

Workers of the future must be flexible. They must be able to
adapt to change. Only a sound basic education equips one to move

ahead with the times. There is no doubt that poverty and unemployment are closely linked to educational levels. One out of every 10 workers in the United States who has failed to finish elementary school is unemployed today. The rate of unemployment for those who have dropped out of school before high school graduation is twice as high as for graduates.

A free education for all Americans has long been proclaimed a pillar of our democratic society. We point to universal education as one of the glories of our nation and as a basic force in its development. This is as it should be — and must be. But candor obliges us to confess that we have fallen short of this dream of quality education, of equality of educational opportunity, for all. One measure of our failure is the fact that 8,000,000 Americans who are 26 years and older have completed less than five years of schooling — the level of "functional illiteracy." Nearly 20,000,000 have completed less than eight years of schooling. Some 54,000,000 did not finish high school.

Our fundamental task remains in our elementary and secondary schools. Here the needs have been recognized and debated for years. Now it is time to stop the debate and to end the neglect of these foundations upon which all education depends. Here we are short of teachers and enough qualified teachers. Here we are short of classrooms and laboratories where effective teaching can be offered.

We must make teacher salaries competitive with other professions if we hope to raise the level of education and also make teaching the proud and favored career it ought to be. During the school year, 1962-63, the average annual salary of public school teachers was about $6,000, and in many depressed areas, the average was under $3,000.

The state of our elementary and secondary school classrooms continues to cry out for attention. An inventory of the nation's public school facilities in 1962 showed that one out of six classrooms in use was more than 40 years old and that more than 10,000,000 children attended school in classrooms averaging 30 or more pupils. To reduce this average to 30 or less we will require more than 66,000 new classrooms — not to mention construction of schoolrooms needed to meet present hazards to health and safety. These figures do not fully measure our need. We also must prepare for the flood-tide of students in the years just ahead. Public school enrollments now stand at roughly 40,000,000. By 1970, this number is expected to rise to more than 45,000,000,

We must repair these serious shortcomings in our educational system and move ahead. Education cannot afford to lag behind in a day of rising requirements. We need more and better teachers and more and better classrooms for our young Americans. But our schools also must respond to the need for education as a life-long process — indeed, as a life-long necessity.

Our educational structure has a tremendous task to perform. Without broad community support, the schools cannot meet that challenge. Without continued and ready response to community needs, the schools only can perform part of their function. It is only through community cooperation that the benefits and potential of existing and new educational programs can be realized. We must work to transform this into reality for the millions who otherwise will live as outcasts in the world of automation and also for the nation which cannot afford to waste its most precious resource — its citizens.

As Pres. Johnson put it, "The Federal Government can provide leadership, information, and other assistance, but fundamentally it is action carried forward in each community that will decide how well we achieve national objectives."

I have faith that we will successfully make the transition into the new world of automation. This is a nation of determined people. We have not faltered heretofore when faced with difficulties and when the times demanded new ideas.

To devote less than our best efforts and our highest determination to education is to sell short the American dream and its promise. To deny educational opportunity to any of us diminishes us all.

Together, with rededication to the American ideal of universal education, we shall enter this Age of Automation with confidence, making the machines of man a liberating boon to man in these last decades of our 20th century.

24. STAY-AT-HOME CLASSROOMS FOR SPACE-AGE ADULTS

NORMAN D. KURLAND

MEN NOW "WALK" IN SPACE and soon they will walk on the moon. What would happen to education if the imagination, daring, and resources that are going into our adventure in space were marshalled for an adventure in learning? This chapter is an attempt to explore some of the possibilities.

For too long, education has sought to cope with its problems merely by extending traditional procedures to handle larger numbers and by the slow and piecemeal introduction of new ideas and methods. But the problems confronting education, created by the twin explosions of knowledge and population, are too great to be handled by traditional procedures. A breakthrough is called for of the dimensions appropriate to a generation that is going to see men visit the planets, communicate with intelligent life elsewhere in the universe, change at will the hereditary characteristics of genes, create living tissue from inorganic materials, transmit information and power by light beams, and achieve the myriad of other potentialities—not miracles — of existing science and technology. Whether our social and political institutions will be able to adjust to the impact of these changes will depend very largely upon the success with which we change our educational system so that it fits — and keeps fit — our citizens for the new world that is upon us.

What follows will seem fantastic, even mad, to those who view educational change from traditional perspectives. Indeed, the great likelihood is that traditional modes of operation and sheer inertia will continue to prevent the large-scale, ordered, and imaginative adoption of new ideas in education. Instead, they will be introduced piecemeal here and there — never enough to realize their full potential, never enough really to meet the needs of the times. Education probably is doomed to lag behind needs and possibilities. With this acknowledgment to the realities, let us consider what might be if we had the wits, the will, the imagination, and the courage to use the knowledge and technology which now are available to us.

COMPUTER-ASSISTED PROGRAMMED INSTRUCTION

Programmed instruction, with or without machines, undoubtedly will have an increasing, albeit limited, role in education. Ordered sequencing of materials, active response, immediate feedback, and self-pacing presentation have obvious educational merit. As more is learned about this method and better programs are produced, it will find an increasing place in our classrooms.

It is the addition of a computer which transforms a useful additional teaching tool into something which, next to the human teacher, may prove to be the most effective teaching instrument yet devised. The computer is far more than a complicated device for presenting programmed material. It can be employed to direct the learner at each stage of his development to the appropriate learning resource, whether it be a programmed lesson, a television or audiotape, a book, or even the teacher himself. It adjusts to the actual learning experience of each student so that no two "programs" are ever alike. The slow learner will be taken through strategies designed to overcome his particular learning difficulties; the fast learner will be moved ahead to materials of appropriate levels of difficulty. Progress will be fully analyzed and recorded, providing counselor and educational researcher with information of a kind never before available: the counselor will have a detailed record of students' past performances and, if the necessary evaluation procedures are built into the program, a secure basis for placement; the researcher will have detailed information on the specific behavior of the learner under controlled conditions at every stage of the learning process. The effects of large and minute changes in the learning situation can be studied exhaustively and hypotheses about learning at last can be analyzed under near-laboratory conditions. At this point, it is hard to estimate whether the research or teaching effects will have the greatest educational significance.

Important as these two effects are, they almost can be considered bonuses beside two others: the equalizing of educational opportunity, and the release of teachers to do those tasks which only the human teacher can do. Under present teaching arrangements, the equalizing of educational opportunity never can be much more than a dream. In most school situations, classes will not be homogeneous or small enough or teachers able enough to adjust adequately to individual differences. Every learner will be handicapped in some way—the fast, by being held down to the pace of the slower, with the attendant boredom, frustration, and loss of powers not sufficiently exercised; the slow, by never quite mastering a subject before being forced to move along to the next topic; and the average—but there is no one average in everything! With computers we can come closer to insuring that the fast learner moves ahead at a pace adjusted to his capacity and that the slow learns thoroughly each lesson before he is allowed to move ahead, thus eliminating the perpetual frustration which must be a major obstacle to his educational achievement. Moreover, once programs are developed for learners of different capacities, it should become possible to understand the obstacles to learning and to develop more effective strategies for helping learners at all levels to learn more and better. It is even conceivable that the difficulty of some slow learners may derive from an inherent incapacity for manipulation of verbal symbols. Machines permit the presentation of non-verbal stimuli—pictures, diagrams, or even things—and thus may make educable individuals who now appear to be uneducable.

Programmed instruction automatically would take into account individual differences in maturation rates. Slow maturers now may be handicapped permanently by being tagged in their early school years as "dumb" and by failing to master fundamentals before they are moved along to more advanced materials. Programmed instruction would adjust to changing capacity for learning throughout the learner's educational career and thus try to assure that each one would achieve to the maximum of his capacity.

Another instructional role for the computer will be in providing simulated experiences as a means of approximating the conditions under which knowledge is applied. Suggestive work is going on in adapting the technique of the business and military game to education. In a "game," the student is exposed to a complex situation in which he has to apply previously acquired skills and knowledge to the solution of a problem. The computer provides both immediate feedback on the results of his "decision" and new information that must be taken into account. Through the mediation of the computer there also can be interaction among several players. In time, complex computer-mediated games may be a widely utilized form of community education and recreation.

There is some fear that machines will replace teachers, but a little consideration will make it evident that the only teachers who will be replaced, if any are, will be the poorest ones. In a programmed instructional system, teachers will have two basic roles — one new, and one old but usually inadequately realized. The new role will be to prepare materials for the machines — programs, televised lessons, filmed demonstrations, audio and visual illustrative materials, demonstrations, and evaluation instruments. Such work will require vastly increased understanding of both the learning process and the subjects to be learned. Intelligence and imagination will be demanded as never before. When these qualities are present, they will be available not just to the handful of students with whom even the best teachers now can work, but to as many as the system cares to have these qualities reach.

The other role of the teacher will be to do what the machine never can do—motivate, counsel, and lead students to those higher-order functions which are the primary goals of education—to question, imagine, invent, appreciate, and act. The teacher need no longer be the purveyor of information or even the developer of basic skills and understanding. When he meets students in formal classes, they will be prepared together to move into the most intricate and challenging aspects of a subject. And the numbers of such formal meetings which will be required will be greatly reduced. There will be time for his own research *and* for the more intimate, informal contacts which all good students find to be the most rewarding part of collegiate life. Under such conditions the teacher can be what, at his best, he always has been—a model, a stimulator, guide, planner, and fellow searcher after truth, meaning, and value. In this way we may yet preserve that vital personal relationship between student and teacher which is so gravely threatened by the onrush of students and the attendant depersonalization of our institutions.

A final benefit of the large-scale introduction of technology into teaching is that it will provide a basis both for raising teachers' salaries to professional levels and for differentiating among teachers of differing abilities. The obvious increased "productivity" and level of professional competence of the teacher who directs a learning "system" and participates in the creation of effective learning materials will justify a reward more nearly commensurate with the training and ability required for the task. The effectiveness, too, of teachers with lesser abilities, working in a team with able leaders and using well-designed programmed materials, will be greatly enhanced.

Lest there be any illusions about technology increasing the teacher-student ratio, let me state that I do not see this as a likely long-run result. The effect of well applied technology will be to improve instruction and alter the functions of teachers and their relations to pupils and each other. But the effect of improved instruction is almost always to put greater demands on the creative teacher. What we can hope for from the introduction of technology, then, is not a saving of manpower, but of "mindpower" and a level of educational achievement more nearly up to the needs of our culture.

LEARNING RESOURCE CENTERS AND THE NEW EDUCATIONAL ENVIRONMENTS

Educational practice, up to now, has been dominated by the classroom in which learners are brought together in small or large groups with one instructor. Even when students are sent off to study on their own, they usually are provided with large reading rooms in which hundreds are expected somehow to concentrate in a hotel lobby atmosphere. In the world of work, when we expect a person to perform important intellectual tasks, we give him a room to himself, and when we really want high performance we provide him with all the aids he may need for his work. As one of the most important and demanding intellectual tasks, learning deserves conditions no less conducive to high-level performance. In recognition of this fact, increasing numbers of schools and colleges are providing individual student study spaces.

Into such spaces can be brought, by wire from a central learning resources facility, programmed material, live and taped television lectures, audio-tapes, language lessons, and broadcast television and radio — all selected at will by the student or available to him on predetermined schedule. Devices are even being developed to give ready access to printed materials at remote locations. From the space, the student's responses can be fed in a variety of forms — audio-visual, electronic, punched card — to the central facility for analysis, evaluation, and recording or to a teacher for response.

Such individual spaces, combined with a limited number of seminar-size rooms and large auditoriums, can provide a learning environment far more adaptable to individual learning needs than anything now available. In such an arrangement, scheduling problems virtually disappear, and learning and instruction both can be organized for more effective realization of individual and institutional goals.

CONTINUING EDUCATION

Five things can be said, with a high degree of confidence, about continuing education in the remainder of this century:

1. Nearly as many adults will be working for college degrees on a part-time basis as will undergraduates enrolled full-time in all of our higher institutions.

2. The demands for advanced education on a systematic, continuous, easily accessible basis by adults will increase, spurred both by the decreasing need for unskilled workers and by the explosion of knowledge. There will be fewer jobs for the under-educated, and anyone quickly will become under-educated who does not continue learning at a high level throughout his adult life.

3. The success with which those needs are met at a high intellectual level will determine in large measure the quality — if not the survival — of American society in the last part of this century.

4. Universities, as presently organized, are not prepared to meet these needs and, being preoccupied with the flood of undergraduates and their increasing research responsibilities, are not likely to organize to meet them.

5. Educational television, by itself, is not likely to meet these needs.

Given these conditions and reflecting on the developments described in the first two sections of this chapter, a solution to the needs for continuing education suggests itself which is so staggering in its potential effects as to border on the fantastic. Yet, given the need and the resources which are potentially available, what follows may be a highly realistic suggestion.

There is every reason to believe that the kind of individual study spaces described above could be designed for installation in conveniently located community centers, such as libraries, and in homes.

Were this done, a central learning resource facility, equipped with a large high-speed computer and extensive library of programmed, televised, recorded, and printed materials, could service whole cities, states, or even regions. If manufactured on a large scale, suitable study facilities, perhaps each equipped with its own small-scale computer, could be made available for a cost that would not much exceed that of a good television receiver ($400-$500). Such a system would provide access to well-conceived learning aids, available when needed, self-paced, and with feedback and built-in self-evaluation procedures. It could be expected to increase the significant educational activity in any community so serviced — a gain not merely in quantity, but, far more important, in quality of the educational experience. Here — not in open-circuit television — is the real mass education medium of the future.

To insure that such a system does not become an instrument for indoctrination of one viewpoint on a scale never before possible, all points of view and approaches must be represented in the resource materials library. This could be achieved not only by the determination of the staff to stock the facility with a full range of materials, but also by an open supply policy. This would permit any individual or group to place in the library any material technically compatible with the system. The storage and catalogue listing of such material would be a small item and a very small price for the freedom it would help protect.

What results might be anticipated from such a system which would justify such a large undertaking?

1. An extension of educational opportunities to every segment of the population of a variety and even quality never before possible and at a cost per student hour of instruction at least comparable with, if not greatly below, present costs.

2. An upgrading of the real educational achievement level of the population commensurate with the needs of an increasingly complex culture.

3. An increase in the general level of political and economic sophistication—a gain essential to the survival and vitality of democratic society.

4. An increase in the demand for cultural resources of high quality so that theater, music, literature, and the plastic arts would flourish as never before.

5. A vast gain in the vocational adaptability of the population. As a rapidly changing technology accelerates the rate of vocational

obsolescence, effective means must be found for continuous up-dating of the training of large proportions of the working force. The proposed system will be the most expeditious means for achieving this objective.

6. An effective adjustment to the greatly increasing amount of non-work time available to everyone. Whether this time becomes "leisure" time, in the richest connotation of that term, or merely is filled with increasingly desperate efforts to escape boredom will depend largely on the accessibility and quality of the education for leisure available. Again, the proposed system will make a major contribution to this need.

COSTS

What would such a system cost? Until detailed feasibility studies are conducted, any estimate is only a guess.

1. For preliminary research and development — $1,000,000. (Some of the necessary work has been done. Research and development should be a permanent part of the operation as it now is in any advanced industrial or commercial enterprise.)

2. To establish and stock a central learning resource facility for a single region, including installation of high-speed computers and development of programs — $50-$100,000,000. Although the initial "hardware" will require large expenditure and, of course, will be essential, the effectiveness of the system will depend primarily upon the quality of the educational materials transmitted via the hardware. Their development will be a major charge. Yet, even here, perspective is called for. If high-quality offerings can be developed for an average of $20,000, then $10,000,000 will "buy" 500 offerings. Even at an average of $100,000 per offering, the costs would be well within justifiable range. This assumes that some items can be incorporated at minimal cost, while others — the video-taping or programming of complex courses — may run into the hundreds of thousands of dollars.

3. For transmission lines, regular telephone lines may be used for part of the service. The estimate of the cost has not been determined.

4. To provide 100,000 individual study spaces in public centers — $50,000,000. This would be done to give the program an initial impetus and to provide for persons unable or unwilling to purchase their own units. The production and sale of home units would be left to private enterprise, which could be expected to launch the development, production, and sales effort comparable to that which

put a television receiver in nearly every home. The estimated total cost of introducing the system in a state such as New York would thus be $100-$200,000,000.

TIMETABLE

Without the full, systematic, large-scale development envisioned above, the system is still likely to be in existence in many localities by the end of this century. Given the decision to implement the above proposal with the needed resources, the system could be in limited operation within five years. Within 10 years it could be expected to reach a majority of homes in the participating areas, and in 15 years have a full-range of learning materials available.

If this seems optimistic for such a large undertaking, remember that it was less than five years from decision to man in orbit and about 10 years from the beginning of commercial television to nearly nation-wide reception. While the pace of educational change traditionally has been far slower than this, and the number of persons involved in implementation is far larger than the space program, with sufficient determination the indicated time table is feasible, as far as establishment of the system is concerned. Full acceptance and utilization will be slower, of course, but the educational needs by the end of the present decade are likely to accelerate acceptance far more rapidly than anything our past experience would suggest.

What is called for, then, is a "Manhattan project" in education to put the new technology at the service of the highest function of man before it destroys him.

STRATEGIC CONSIDERATIONS

The proposed system could be developed for formal education from the kindergarten through graduate school. Two considerations argue against this approach:

1. An effort to introduce the system on the scale proposed would run into all the entrenched interests, habits, and values of established institutions. The resistance certainly would slow down the program, and the compromises required to make even a little headway probably would vitiate the best effects of the system. In concentrating on advanced adult education, the system would be entering a field now serviced by a wide variety of institutions, none strong enough to resist the program; and, in any case, few are doing anything in the areas in which the system would be most important.

2. Educational considerations argue for beginning as proposed. Assuming that the proposal is not implemented, the educational needs of youth will be met, more or less, and new technology will be introduced, although at a slow rate. There is little prospect, however, that the needs for advanced, continuing education will be met on anything near the scale and quality required. Thus, the proposal will meet a large unfilled need in an area in which resistance to its introduction will be minimal. Success in this area, of course, will have profound effects on the schools, bringing about changes far more rapidly than would direct introduction of the system.

There are those who will feel that this proposal puts excessive emphasis on "hardware" and ignores the central importance of teachers and ideas. Without going into a detailed argument on the point, the following considerations will suggest the lines along which discussion might proceed:

1. There is, certainly, no substitute for a good teacher, and such a teacher can teach under any conditions. In mass education, however, it is unrealistic, unfortunately, to think in terms of good teachers for every student under any foreseeable or existing arrangement. Given a vast majority of average to inferior teachers, the question is how can we help them to do a better job and at the same time extend, without destroying, the effectiveness of the really good teachers? This is one objective of the proposed system.

2. The environment in which teaching occurs and the tools teachers work with profoundly affect the character of education. The printed book certainly changed education, and the kind of buildings we now have is, many believe, an obstacle to improved education. But most important, the right changes in "hardware" may do more to stimulate fundamental thinking about the nature of the educational process than the most well conceived efforts at curricular reform.

3. The emergence of this system undoubtedly would generate great demand for direct contact with teachers. Once people get a taste for education through independent study, they generally want the experience of sharing ideas with others. Increased opportunities for such experience would be an inevitable result of the proposed system. Whether in privately arranged group meetings or in specially organized formal seminars or workshops, individuals would find ways to satisfy the need to exchange ideas with fellow human beings.

There is more at stake than whether the role of the teacher will be kept, modified, or abolished. The central question is the impact on the individual. Will such a system transform him into a mere extension of a machine—mindful of the things needed to keep the social machine operating smoothly, mindless about the things that make men human? Whether man is mechanized and enslaved by his machines or freed by them depends on how he uses them. Every external extension of the human hand or brain has put some aspect of human functioning outside of the individual. Is man lessened thereby or freed? Though this debate will go on as long as man survives, the issue of how our vast technological capabilities and material resources are to be put to use in education is before us.

And the issue is *how* and not *whether*. The need for change is here and cannot be denied. Already other agencies whose concerns in the past have not been primarily with education — business, industry, government — are considering how they may meet the need. If educators leave to others the determination of how new needs are met and new resources used, they will have little to complain about if the results are not to their liking. They must lead and not follow in adjusting their practices to meet changing needs and in exploiting new resources to help in meeting the needs. They should welcome the contributions of technology for what they can do for education. The hope for the future lies not in denying powers that history has put in our hands, but in using those powers for the enrichment of life.

25. EDUCATION
FOR THE WORLD
OF WORK

VIRGIL M. ROGERS

THE TECHNOLOGICAL AGE in which we live and work, and interrelated problems that evolve, are dramatized effectively by a Lichty cartoon, "Grin and Bear It." The vagabond, having coffee around the fire with his guest, remarked, "In addition to business administration, I took sales psychology, executive training, and office supervision; then I couldn't find a parking place." One university president quit his job, I am told, because the most vexing administrative problem for which he could find no solution was parking space for the faculty.

Secretary of Labor Willard Wirtz recently described the impact of automation upon the worker, management, and the public in these strong terms:

> The most dangerous myth, in immediate terms, is that machines produce as many jobs for men as they destroy and therefore represent no threat to workers. This is a half-truth and therefore a half-lie. The truth is that machines permit the extension of men's work activities. The implied lie is that this will happen automatically or without the exercise of full human responsibility.
> The machines now have, in general, a high school education — in the sense that they can do most jobs that a high school education qualifies people to do. So machines will get the unskilled jobs, because they work for less than living wages. Machines are, in the most real sense, responsible for putting uneducated people out of work.
> The jobs the machines create, furthermore, are usually for different people from those they displace. This doesn't matter if labor is viewed as a commodity. What it means, however, in more understanding terms is that the bargain a machine strikes with a man is that it takes one job and offers in return another

— stripped of the worker's seniority, accrued vacation benefits, pension rights, and the value of the skill he had spent a lifetime developing.[1]

Gilber Burck, writing on "The Boundless Age of the Computer" contends that the invention of the computer historically may prove to be more revolutionary and beneficial to mankind than the printing press, the wheel, the steam engine, the electric motor, or atomic energy. He speaks in these glowing terms of its achievements:

Certainly no other single item of capital goods has changed the basic terms of so many human activities in so short a time. Within a few years, as the engine of modern information technology, it has profoundly altered the techniques of science, has begun to make government efficient, and has provided a new basis for the strategies of national defense. Above all, it is radically changing business' production methods and the art and science of management. Although the machine is the bête noire of critics who fear it will accelerate unemployment and compound the worst problems of modern society, it seems destined to shine as a powerful instrument for making business more creative and efficient and hence for raising the nation's real income per person, for eliminating a vast amount of drudgery, and for increasing leisure. In short, for measurably expanding free man's range of choices.[2]

Harold Wilson, in a recent speech to the British Labour Party, may have been more nearly correct than some of us would like to admit when he said, "If there had never been a case for socialism, automation would have created one." Then he called for a marriage of science and socialism to accelerate a logical social progress instead of trying to repeal the 20th century.

Today, machines provide the equivalent of about 30 slaves for each of us every day, while millions of Americans live in misery, squalor, and disease, and without hope of finding the means of earning a living for the family; this means that we have cause for critically examining automation, education, and work.

This chapter will attempt to deal with education and the world of work. It will be limited largely to the preparation for work below the level of the highly technical professional fields of endeavor which call for university and graduate work, although the kind and quality of education anyone receives in the elementary, junior, and senior high school, or during the junior or community college years, will affect his adult life profoundly, whether he goes on through the graduate school or terminates his formal schooling earlier.

We shall assume, without taking time for documentation and defense, that education is the primary instrument through which we can change our human situation and hopefully improve it. In fact, it is about the only way, if we include all forms of education.

[1]Address to midyear graduation class, University of Michigan, Ann Arbor. Quoted in *AFL-CIO News*, Jan. 18, 1964, p. 4.

[2] *Fortune*, March, 1964.

Therefore, what we put into the courses of study, the design of the program, the richness of offerings, and the quality of administration and classroom leadership will determine in large measure the direction the nation will go in the years before us.

Having in mind the problems related to work, employment, job training, preparation for the adult world of work, and opportunities for earning a living with some degree of job satisfaction and proficiency, what is the current situation, educationally speaking?

We have more children, youths, and adults in school than ever before, both in numbers and percentages. On the whole, well-financed school systems are doing a better job than ever before. In fact, many universities are in the process of upgrading freshman courses in English, foreign languages, mathematics, and science because so many students are entering college and finding the freshman courses repetitious of the senior year in high school. More adolescents are being prepared for college entrance and more are clamoring for admission than at any time in the history of formal education. This type of problem is rather pleasant; we almost can be proud that we have managed to bring it about. Much less pleasant is a great educational and social situation rising in our midst, which we ignore at our peril. We refer to the fact that more than 1,000,000 youngsters have a place neither in our educational institutions nor in our working community; yet they are of school age and are old enough to hold jobs or go to war, should the country call them. Most of them are anxious to work or go to school or do both. However, one out of every three pupils who enters school, for one or another reason, will not finish a secondary education. This is tragic for the individual and for the nation; it also is wasteful.

There are over 1,000,000 dropouts per year from our schools. Most never come back to the regular classroom. The dropouts mostly have nothing to do and their plans take them nowhere; like the vagabond, they are not in any hurry and they are not going anywhere. They will form a part of the hoard of 55,000,000 Americans who have not completed secondary education.

Unemployed youths, in some respects, are in a more difficult situation than unemployed adults because they are not even getting an initial chance to prove themselves in the world of work. The total unemployment rate hovers above 5%, whereas the current rate for ages 16-21 is about 15% or worse. In the age range of 20-24, the unemployment rate is almost twice as high as the national average. The more dismal part of the picture is that for dropouts the rate is twice as bad as for high school graduates and is even more serious for those who, by accident of birth, happen to be non-white.

The prospect for employment as laborers, farmers, and handymen—in the relatively unskilled job at the bottom of the ladder —will continue to decline in the future. Additionally, coming into the young adult age bracket are some 26,000,000 between 1960 and 1970. Of this group, about one-fourth will be dropouts, and millions of others will lack essential skills to train or retrain readily for new jobs, some of which are as yet non-existent.

Without going into the social implications of the picture, we shall turn quickly to some suggested partial, practical approaches for school and university leaders as well as professionals whose communities now are facing some of these issues.

SOME STEPS TOWARD EDUCATING FOR THE WORLD OF WORK

1. Let us assure every child the opportunity of attending a comprehensive high school of sufficient size to give reasonable choices with reference to vocational interests and personal needs. Provisions should be made for easy transfer from one curriculum to another, with a minimum of effort or loss of time and credit. No pupil would be under pressure to make vocational choices before he is mature enough to understand the problem. We would avoid this hand-me-down from the European schools, despite H. G. Rickover's oft-repeated counsel. Parenthetically, an American revolution in secondary education is underway in Britain.

2. Provisions for modernized industrial arts and home arts programs should be made available to most students in high school. These would be based upon the needs of current-day family living, with units in selecting, buying, and using consumer goods. There would be required some skills in the use of tools and machines, and each student would get some feeling for the use of these. He would be oriented to a world of mass production and industrial operation, community organization, innovation, and automation. Such training would equip the young citizen as a consumer, worker, voter, parent, and taxpayer, with some essential skills to face the adult world of the 1960's and 1970's.

3. Programs of work-related education should be available to students for a threefold purpose. First, to become work oriented — appreciative of the importance, value, and satisfaction of holding jobs. Second, to have a part-time paying job when need for partial

self-support to stay in school is indicated. Third, to get practical training and experience in a salable skill while finishing secondary school.

4. Major emphasis should be placed on basic skills or tools for learning and communicating, including reading, writing, oral communications, arithmetic, and human relations. Intensive specialized skill training for a job should be delayed until post-high school or on-the-job training. This becomes increasingly necessary as the trend toward multiple-employment careers grows. Retraining and the capacity to adapt to changing occupational patterns may mean the difference between chronic dependence on the dole and job security. We must help youth understand that today a man's skills may well become obsolete two or three or more times in his working lifetime.

5. The modern industrial community should establish, under the auspices of public schools, with the help of a community-wide representative advisory committee or board, a community skills center for youth and adults. The center would provide for vocational training, retraining, upgrading, orientation to new vocational fields, and extensive counseling and job-seeking assistance. These centers in some communities would be attached to a part of the community college program.

The center would house the heavy-duty machinery for specialized job training on an individual basis and would be adapted to the needs and capacities of those who sought, free of charge, its services, either on a full-time or a part-time basis. The combination of people without jobs and jobs without people to fill them should concern every thoughtful citizen and should constrain the educator to re-examine most critically the adequacy of the schools' offerings.

6. Every youth capable of acquiring a skill for self-support should be helped to continue through secondary school and to attend a community college or technical institute, or some other specialized training program.[3] The student never should be lost track of from the day he enters school until he has matriculated at a college or university or has been accepted into a satisfactory job situation. To allow a contrary course is to court disaster for the individual and to invite deep trouble for society. To the skeptic, we should say, "Look about you in your community for confirmation of the truth of this statement." The two-year community college must be both academic and vocational and adapted to the needs and conditions

---

[3] See "Universal Opportunities for Education Beyond the High School" (Washington, D.C.: Educational Policies Commission, NEA, 1964).

of the area it serves. It may well be a combination of a two-year liberal arts college, technical institute, community skills center, and adult education opportunity school. It should be free to all who enter its halls, library, shops, studios, and counseling center.

It should be the aim of the public schools to let no one depart from them, even through the processes of graduation, without reasonable preparation for the next step in education or in an occupation, or without preparation for work. In this connection, school attendance laws and child labor laws should be re-examined and revised to give the counselor and the school dropout and potential dropout more realistic choices, with reference to work and study programs. The job-bound youth should be looking toward the day when he will be accepted in an employment situation for which he has prepared, and he should remain in school or other work-study arrangements until, through the facilities of the school or the community, this has been achieved.[4]

7. The new secondary curriculum—in fact, instruction at all levels—should educate for acceptance of new meanings of work and leisure. The worker will be increasingly less a producer, a creator, a builder, and will be more of a monitor, a watcher of machines and controller of panels, or a caretaker. This kind of work will call for alertness, yet it may be boring, create frustrations, and cause morale problems not dreamed of before. The problem of the school is to learn how to educate for work in a highly technical society.

The child's education should include increasing attention to recreation skills, hobby interests, and familiarity with the rich resources of the library and how to make the fullest use of them. The educational program for the young citizen preparing for the world of work will incorporate cultural enrichment by encouraging greater appreciation of the fine arts and volunteer service to the community during the increased leisure time made available by the already shortened work week, unknown in previous periods of man's formal working day. There is great need in all of our communities and universities to recognize that the age for beginning employment is rising and the age for retirement is declining at the very time when the work day and work week are growing shorter (from an 80-hour work week in our great-grandfathers' day to a 39-hour work week in our day) and that education for intelligent use of the unallocated

---

[4] See Daniel Schrieber, editor, "The School Dropout," Project: School Dropouts (Washington, D.C.: National Education Association, 1964).

hours is becoming a major concern. Often the concern over the debilitating effects of too much leisure is not for ourselves but for the other fellow.

Our communities are in dire need of volunteer workers to help the officials cope with the myriad problems of modern society, including transportation chaos, water and air pollution, a trend toward destruction of the last vestiges of the wilderness, spreading slums, overcrowded hospitals, juvenile delinquency, inadequate library service and city recreation, adult education, and a number of others. Here is an outlet for constructive use of part of the workers' leisure which can relieve boredom and "vegetating" with great vocational satisfactions and spiritual rewards and which would contribute to community betterment and to checking the current drift of urban living toward vast industrial slums and ghettos. This is an indispensable element in educating for the world of work and for leisure.

We recognize there is a dream world of affluent living which is reducing the workload for many while causing permanent unemployment for others; also while providing freedom, leisure, and more playtime for some, it is bringing with it a threat to our once basic beliefs for many. The basic beliefs that we succeed through hard work, thrift, free enterprise, experimentation, ownership, and the taking of risks are largely disappearing in the new world of work, at least for some. What are the substitutes? As one philosopher queried, "Must it become inevitable that the wonderful world of automation will destroy all the character values that created it?" It need not. The answer is largely up to the educator and those community, state, and national political leaders who provide the support for the public schools, colleges, and universities.

8. There must be closer cooperation with Federal sources of help. A recent Federal vocational training law permits states and communities to broaden and extend their vocational programs and develop new programs, provides part-time employment, etc. It gives all persons of all ages opportunities to continue with their education. The act makes it possible for those entering the labor market to upgrade their skills or learn new ones; those with special educational handicaps have greater access to vocational training or retraining, in light of actual or anticipated opportunities for gaining employment. The training must be suited to their needs, their interests, and their ability to benefit from such training.

The youths can earn up to $45 per month but not in excess of $325 per year while they are working and studying. They will be employed by the school, city, or state but will be considered as employees of the U.S. government. This means that young men and women, or older men and women, now can receive training on a much broader vocational basis than has been provided in times past. Also, the amended Manpower Training and Development Act of 1962 lowers the minimum age for youths receiving training from 19 to 17 years (subject to one year of waiting) where the individuals are in the classified group of dropouts.

We must recognize that work is man's way of identifying himself as a worth-while citizen. Destroy this for youth and we remove the under-pinning for self-respect and human decency. The Federal sources of help should be exploited in behalf of youth.

9. Educational planning calls for a modified point of view toward women's education and women's place in the world of work outside the home. It is a fact that the U.S. is maintaining, in educational and professional opportunities, a double standard based upon sex; and it is a further fact that in the 20th century we no longer can afford such a luxury.

We are failing to tap a great reservoir of talent among women for scientific training and the professions. This we cannot afford politically, economically, or socially. Note the absence of women in science, mathematics, research, the laboratory, and the major professions—all at a time when the nation's needs call for more technicians and professionals in all these areas.

This situation can be corrected in short order if we do as some European nations now are doing and have been doing for 20 or more years: simply stop discriminating against women by counseling them out of these fields. The tendency to discourage promising high school and university women students from majoring in science and mathematics and most of the chief professions is well-known and understood. Yet at the same time we continue hypocritically to preach an educational doctrine of the worth of the individual and the importance of developing each individual's unique talents. There is a high degree of correlation here between these practices and the widely recognized discontent among American women which has been making copy for the magazine writers for a couple of decades.

The scarcity of women teachers in science and mathematics at all levels of education is mute testimony to the prejudice and poor judgment of those who discourage their work in these areas. The stories that women relate of discouragement and downright opposition in the fields of medicine, law, engineering, dentistry, and university teaching are all too familiar to those who have been associated with youth struggling to find themselves as they plan educational careers.

In answer to the criticism that "Women prepare to teach and don't practice their profession," the evidence indicates that many of the women who leave the profession to have their families do return to contribute many more years of service. It is anyone's guess how many more would do this if only the climate were made more favorable. It is a statistical fact that women spend many productive years in their specialized fields. Despite the resistances they encounter, a few do become professionals — college teachers, physicians, lawyers, business executives, engineers, chemists, biologists, social workers, psychologists — and they usually spend most of their adult lives in the professions.

Today one-third of our working population are women. The prediction is made that, in 25 years, one-half of all jobs will be filled by women. Yet, less than 3% of today's scientists are women. Why?

At a time when there are thousands of highly technical positions waiting to be filled and when our world competitors have dropped the bars of prejudice and opened most of the professional doors to women on the same basis as men, would we not be wise to re-examine our theories and practices with reference to women and the professional labor market?

The total effect of the new industrial revolution can have untold benefits and satisfactions for mankind if we have the wisdom to allocate our total resources intelligently to assure the esssential high-quality education that the Space Age requires. If we are to avoid being swamped by a gigantic technology we have brought into being, then the nation, the state, and the community must rally to the vigorous support of education as the nation's great hope for the future. To fully appreciate this truth and to help translate it into understanding among students and faculty as well as laymen concerned with education — this is our task. This means the congressman, the state legislator, the governor, the university trustee, and the local school board member all must be helped to understand that only quality education programs are acceptable for the nation's children, youth, and adults who need more schooling, and that education calls for a substantially larger share of the nation's gross national income. We should have no hesitancy in demanding more for schools and colleges after being reminded by the Federal budget makers that we are spending about as much Federal and private funds for research as the entire nation is spending on its public schools, and that more money was spent to house the 1964-65 New York World's Fair than was spent on public school building construction in 1963.

This is a time when those fortunate ones in the privileged communities, colleges, and universities of the nation, with their high-quality and high-cost education programs, should be mindful of those millions of their less fortunate fellow citizens who are without work and hope, whose older youth have no tradition of college attendance in back of them, and whose children very likely spend the school day in educational slums where they are being conditioned as another generation of have-nots to accept their place on relief — or worse, to look for supposedly easy cash through theft or violence. The President, in his message to the Congress, Jan. 8, 1964, so ably stated the case against poverty and for the culturally deprived child when he said:

> The richest nation on earth can afford to [win the battle of poverty]. We cannot afford to lose it. One thousand dollars invested in salvaging an unemployable youth today can return $40,000 or more in his lifetime. . . . Our chief weapons [in the attack on poverty] . . . will be better schools, better health, better homes, better training, and better job opportunities to help more Americans, especially young Americans . . . escape from squalor and misery.

For those who are so deeply involved in the business of trying to develop new patterns of education for a changing world of work, these words from a fellow-educator-turned-statesman were noted with peculiarly understandable pride.

While we have an enormous imbalance for most Americans, such as between the amounts of time allocated to labor and leisure, I am inclined to go along with the Irishman who, after hearing Sen. Edward Kennedy speak in the 1962 campaign and recalling the opposition's criticism of his youthfulness, limited experience, and lack of contact with work or payroll, sidled over to him as he left the factory yard platform to greet him. The old timer, with a bit of a brogue, said, "Teddy, me boy, I hear ye've never done a day's labor in yer life. Well, let me tell ye lad, ye haven't missed a thing."

The late Adlai Stevenson was getting pretty close to the heart of the matter when recently he said, "It is the educator, not the engineer, not the business man, not the union official, not the bureaucrat, who must ultimately bear the responsibility for cushioning the impact of automation on our American society."[5]

---

[5]Address before graduate faculty, New School for Social Research, *New York Times,* April 30, 1964.

The college professor, the school administrator, and the classroom teacher must comprehend quickly the incredible rate at which the stature of the educator is rising, and also comprehend the enormously enhanced role of the school and university as the American people increasingly turn to them for help. This trend will be accelerated substantially, despite the roadblocks of parochialism in racial and religious concepts of education, as the American people more fully comprehend that the population expansion and the automation of men's jobs are on a collision course. Julian Huxley points this up when he says that the population expansion is the most dangerous force in the world today — more dangerous than the atomic bomb, because he thinks we will learn to control the bomb. With reference to work and automation, he says. "Machines are going to do the jobs now. Man has got to learn to live." We must accept the fact that there is no easy way out of the chaotic pattern of work-leisure-profits-poverty that besets our society.

The latest phase of the evolution of human society need not necessarily end in madness; but it certainly will fall short of producing a better society unless we learn to live by the principle that the well-being of each man is ultimately dependent upon the well-being of all men. In our day, this means giving some thought to the problems being created by automation.

26. THE ROLE OF WORK IN THE SOCIALIZATION OF THE ADOLESCENT

DALE B. HARRIS

To DIRECT OUR THINKING toward the socializing effects of adolescent work experience, let us summarize a fairly large body of social-psychological concepts and data in a series of propositions.

1. A simple definition of work is an activity involving muscular and/or mental effort to produce effects which are valued by others and, hence, is rewarded. Nowadays we think of this reward as pay, though other rewards have been and still are possible. Leisure is that time left over when work and personal maintenance have been taken care of.

2. The American ethos traditionally has accorded a significant place to work as an agency for character building. This ethos has emphasized the value of diligence and effort and the denial of immediate gratification in favor of distant and larger rewards. These elements may be found in many aphorisms and folk sayings, which link such beliefs to the development of the good man and good citizen. While in an earlier day, leisure was frowned upon as idleness, today it is viewed as a reward to be earned by work.

3. The adult's work role is a major determiner of his social status and, through the cultural and economic constraints imposed by this status, of the social status of his children.

4. In the American culture, late adolescence is a period when upward movement in the class structure is most likely to occur. It is in

these years when a person may change his geographic location, when he may acquire special skills or make a fortunate marriage — all of which have been useful devices for improving his status.

5. More recently, education has come to be a prime elevator in the class structure, a way for gaining prestige directly, but more importantly for acquiring special knowledges or skills which will supply the individual's work role and which may permit him to occupy a position of greater status than his parent.

SIGNIFICANCE OF THE ADOLESCENT PERIOD

In America, we soon put aside the strict Puritan notion of the necessity for serious busy-ness in childhood, recognizing the right of children to *play*. Adolescence, however, here and in many cultures, has been regarded as a transitional period in which play is put aside for work experience or training in the work tasks expected of adults.[1]

In an earlier America, adolescent effort, whether supplementing family labor on the frontier farm or adding to family income in the urban industrial economy, made a significant contribution to adults while the adolescent was still under the family roof. He established himself as a useful contributor, often fully demonstrating his capacity to do "a man's work" (or "a woman's work") before making his break from the family and establishing himself as an independent agent in society. While the child might play, the adolescent must work.

Though such practice is largely in the past, many beliefs still linger from that past as desirables or "oughts." For example, many older adults today believe that characteristics such as responsibility are formed by childhood work experiences. Many still affirm the character-building qualities of hard, competitive work.

We have been of two minds, however, concerning work for young people. In the latter part of the 19th century, as an industrial economy rapidly developed, child and adolescent labor came to be viewed as evils to be abolished. That movement, getting under way in the last years of the 19th century and pushing ahead vigorously in the first four decades of the 20th century, proceeded sucessfully. Child labor laws effectively eliminated children and youth from job after

---

[1]The play of childhood has come to be equated with leisure, in the eyes of the adult world. It can be questioned, however, whether adult leisure retains much of the spontaneous, enthusiastic, exploratory manipulation and learning which characterizes children's play. Often, adult leisure is competitive, or used to display or enhance adult power, privilege, or status.

job. This elimination was seen as a social good by humanitarians and as economically desirable by those who wished to eliminate cheap competitive labor in order to improve the lot of adult workers. Some of the earlier mythology concerning the value to character of hard competitive effort has been transferred in our schools to the areas of physical education and competitive sports.

Concurrently, a rather curious counter-trend also has appeared, often among young people themselves. While we steadily have pushed up the legal age for school leaving, there has been at the same time a steady increase in the proportion of school-age youth working part-time. Increasingly, knowledgeable schoolmen have pointed out that simply keeping children in school is not sufficient. There are many young people for whom a work experience is considered as valuable as the organized academic learnings of high school. We have seen the National Child Labor Committee reverse its role from emphasizing the evils of child labor to pointing up the positive value of selected supervised work experience for young people. We have seen this Committee develop the community registration bureau for summer jobs for youth. We have heard increasingly of the dangers attendant upon a large population of out-of-school and idle youth.

YOUTH'S WISH TO WORK

I have long been impressed by the evident desire of young people to work while still in school. A number of elements seem to contribute to this desire. There is, of course, the advantage of having money to spend in a culture where money is a significant key to adolescent wants — money to maintain a car, money for entertainment, for sports equipment, for modish clothing. Money is consistently at the head of problems listed by high school youth, and one study shows that this primacy of money as a major problem for youth has not changed since Depression days,[2] even though another study has indicated that the financial resources commanded by the older adolescent has increased by more than 1,000% in the generation between the 1930's and the 1950's.[3]

Nor can the desire to earn money be charged altogether to need. Young people with ample family allowances often express a strong

---

[2] Dale B. Harris, "Life Problems and Interests of Adolescents in 1935 and 1957," *School Review*, 67: 335-343, Autumn, 1959.

[3] E. G. Williamson, W. L. Layton, and M. L. Snoke, "A Study of Participation in College Activities" (Minneapolis: University of Minnesota Press, 1954).

desire to earn. This fact suggests that work for pay satisfies some other important need of the young person. In our status-geared society, a person's "worth" is measured in part by the fact that he can command an income. Also, like it or not, this "worth" tends to be seen as commensurate with the size of that income. The teen-ager who will not do chores for pay at home but wishes to work for a non-family employer is indicating, in effect, that the employer stands as a significant representative of society who says to him as employee, "You are a worthy person; I need your help, and your pay check is tangible evidence of your value to me." The family, the young person intuitively recognizes, has a moral obligation to him. The employer recognizes him for his merits and not because of moral obligation. Thus, work for pay can be an important symbol to the adolescent struggling to realize his self-image and a sense of identity while, at the same time, weaning himself from dependency on his parents.

Linked to the recognition of merit is the status significance of occupation in itself. Society generally views a work role in terms of prestige. Jobs are graded along a continuum of desirability — indeed, of respectability. Youth, however commonly view occupation in terms of a self-development and independence. Young people in the mid-teens, as shown by the University of Michigan Boy and Girl Scout studies,[4] regard the immediate post-high school years in terms of further education, work, or marriage and interpret all these roles in relation to self-development and self-realization. Hence, any work is seized upon as a way of realizing or enhancing the self. It has been suggested that the drop in job satisfaction, which industrial psychologists commonly report as characteristic of the mid-20's, may signal a shift from an adolescent to a more mature view of the job.

A third element in the value of work experience for the socialization of the adolescent is found in the social significance accorded the personal characteristic of responsibility. Industry, business, and the professions all want a stable, dependable, and productive individual. Yet, the adolescent often is regarded as unstable and irresponsible. Many parents and employees of youth cite their principal problem is that of developing dependable, conforming behaviors and attitudes in the teen-ager. Studies of vocational maturity have made a beginning in assessing this aspect of adolescent personality. These studies have constructed reliable measures of "acceptance of responsibility," for ex-

---

[4] "A Study of Adolescent Boys" (Ann Arbor: Survey Research Center, University of Michigan, 1955); "Adolescent Girls" (Ann Arbor: Survey Research Center, University of Michigan, 1957).

ample, but they have not yet determined the predictive significance of such measures.

The picture here is incomplete, but if the kind or quality of early work experience can be shown to correlate with work habits and attitudes, such outcomes would be socially very important. Some research suggests that young people develop responsible attitudes toward tasks which they see as needed but build attitudes of carelessness and indifference towards tasks which they do not view as serious and demanding.

WORK AND YOUTH'S SENSE OF WORTH

Dynamic psychology in recent years has made much of the feeling of self-worth, the self-image, and the sense of identity achieved during the teen years. We already have remarked on the importance of work considered pay-worthy by an unrelated, objective adult who represents society to the young person. It is possible that work experience, properly designed and interpreted, can be a most important reinforcer of an attitude of self-esteem. About a decade ago, the U.S. Department of Labor developed significant materials pertaining to the supervision of the adolescent worker.[5] These studies stressed how important to the sense of self-worth it is that the young person discover he can make useful suggestions on the job. These materials stressed to supervisors the importance of understanding this principle as a means to training the useful and productive worker. These studies also stressed the importance of regarding failures in early work experience as inevitable in exploration and development of abilities. Yet, too much floundering and too much failure, as clinicians amply have demonstrated, can have a serious negative effect on the self-image despite firmly laid foundations in childhood experiences of acceptance. That young person is fortunate who is able to get work experience which reveals his developing abilities adequately, providing positive rather than negative reinforcement for his sense of identity.

Industrial and personnel psychologists frequently point out that two important work adjustments are those to authority and to coworkers. More individuals seem to fail on the job for these reasons than for lack of specific skill. Although it has been said that industry too often interprets docility in the worker as "responsibility," the

---

[5] U.S. Dept. of Labor, Bureau of Labor Standards, "Job Supervision of Young Workers," April, 1953, Washington, D.C.

young worker somehow must learn to take directions and supervision and be willing to progress more slowly than he sometimes expects towards his goal. In other words, he must be willing to serve his apprenticeship and to "win his spurs." Industrial psychology has shown that the young adult is dissatisfied more often with the job than the older worker; somehow the younger worker must learn willingness to go through with his training program and to bring his skills to the level of the reward he hopes for. This is difficult when work operations are simple, dull, and intrinsically uninteresting.

Another aspect of work attitudes is the young worker's relationship to a responsible adult. As jobs become more specialized and fragmented, requiring less craft or skill, it is more difficult to locate appropriate work experiences which reinforce responsible work attitudes. The teen-ager who can work as a part-time helper to the craftsman is in a much better position to learn consistent attitudes than the youth who pushes a broom or the errand boy in the large office. The boy who helps load cars at the super market gets much more direct personal reinforcement than the one who fills shelves in the stockroom. Contact with adult models seems to be helpful to the formation of the desired attitudes, and such contact seems increasingly hard to get. Both industry and business and organized labor often seek to avoid bothering with the teen-ager. He is an uneconomical producer on the one hand and too economical on the other!

THE PRESENT DILEMMA

Although we can make a substantial case for the importance of teen-age work experience in the transition to adult status, and although we can demonstrate that adolescence is an important period in the formation of work attitudes, we are faced today with a serious dilemma. On the one hand, our psychology of adolescence points out that the teen-ager has an amazing capacity for energy mobilization; that he has many qualities and attitudes which in adult life are identified as bizarre, deviant, even sociopathic; and that he has a driving need to establish mature roles, which lead him into much trial-and-error behavior. On the other hand, social psychology points out that the adolescent today makes his transition to adult status in a very rapidly changing culture. Mature, stable adults, who are bewildered by the loss of familiar behavior norms and landmarks, give, at best, sympathetic but inconsistent and, at worst, resentful guidance to young people. Institutional and ritual supports to the development of roles which existed in an early America have disappeared. There is, today, a relative lack of restraint on and supervision of youth's behavior. There is considerable evidence that our contemporary culture exacerbates two very powerful adolescent drives—the drive toward aggression and the drive toward sexual expression. They spell out the bases for much of our so-called youth problems and delinquency.

Presumably, a secure place for young people in meaningful school experience or in significant job experience would be a considerable safeguard against behavior aberration and deviation in the process of adolescent transition. Unfortunately, both these experiences are lacking for many young people. The drive toward stepped-up academic education with its emphasis on excellence bypasses many youth who lack academic abilities or cultural background, or both. Too much so-called vocational education is wholly inappropriate to today's vocational opportunities and requirements.

More serious is the employment situation. There is an over-all national unemployment rate of 6% or 7% which persists despite efforts to get the economy moving. It is well understood that marginal groups are the first to suffer when jobs become scarce. The adolescent, like the minority group member, is particularly vulnerable. The present unemployment rate among high school graduates not in school in the 16-21 year bracket is at least 10%, and may be higher. The unemployment rate is at least twice as high among school dropouts. In the slum areas of large cities, about half of the high school graduates and almost two-thirds of the dropouts in this range are unemployed.

Indeed, in the years ahead we probably must reinterpret radically the place of work in adolescent socialization. Work experience as a means of fulfilling the young person's desire of independence, recognition, status, and the like may be virtually gone. The so-called entry occupations are rapidly becoming meaningless. Even beginning jobs require trained ability and considerable technical skill. Once into one of these jobs, however, advancement is rapid. Thus, the socialization functions of the quasi-apprenticeship are minimized. Moreover, the rapid advancement for some and the complete lack of opportunity for others sharpen the contrast in status of the have-nots and the haves among the young adults. Lack of opportunity and lack of ambition create a vicious circle, turning ever more rapidly. The marginality and the anomie of the older teen-ager increases. For the so-called underprivileged in the large cities, a few years on the street means they probably are lost permanently as productive contributors.

There have been a number of suggestions for alleviating this condition. Young people have been used in community-sponsored civic projects both for pay and as volunteers. There is the campaign to keep young people in school. A renewal of the C.C.C. and a domestic Peace Corps have been suggested. The annual foreign trek of thousands of high school and college youth, many of them with commitments to observe, to study, and to write reports which will qualify for course credit, may be a substitute for the summer job as a socializing agency.

None of these devices has reached many youth as yet and none promises to be a very fundamental solution. Indeed, there are those who insist that we are not very many years away from having about half the population, regardless of age, permanently unemployed, at least in the sense we have used that term in the past.

REDEFINITION OF WORK AND LEISURE IN TOMORROW'S WORLD

Not being a divergent intellect, I can offer no dazzling solution to this problem. I join with those who say that some fundamental reinterpretation of the nature of work and leisure must take place. This reinterpretation, it seems, must go deeply into concepts which undergird our entire culture. Perhaps, we must do no less than completely revise our notion of work, building a wholly new concept which embodies any effort leading to the development of potentiality considered very broadly.

At the moment, most of us think of work as something we do for pay, often with somewhat less than enthusiasm. We think of leisure in terms of sports, travel, beaches, or the good life on the backyard patio. Perhaps the new concepts of "work" and "leisure" will be much closer together, with the result that intellectual and social activities which lead to enhancement of the self will constitute the "leisure-work" in the world of tomorrow.

This concept to some will seem hopelessly idealistic — and maybe it is. As an educator, however, I believe that we must interpret education as a continuing activity rather than as something assigned to the childhood and adolescent years as preparatory to the adult life of work. This assuredly, is not a new concept, but we somehow must engrain it into the culture more widely and more deeply than we have succeeded to date. We may have to blend somehow the notion of the personally and socially enhancing with the idea of the economically productive. Such an emergent appears to be implicit in John K. Galbraith's "The Affluent Society."

Some such concept follows from Hannah Arendt's penetrating analysis of "The Human Condition."[6] It would appear that at one time man was ruled by his need to labor; later he won a measure of freedom by work. His present preoccupation with what Dr. Arendt regards as a kind of hedonism may be a temporary lapse.

It has been suggested that the responsibilities of "work" in the world of tomorrow will devolve on fewer but more highly trained technical and scientific personnel. It is likely that these people will continue to carry heavy loads of responsibility, as they have in the past. How we will identify the adolescents who are slated for this responsibility and make them content with carrying the stress imposed by it, while larger and larger numbers of the population win freedom from such demands, remains to be seen. Perhaps they will vie energetically for the privilege. If tomorrow we interpret leisure in the sense we interpret it today, which is essentially self-centered and hedonistic, we may be due for serious social confusion. Or we may get a society which is much more highly stratified, with those carrying responsibility being accorded great privilege and special reward. Or if we evolve a concept of work which includes the development of individual ability and the cultivation of relations among people for the improvement of society generally, we may accommodate this seeming discrepancy between the few highly responsible and the many carrying much less responsibility for the maintenance of the society.

I am assuming of course, that the prime characteristics of adolescents—their available energy, the desire to explore roles, the desire to assume independence, and attitudes and personal qualities that strike adults as rash, brash, or even dangerous — will not change in the years ahead, as they seemingly have not changed during man's long record of discontent with youth and their ways. One of society's primary tasks, which cannot be avoided much longer, will be to discover how to exploit these qualities in socializing the individual in a society where many — perhaps a majority — will be "idle" as we now interpret that concept. Clearly, we no longer can leave the getting of socializing experiences to the ingenuity of the individual youth, making his own way in the market place—and, least of all, in the present-day academic market place.

---

[6] Hannah Arendt, "The Human Condition" (Chicago: University of Chicago Press, 1958).

27. TRAINING 1974:
THE REVOLUTION
IN LEARNING

JOHN W. BALL
DONALD J. LLOYD
ALBERT J. CROFT

THERE IS ALWAYS A STRONG SUSPICION, when a title is divided in the middle by a colon, that it means there are really two subjects and the writer could not make up his mind which one to choose. In our case, we hope the colon is meaningful; it suggests that the revolution in learning will produce a new and different kind of industrial training by 1974. Our view is that, as a result of much new research in the behavioral sciences, our concepts of how people learn best—and remember and use the learning best—now are undergoing deep-running changes, that these changes are being accepted more thoroughly and rapidly in industrial training than in the schools or elsewhere, and that the new learning methods and systems will change seriously the nature and status of manpower training in the hierarchy of industry within the next few years.

Fortunately for industry, this revolution (not evolution) in learning comes at a time when our need for it may be greatest. For ours is truly an age of science and technology. Since World War II, the whole shape of industrial production (already mature in a historical sense) has been changing radically; we now are required to adjust to constant, far-reaching, rapid technological change as a way of doing business. Such a pattern of swift technological change automatically requires training, re-training, and up-dating with a speed and effectiveness we do not now possess, severely expanding the familiar problems of industrial training.

Obviously, the decade between now and 1974 will be a wild one, geometrically increasing demands on training, along with a revolutionary new basis for helping to learn. Where will we be in training by 1974?

In the past, most of the effort in industrial training has been grouped into four areas: apprenticeship and orientation for new employees; job training to improve skills, accommodate production changes, or upgrade workers; specialized training in such varied areas as safety, supervision, human relations, executive development; and a wide variety of general education programs, both in and out of the plant, to increase the trainability of industrial personnel. In these areas, industrial training staffs have devised training projects to be implemented in special classes offered by training personnel, administered on-the-job by line supervisors, set up by contract for out-of-company presentation, or accomplished by self-instructional materials on off-duty time.

It was this system of industrial training which we were prepared to use as the tornado of swiftly increasing technological change struck us in the years since World War II. Now the speed and scope of that change have begun to outdistance the capability of traditional training to keep up with the change, and a whole host of problems has become apparent.

Clearly, an attack on these problems cannot be mounted in a vacuum, within the enclosure of an industrial company; improvement will require liaison between the training people of a given company and the rest of its corporate structure, as well as other companies and other industries. Then, a complex network of relationships is necessary between a company, its associated labor unions, various government agencies, industrial associations, universities and research centers, specialized consultant companies, and many others. The basic issue, however, lies not just in constructing an adequate organization and inter-agency system for better use of existing training methods and materials, but in developing the means by which more people can learn much more quickly and effectively. For if we do not provide greater *access* to learning, basic to all types of training, then we will continue to fall further behind the speed of technical change.

Unless we make some basic and large-scale improvements, it is more than possible that large parts of our work-force may be misfits in the technological structure of 1974. It is for this reason that we need to examine and evaluate the so-called "revolution in learning" now on the nation's drawing boards and to predict its impact on industrial training.

THE REVOLUTION IN LEARNING

The most significant aspect of the present ferment in training is that research findings in the behavioral sciences are finally being applied in practice. In the physical sciences, the step from physics to engineering design has grown much shorter in the past couple of decades, but, until lately, the step from experimental psychology to training design seems to have grown longer rather than shorter. This trend is now reversed, and, in addition, interdisciplinary research, drawing together such fields as psychology, social psychology, sociology, anthropology, and linguistics, is just beginning to show its relevance to practical training needs. Note the growing interest in such interdisciplinary fields as communications, organization theory, information theory, learning theory, open systems theory, international development theory, computer-based business decision-making, and many others. As the behavioral scientists begin to understand each other and grope toward unified views of man in an industrial society, they find themselves sought out by business and industry. We are caught in the tides of major social change and in need of new insights.

As behavioral science moves to accept this challenge, it has made questionable some hoary assumptions about how we learn, who can learn and how much, and how to create training environments favorable to learning. One of the most seriously shaken assumptions is the meaning of the "I.Q." Most training is conducted on a built-in, but erroneous, belief that human beings distribute themselves along a bell-shaped curve in all aspects of competence, potential, and teachability — all this because people tend to come out this way on the much narrower dimensions measured by a set of "I.Q. tests."

The decade ahead will show a significant decline in faith in the I.Q. as a measure of men generally, but especially as a determinant of trainability in industry. In tests of the best self-instructional materials now available, I.Q. correlates with speed of completion but not with achievement, error rates, or retention. The I.Q. is, in effect, time-bound; it correlates with learning when a clock is held on the learner. Thus, though it will take longer to train the slow ones than the fast ones, the lowest quartile of employees may be brought through training up to the same standards of useful and competent service in the company as any other quartile. By 1974, learning studies will have forced us to discard the presumption that men are born so unequal that a company simply must bear the human and economic waste implied by the lower half of the bell-shaped curve of the I.Q.

Another assumption to be discarded is that learning is necessarily advanced by a teacher facing a small number of students. If the teacher is not very competent and his materials are not well organized, or if the whole assembled class proceeds without regard to sophisticated learning theory, the learners might do better by themselves with a book. But the growing spectrum of educational technology will free the learner from mediocre instruction more surely than the book can. Films, TV, and programmed instruction (all of these using the best instructors in a team teaching situation) will bring top teaching to students who have seen all too little of it. In 1974, *top quality* training will reach many more employees by going beyond a costly and questionable dependence on face-to-face classroom teaching.

Perhaps the most basic assumption to be questioned is that teaching or training cannot be held strictly accountable for its end product and must not be measured by what happens afterward in the real world. It now is becoming possible to identify a series of specific behavioral units in a job situation, train for these units, measure the extent of change in the trainee after training, and then cost-account the process for a pragmatic validation of the training program.

Advances also are being made on some of the more subtle and stubborn problems of training. One of them is teaching "why" as well as "how." Training often has settled for "how" — the simple habituation of unthinking routine performance — because of assumptions mentioned earlier. But those who have seen the American Petroleum Institute PILOT series of programs know that it teaches a good deal of "why" to refinery operators even though the average trainee taken as a target for these programs left school in the 10th grade and is resistant to all classes and all but the most explicitly practical manuals. There is no doubt that other ways, too, will be found to teach large chunks of "why" to large numbers of ordinary employees.

Teaching "how" *and* "why" is difficult enough, but now training also must prepare employees for a dynamic, fluid situation instead of for one that will continue to be very much what it is. Nearly all workers must be prepared to see their work changing and themselves changing in relation to it.

As static thinking must give way to dynamic thinking, so linear thinking must give way to process thinking. Instead of trying to teach refinery employees simply to do A in order to produce B, more and more we need them to understand that G, H, K, and X all interact. B must be produced while all these others are kept balanced, but if an employee simply does A to get B, he may produce disastrous effects on G, H, and K, to say nothing of what happens to X in a little while.

To move from linear to process thinking is not merely to abandon the simple for the complex; it is to move to a wholly different way of sizing up problems. Teaching must face a problem of action as a set of many elements where each interacts with all the others now and continuously. Human "control" of these elements consists of trying to shove the whole system slightly one way or another while it is in motion, with an eye always to the fringe effects. This same structural intersection of variables exists in higher level business decisions, in human relations, in complicated accounting practices, in laboratory experiments — in fact, in everything. Following Whitehead, Bridgman, and others, this kind of thinking virtually has remade the physical sciences. It now is beginning to have a similar effect in the behavorial sciences.

We do not live in a simple world where doing A produces B in linear sequence, yet that is how we have trained people to work and think. By 1974, most industrial training will have met the imperatives of technological change by orienting to the dynamics of intersecting variables in process — and will have become more efficient, more successful, and more interesting than ever before.

NEW DIRECTIONS IN TRAINING METHODS AND SYSTEMS

The values of these approaches to our practical training tasks are becoming clearer. In order to illustrate these values, let's turn quickly to three instances already operating in industrial training programs.

The first is the simulator. Very impressive is the refinery tower control room simulated at the Whiting refinery of American Oil Company. Hooked to a computer and capable of facing the trainee with an almost infinite profile of *process* problems, here is high-level training in the idiom of the new learning theory.

Added dimensions of training depth will be provided in the future by improved and simplified simulators, which can give the trainee experience in manipulating the variables of a multi-dimensional process without the risk of injury to himself and others or of damage to costly equipment. Our guess is that the cost of a simplified simulator will fall, in all likelihood, below $1,000.

A second instance is programmed learning. The preparation of high-quality, self-instructional materials can be guided by the top technical minds of industry, cleanly planned to hit the specific task priorities of the new technology, carefully validated through use by real trainees in the field, and priced far below the cost per trainee of assembled training.

Programmed learning will lead to a virtual elimination of time, space, and institutions as training boundaries. Self-instructional materials of high quality will free the training situation from the cage of the classroom and the class schedule; wherever and whenever there is a man to be trained, he will have full access to the best training in his field. He will not be prevented from learning something he needs to learn or wants to learn just because his company is small or does not happen to offer certain training. Although programs by no means will replace all other forms of training now in use, they will be the dominant training mode in a great many technical and non-technical fields, and they will average over 200% greater effectiveness in providing retention than standard class-textbook modes while requiring less than half the training time. The cost per hour of training will be ordinarily under a dollar.

A third instance is the new look in seminar-type training. We are all familiar with the new slants on assembled training which cycle in and out over the years, each leaving a valuable residue as it passes: sensitivity training, business games, role-playing, brain-storming, and many more. In addition, we have developed many new media for audio-visual instruction. This kind of innovation will continue.

However, we think the most *basic* development now occurring is the trend toward joining behavioral research with the best combination of assembled seminar devices. One of the best examples of this method is the executive development project of the Sun Oil Company. This approach brings us now to the question of "system" development in training, for that is what the Sun experiment is — a total system, coordinating a set of training and research tools.

NEW SYSTEMS FOR TRAINING

Based on concepts and tools from the growing field of interdisciplinary behavioral research, it now is becoming possible to construct a total system for nearly any training project. In general, such a system can be described in five phases:

The first phase is audience analysis: a close, careful research into the knowledge, attitudes, values, and needs the trainees now have.

The second phase is identification of specific behavioral objectives for the trainee and the sequencing of these into an over-all instructional outline. It is our belief that most training is, to some degree, found wanting because its specific objectives are not fully defined, especially in a behavioral sense, so that they can be verified in action. The experience of the next few years will aid our discrimination in identifying behavioral objectives as a basis for both training materials (especially programmed learning) and training programs.

The third phase of this approach is development of a design for training utilizing the instructional outline described above. Selection of a mode or modes of training is part of the design function. The appropriate mode may be a film, a self-instructional programmed book, a manual, an assembled seminar built around a lecturer or a group discusssion technique, or a combination — say, a programmed basic structure for an assembled seminar to build on. A design specialist will write a detailed description of the training plan and consult as needed with training staff members, who will develop the needed materials and put the plan into action.

The fourth phase in this approach is field research, in which the effort is to determine the effect of the training on the trainees' work and evaluate its results in practice. The presumpion here is that we must determine not only whether that which we wanted to teach really got taught, but also whether it makes the business difference we wanted to make.

The final phase of the system is to develop channels for feedback of results on all of these phases in order to evaluate and refine the instructional material and design the next cycle of assembled training. Working from this feedback of results, it is possible to estimate the levels of learning needed for specific tasks and, from these, to develop cost estimates which allow careful budgeting of all training.

In brief, the training system components are: analysis of audience, construction of behavioral objectives, design of training materials and methods, field evaluation research, and the use of all relevant experience for next-cycle planning and for cost and budgeting analysis.

When successfully administered, this kind of training system provides a clean-cut pattern of training, hard-nosed budgeting and planning, and a realistic evaluation and defense of training results. It is our belief that the construction of such a system must be tailored individually to the needs of each company and that it requires the application of interdisciplinary know-how across the board, especially know-how in the behavioral sciences and in information theory, organization and systems theory, and communication.

Based on the above system outline, a training staff could develop, through selective use of the following options, the following specific training program for any subject area and provide cost-result estimates for each phase:

a detailed instructional outline of the materials to be covered and the behavioral objectives to be pursued;

a set of booklets or a series of units of programmed instruction presenting background material for pre-seminar study or for self-instructional use independent of a seminar;

a detailed seminar design, based on the outline, including such factors as staff identification, modes of presentation, types of trainee participation, and specifications for audio-visual materials;

presentation of the seminar according to the design;

a system of pre- and post-tests to measure trainee achievement;

a system (simple or multi-dimensional) for follow-up of trainees on the job to measure attitude changes and to estimate effect of learning on productivity and over-all effectiveness;

a full evaluation and report of the total project, including summaries of all designs, statistics, and conclusions;

a proposal for revision and further development for the next training cycle;

and a breakdown of the training project into behavioral units, with cost estimates for each in order to allow training cost-results accountability.

Let us attempt a kind of summary. Given the present kinds of training needs, precipitated especially by the speed and scope of technological change, and considering the extension of trends already apparent, what will industrial training be like in 1974? Here is our projection.

In spite of advanced automation and computerization, industry will be doing more training than ever before, at greater depth than ever before — and doing it better than ever before. Not only will industrial training approach the point of catching up with the major research breakthroughs in learning theory, information theory, communication, linguistics, systems theory, organization theory, and related areas, but also, by 1974, a concept of research/training as a dual process will be well established and operative. Field research on the training audience will help in the shaping of training materials, which will be accompanied in use with field research on the multiple dimensions of their effect. Such research will not be a product of the ivory tower; it will be fully functional and practical. It will provide training based on knowledge and control rather than on guess and hope.

Finally, as a result of years of experience with such field research and with the training materials resulting from it, there will be a new concept of the organization and management of training. The mystique and the magic will be replaced by research-based prediction and prediction-based planning. It will be possible to provide cost accounting for the training function in terms of such units as specific skills and concepts. Thus, the Training Department in 1974 will speak with a new precision and a new authority.

28. FREE TIME — THE NEW IMPERATIVE IN OUR SOCIETY

DONALD N. MICHAEL

DISCUSSIONS about the future of free time contain a fascinating collection of preconceptions which, in many ways, obscure, prejudge, and beg the questions we face in dealing with free time tomorrow. For, those most concerned about tomorrow's free time are, generally speaking, those with the least of it now, those who will continue to have the least of it, and those who, by training and viewpoint, would know very well what to do with it if they had it.

True, one cannot be terribly scientific about the future. But certainly on the basis of our knowledge about people and societies, and on the basis of some fairly good techniques for defining alternative futures, it is possible to detect areas needing systematic programs of research and action so we may avoid future problems and embrace the opportunities. After all, we plan far ahead to formulate our national defense against external threat and to put a man on the moon. We should be doing no less in dealing with the internal threats and opportunities for our social processes that the future may hold.

I would like to explore plausible properties of the social environment out of which we shall have to invent and implement our means for trying to meet this new imperative of free time in the next 20 years. This period includes most of those whose impact on the world will be significantly modulated by the present value systems. Beyond 20 years or so leads us into sheer fantasy.

Let me make explicit one primary source of the growing preoccupation with free time. In one way or another, probably faster rather than slower in the U.S. at least, the application of cybernation —*i.e.,* the combined use of automation and computers — will mean that, for many more people than now, there will be more time free from economically necessary work. For cybernation will increase productivity and thereby will provide the potential for well-paid, shortened working hours *and* for unemployment. The questions then arise: What will people do with this additional free time? If they do not do well with it, what are the consequences for them and for society?

To begin to recognize the problems and opportunities our society faces in dealing with free time, we need first an explicit picture regarding such questions as: How will free time be apportioned? Who will have leisure? When in their lifetime? Let us look first at some of the implications related to how free time may be allocated.

While the number of hours worked per day could become less, this is unlikely, given the increased needs, in a cybernated society, for continuous-flow operations. Shorter work weeks are a possibility, but this, too, presents problems in operational efficiency as organizations shift from one work-force to another. What seems to be more likely are longer vacations and "sabbaticals," which may occur each year or be granted every few years. And the perpetual vacation for the retired will begin for many sooner than it does now. Thus, at any period of the year, a substantial portion of the population may well be faced with the opportunity or problem of living with a large block of free time.

It is worth pointing out that the continuous processing advantages of cybernation probably mean that more organizations than now will work 24 hours round-the-clock. This means there will be more opportunities for free-time activities, day or night, than conventionally have been associated with one part or another of each 24 hours. Thus, whatever one does with free time, there probably will be more hours in which those activities will be available. Similarly, the trend to use tourist and recreational facilities year-round will increase as more people take longer vacations at more times of the year.

Along with the abstract state of more free time, there very likely will be a growth in the present trend of using free time to get started and to finish up — in other words, waiting. For example, as the population grows and as more people reach the age where recreation consumption requires specialized facilities, there will be a growing shortage of recreational resources for some years at least. Whether one drives hours to a recreation area or waits around on the first tee or boat landing, waiting will be a greater component of free-time activities. Waiting at the recreation site may be the modern equivalent of sitting around the old drugstore or standing on the corner whistling at the girls. In fact, all this waiting around, willy-nilly, may begin to develop attitudes and physical habits which could be a prelude to more tranquil uses of free time.

An important aside: Within a family, this additional free time may not be an unmitigated blessing. The state of the family and the state of marriage suggests that not all husbands and wives will relish more hours together; and not all parents and children will relish more hours together either.

Who will have the free time? One thing we can be sure of for the next few decades at least is that the top-level managerial and professional elites, for the most part, will not have any more free time than now. Some artists, some mathematicians, and the like will be exceptions, but most first-rate professionals will continue to work long hours simply because there will not be sufficient new professionals, especially in the light of the growing population — 230,000,000 by 1975 — and the growing complexity of its social welfare needs. Moreover, those seeking membership in this professional elite will begin studying earlier and study harder in school. As such, they probably will have less free time, *i.e.*, shorter vacations and more homework. And, because of the shortage of top-level professionals, it is very likely that those in the group who wish to work longer than the usual retirement age will be encouraged to do so.

While free time in the top-notch professional class will be a problem only by its absence, many of the wives of non-professionals and the occupationally non-skilled wives of professionals may well have much more free time than now. This may seem surprising, given the household and child-raising work schedules that even reasonably affluent wives and mothers face today. But a new source of babysitters and other home services may arise from the surplus of unemployed women displaced from clerical work by computers. This will tend to free these affluent wives to pursue their own careers, or, in the absence of career-oriented skills—which often will be the case —it will free them for leisure.

Then there will be that large portion of the population composed of the semi-professionals, the skilled, and the more mediocre professionals who will contribute enough in their social role to command good or adequate salaries but who will not be so rare as to be needed for 40 hours a week. There may well be considerable variability in work hours from regular "overtime" down to around 30 hours. It is this group that will have both the money and, to some important but often insufficient extent, the education on which to base future patterns of free time utilization. Also in this group will be those adolescents whose career plans are not such that they must study long hours and whose family affluence encourages them to consume the commodities of free time.

At the bottom of the heap will be a substantial population, poorly paid or unemployed; as we know, about a quarter of our population now is living in poverty. These will be the slum dwellers, a disproportionately large percentage of the Negro population, the poverty-stricken from the rural areas, the mentally underendowed, the unskilled, and those made unskilled by cybernation, since cybernation does not upgrade all jobs — wishful thinking and propaganda notwithstanding. Here, too, will be some of those middle managers who will have lost their jobs to cybernation. Also in this group will be high school dropouts and the students from schools which will not provide opportunity for longer study hours or the stimulus to use them. All will have plenty of time on their hands but not the money or the motivations to use it as "free time." In most cases, they will not have education to do so either.

Increasing numbers of retired and aged will find they have more free time; and for many in the population, retirement will come earlier as cybernation and the exploding size of the young work-force pressure the society to move the economically unproductive out of the labor market by this polite device of personnel management and public relations.

Those are just some of the categories of leisure and workers, but even this preliminary selection of categories emphasizes that education, money, privilege, sex, and stage of life each will affect the amount and type of access to the free-time environment. Let us examine, then, some of the problems and opportunities these groups may provide for discovering and establishing standards for the use of more free time.

Consider the adolescent and young adult. This group, more than any other age group, probably contains the greatest proportion of souls seeking a sense of self and of calling, and it is the group freest to experiment with self and environment in the quest. Most of these experiments are conducted during free time. Typically, it is this group that has made the Peace Corps possible, and, if politics permit, it will make the domestic equivalent possible, too. And it is from this age group that we get the most intense expression of personal styles and preoccupations, such as endless devoted hours of tinkering with and technically refining hot-rods or forming highly competent lung-diving teams. While the proportion of youths with either a social or personal calling or preoccupation, which they intensively refine, is probably not very great, at least it is a core group. Their styles of self-refinement and craftsmanship might provide a model for their jaded or flighty peers who also, perhaps unknowingly, are seeking meaning in life through the obsessive pursuit of fads and fancies. (Incidentally, youth might work effectively with tomorrow's aged and retired in the joint development of free-time activities for themselves and for other age groups. There are, after all, not totally forgotten traditional roles of companionship between youth and grandparents which might be re-established and enlarged in this new age; often enough, these might be free of the deep-running conflicts between youth and parents.)

On the problem side, in future years many of these youths who are devoted to craftsmanship or are commitment-oriented are very likely to be more heavily time-involved in education. Most of those young people who lack the motives or the abilities to be so involved very probably will continue to be the consumers of fads, partly because their academic and temporal isolation from the others will be greater, thereby reducing the opportunities to copy them. Partly, the consumption of free-time fads will continue because a substantial segment of our economy and mass media depends on the exploitation of youthful motives to be like one's peers and to seek out novelty and styles which give the possessor the security of being "in" and a comfortably snobbish distinction, for a few fleeting weeks, from those who are "out." And, too, while it is enticing to speculate on the possibility of standards of motivation and avocation radiating out from those already using their free time productively, relatively few do so. Surely, parental values and the social milieu more often make the rule than the exception. These values and circumstances are unlikely to yield easily to programs and proselyting by any methods reasonably and widely available in a pluralistic society.

What about those adults who will have both more free time and sufficient money to indulge themselves? On the positive side, the percentages of the general population who do paint pictures, go to concerts, and read books are small compared to the percentages who spend time watching TV and basketball, but, nevertheless, the percentages are increasing. Also increasing are percentages of adults going back to school — and not only to collect credits for degrees. Traveling has increased greatly, as has active involvement in sports and recreation. So, to some extent — though to precisely what extent is unknown — some larger proportion of people than in the past has been using its free time and discretionary funds in active and more rewarding ways.

Even though active participation in the use of free time has increased, it is doubtful that new national patterns of free-time utilization have been established or are about to be. Much of this activity is for the sake of consumption as such and because it is the thing to do — such as going on safaris even though one is not remotely interested in animals or Africa. But there is the chance that some of those who buy something for the sake of possession may find that they possess something more than they expected to and, willy-nilly, they may discover a rewarding means for the expression or preoccupation of self. And it may be that, within this group, those who enlarge their own leisure-time selves may attract others to seek the satisfactions that they find — even if these others are only motivated by the ubiquitous dynamics of status seeking.

However, for the most part, adults are unoriented toward, untrained for, and unexposed to a qualitatively wide range of free-time, leisure-oriented activities. Also, they are mostly the products of a Protestant ethic which equates leisure with idleness, the devil— or at least makes most people uncomfortable if they are not working. And they are indifferent or anxious about the larger world. Indeed, many of them will become more anxious as the increasing rate of job obsolescence — from blue-collar through junior executive — deprives a good part of the working population of the sense of having found their life's occupational niche. And for many, the deeper adolescent insecurities about self never disappear. Moreover, many adults are also the products of an economy and a national style which equates high consumption rates with success and status. These factors, variously interacting and influenced by advertising, the mass media, the product packagers, and the product makers, probably will contribute enormously to the pursuit of novelty and gadgets as the proper expression of avocational preoccupation. Instead of seeking self or society through work or leisure, the abiding obsession seems to be to avoid them.

The wives of the overworked top-flight professionals also present a potential opportunity for developing the effective use of free time. Their free-time activities might become the approved style just because it is done by the right women. Their activities, the styles they set, and the things they do may attract other women (especially from the well-paid, fewer-work-hours strata). And to the extent that what they do is not sex-typed, they may demonstrate for husbands and youths a wider range of free-time activities.

Again, there are negative factors to be considered. One is that most wives may prefer to keep conventionally busy rather than face the challenge of free time. Another is that so many of the top professionals with sensitivity and the concern for the productive use of free time will be too work-occupied to respond to their wives' discoveries and styles. To be sure, not all top professionals reaching retirement will work the extra years they are invited to work. But it is worth speculating whether those who do voluntarily retire, in the face of rewards from their working role and the persisting ambiguities and ambivalences of a retired role, will be mavericks in some sense. Therefore, they are not as likely to be the best cynosures for free-time utilization standards.

The older and retired seem to offer potentially the best medium for the constructive and elaborate development of free-time activities. In the first place, by being older and retired, they *ipso facto* have done their work. Thus, according to the Protestant ethic, they are entitled to rest, relaxation, and recreation. If other things were favorable, they could approach this free-time period with psychic comfort and cultural approbation. Then, too, many older retired people today and over the next several years will come from ethnic-oriented backgrounds where craftsmanship and the quiet use of leisure have deep roots: gardening, wood-working, needlepoint, etc. (However, even the future satisfaction of handweaving is somewhat in doubt. A recent full-page advertisement informed us that the looms of a major manufacturer now turn out fabrics with "planned imperfections" that simulate handwoven fabrics.) There is the chance that, by careful cultivation of these styles of leisure, these people could set standards and also be the teachers for younger members of the society seeking the state of mind and mental and manual abilities to make leisure more rewarding.

On the negative side, there are now many older people or retired people, and there will be proportionately more, who cannot make the shift comfortably from the Protestant work ethic. Moreover, for many, retirement—especially early retirement—probably will imply that somehow one's contribution to the work-force is no longer needed (perhaps one is being replaced by a machine), that one is not so socially valuable as one's contemporaries who have remained in the work-force or been enticed back into it. And this shift will be all the more difficult because, for many years, we will not have developed a leisure ethic, because so very many of the older population desperately lack the financial security for necessities, and because so many of them will be unskilled and uneducated about themselves or their environment. For all of these reasons it will continue to be difficult for a substantial proportion of the older population to make an easy and large contribution to their own or to others' creative use of leisure time.

Underlying the possibilities and problems associated with more free time as used by these specific groups are basic issues generally ignored or begged. I shall make some of them more explicit, since meeting successfully the challenge of free time will depend very much on our willingness to face up to these basic issues.

In the first place, when we fancy the proper and hoped-for societal expressions of free-time utilization, we tend to base our plans and expectations on our beliefs about the characteristic free-time behavior of the Greek citizens of the city states or the behavior of the cultured leisure class of Europe two centuries or so ago. These beliefs are in error. True, for many Greeks, some part of their free time was spent on civic activities — activities which now are very much part of our growing professionalized work world: politics, government (they had 501-man juries), bit parts in theatricals, philosophy, and so on. Also there were not so very many Greeks per civic unit among which to apportion these various activities (perhaps 30,000 citizens out of 100,000 total population in Athens, for example). But it is also true that for the Greeks a lot of free time was frittered away drinking with friends, fighting wars, and enjoying the very frequent festivals put on at government expense. Incidentally, women were denied all public and civic participation.

As to the leisure classes of recent history, even this small elite, trained from childhood in self-indulgence and use of free time, for the most part either was bored or preoccupied with intrigue, the pursuit of love and license, and given to various forms of violence (from fox hunting to assassination and warfare). Some were creative, pursuing farming, politics, and science — all areas now well past the point where most amateurs can contribute significantly to them. And, too, the masses worked and the elites had the free time. Now we are faced with a social inversion, with the masses leisured while the elites work. (This was last tried in ancient Rome.) If my reading of history is correct, we are on our own and will have to invent our own ways of making more free time a blessing rather than a curse.

In the second place, we strongly tend to assume that free time should be a creative part of life. Somehow just sitting in front of a television set hour after hour or pursuing more gadgets for the chromium-plated, electric-fired hamburger grill have been deemed inadequate for the proper conduct of the good life by common consent of those who brood over the values and direction of society. Even discounting the personal leisure-time preferences of those who think about leisure for others which they themselves won't have, and discounting the transposed Protestant ethic implicit in the justification of leisure through self-improvement, this assumption needs much more careful examination than it has received. For within it are two profoundly important questions regarding the whole future conduct of this society.

Is the goal of self-fulfillment through creative free-time activity at all compatible with the requirements of an economy which depends upon the voracious consumption of leisure-time gadgets, mobility, and all those other things which one gets now and pays for later? Actually, the careful cultivation of self through hobbies, avocations, and any other activities involves the careful cultivation of technique and insight much more than it involves the steady acquisition of things. Their acquisition should not be at the pace needed to keep an economy, dependent in large part on free-time activities, running at full steam. The basis for a prosperous economy could be changed, of course, and, in doing so, both public welfare and private leisure might benefit handsomely, but such a change would be radical in many eyes.

The other major question has to do with the extent to which we really mean to pursue excellence during free time. As of now, it is not evident that anyone can be a good musician or a good painter or a good anything. Over the time period we are speaking of, the best most people can expect to be is mediocre at whatever they undertake. We have no good basis for assuming they can be otherwise, living as they do in a prefabricated society where youths now snap together pre-formed plastic ship models rather than starting with balsa wood and a razor blade, where airplane glue is for sniffing instead of for fabricating, and where the camera is steadily becoming more automatic. Now, if we are interested in simply having people dab paint or scratch away at musical instruments as additional ways to fill free time, that's one thing. Then all we are doing is simply extending the variety of diversions available for free time through the general mass-market approach we apply to the rest of our activities. As such we have not changed the quality of free-time utilization. (Incidentally, let us not assume that starting out at the mass-market level of fully automatic cameras or painting-by-numbers leads naturally to higher orders of aspiration and attainment. We know nothing about the operation of such processes on a large scale.)

If we really are concerned with pursuit of excellence, that's something else again. Then we are rejecting the mass-market approach, placing the emphasis on individual accomplishment and variously deprecating or separating from the talented those who can be no more than mediocre. It will take a subtle value system, indeed, to insure that, on the one hand, those who can excel are encouraged to do so and that, on the other hand, the limits of others will not result in their discouraged withdrawal into trivial leisure. Perhaps even greater ingenuity will be needed to keep this difficulty — especially in a mass-consumption society — from being resolved by the further abandonment of standards of excellence in order to make mass mediocrity rewarding.

We have the problem of how to organize free time for, and justify it to, the dispossessed and underprivileged at home and abroad. They will possess neither the resources nor the training to partake in the creative leisure activities we are thinking about. But they will possess resentment and alienation as they watch the well-to-do fill their free time with travel and gadgets and even the "higher" types of self-fulfillment. We must face the inevitable correlation that large numbers of people will have free time because they will be economically useless in our kind of society. They will have free time because they will be no longer valuable for the processes of production and distribution. It is for these people that society will have to invent forms of social being that will preserve their self-respect. The well-to-do can get along even with the old forms of free-time passivity, given enough access to sensation and diversion. But, because of the rural and urban slum residents, the underprivileged Negroes, the intellectually and emotionally under-endowed, the poverty-stricken youths and the masses in the underdeveloped nations, the abundance of free time will require the invention of new things to do for all of us if we are to retain our self-respect and way of life.

What are the alternatives to history's bread and circuses and how do we provide them in the relatively short time available before the haves and have-nots in education, free time, and funds become so separated as to undermine our whole way of life at home as well as abroad? If leisure is to be self-fulfilling, it cannot be as it has in the past at the expense of other parts of the population. The easy answer, of course, is to say that those with leisure should spend it helping to educate and support those without the intellectual, emotional, or economic wherewithal to share their leisure with them. And we have the splendid example of the Peace Corps and related activities to demonstrate that this can be done. But generating a *noblesse oblige* state of mind in the majority of those in the society who will have income and time to contribute to social growth, through taxes or directly, hardly will be easy. Even the Peace Corps has recruitment problems.

The last fundamental issue is that of education for valuing free time. How do we educate one segment of society to expect to have and to use productively more free time and, at the same time, educate another segment to expect to have little or no free time and not to want it? How do we encourage more students to study longer and harder and, at the same time, develop in other students styles for free-time use—free time which will be comparatively greater for them than for the other students, even during their school years? Do we try to develop habits for free-time tranquility, and, if appropriate, how do we do so in schools which are oriented toward efficiency and work? If, as frequently suggested, life-long education will consume quantities of free time, how do we go about inculcating the appropriate motivations? After all, very few people, even among the professional community, voluntarily indulge in continuous re-education on any substantial scale. How do we get into teaching and guidance those with free time and talent who lack prerequisites for accreditation in the educational institution? And how do we arrange our educational institution, from parents through teachers to fund sources, to encourage the teaching of values and behavior appropriate to tomorrow's world—values and behavior which, if we are right in our prognosis, will be different from those generally emphasized today?

All in all, I suspect that working on the research, program development, and political and social action which will be needed to meet the imperative of free time will insure that those of us concerned with it will never reach the promised land. For we will find our hours far too few as we work to invent means for keeping the hours of others from being too many.

29. WORK, LEISURE, AND EDUCATION

WILLIAM W. BRICKMAN

AS MAN BECOMES SUBJECTED increasingly to the impact of automation on his habits and way of life, many problems and issues arise. Competent observers have pointed out dramatically that the need to work will be reduced greatly in the decades to come as machines perform the functions that had been done previously by man. The basic activities of production of the necessities and luxuries of food, clothing, and shelter will be taken care of by the automated machines. The role of man will be administration and supervision.

Of course, one might think of the very important problem of unemployment.[1] This is a question that must be pondered by all who are concerned with the stability of society. However, let us assume, for the sake of argument, that somehow the leaders of government, management, labor, and society will find a means, in the age of automation, of keeping unemployment to a bare minimum.[2] We now can address ourselves to the problems that would emerge in an environ-

---

[1] The U.S. Congress found that "the skills of many persons have been rendered obsolete by dislocations in the economy arising from automation or other technological developments, foreign competition, relocation of industry, shifts in market demands, and other changes in the structure of the economy; that Government leadership is necessary to insure that the benefits of automation do not become burdens of widespread unemployment . . . " Manpower Development and Training Act of 1962 As Amended (42 U.S.C. 2571-2620).

[2] See A. H. Raskin, "Automation: Road to Lifetime Jobs?" *Saturday Review,* Nov. 28, 1964, pp. 14-16, 68.

ment in which large numbers of individuals have considerable time on their hands.

Apparently, man always will be engaged in some time-consuming work. The amount of time, however, will be considerably less than it is at present. Accordingly, then, man will have more hours for non-work or leisure time. What one can and should do in the way of suitable leisure activities is the subject of this chapter.

Let us glance at some of the definitions of that key term, "leisure." The "Oxford Universal Dictionary on Historical Principles," tracing the word through Middle English and Old French to the Latin *licere* (to be permitted), defines leisure as "freedom or opportunity to do something." From the historical usage, it is clear that the term is connected with the concept of free or unoccupied time. Among the contemporary writers, Marion Clawson, of Resources for the Future, defines leisure as "all time beyond the existence and subsistence time."[3] To a philosopher, "Leisure time is that portion of the day not used for the exigencies of existence. . . . It is a separate period in which no work is done."[4] This definition does not rule out "the performance of necessary work," but it does insist that leisure should not be used, as a rule, "for the sake of work."

It is clear that time is related to leisure in a directly proportional way. What is necessary to consider is the allocation of time in accordance with the principle of wise, rational choice, as well as the types of education which would enable a person to make proper use of increasingly abundant time.

What happens when time hangs on one's hands is well known. It is proverbial that idle hands make mischief. The week-end riots in Britain in the spring of 1964 testified to the fact that adolescents did not know or did not care about the constructive uses of their leisure time. The teen-age gang "rumbles" in the U.S., the attitude of the *Stilyagi* in the Soviet Union, and the adolescent unrest in other countries all over the world yield further proof that society and the school have not labored sufficiently and successfully to convince young people of the crucial necessity of the intelligent use of leisure.

Those whose memories go back to radio will recall the wry quips of that literate humorist, Henry Morgan. On his program, Mr. Morgan would illustrate the consequences of the introduction of modern,

---

[3] Marion Clawson, "How Much Leisure, Now and in the Future?" in James C. Charlesworth, "Leisure in America: Blessing or Curse?" (Philadelphia: American Academy of Political and Social Science, 1964), p. 1.

[4] Paul Weiss, "A Philosophical Definition of Leisure," in Charlesworth, *op. cit.*, p. 21.

time-saving devices in the economy and at home. For example, the introduction of an express highway meant that a driver could get home faster and have more time to argue with his wife. In contemporary terms, the reduced working day often encourages a longer period of exposure to television. During the past decade and a half it has become evident that "watching television became the most firmly ingrained social habit. By 1955 a leading marketing organization was reporting more total time spent in watching television than in any other single activity except sleep. An electronic marvel had become the aural-visual link between the American home and the larger society."[5] Even the ardent admirer of television will admit that this form of audio-visual communication leaves much to be desired as an outlet for the constructive use of leisure time. Nor has it been firmly established that no relation at all exists between the detailed scenes of vice and crime, as depicted on television, and the behavior of young people.

With all this as a preliminary, it would be appropriate to recall the role of leisure in the history of education. It was the ancient Greeks who showed the connection between education and leisure by using the word for leisure, *schole,* to designate a place of instruction, or a school. It is noteworthy that European languages generally refer to the locale of learning by a word derived from the Greek *schole: schola* (Latin), *Schule* (German), *shkola* (Russian), *scol* (Anglo-Saxon; *school,* modern English), *escole* (Old French; *école,* modern French), *escuela* (Spanish), *scuola* (Italian), *school* (Dutch), *skole* (Danish), etc. The more common Latin word for school, *ludus,* meant play, game, or pastime. In the classical sense, *schole* actually meant "spare time spent in rest and recreation."[6] In point of fact, the Greek word for school was *didaskaleion,* a place where teaching is carried on. As time went on, the young consumers of leisure time in ancient Athens must have gotten tired of sports, amusements, and the like, and they tended to show an interest in intellectual forms of leisure. The word *schole* began to take on gradually an educational connotation. Both Plato in his "Laws" and Aristotle in his "Politics" made use of the term in an educational context. Dionysius Halicarnassus, in the first century B.C., wrote of a school *(schole)* of philosophy or

[5] Paul F. Douglass and Robert W. Crawford, "Implementation of a Comprehensive Plan for the Wise Use of Leisure," in Charlesworth, *op. cit.,* p. 51.

[6] Arthur F. Leach, "School," in Paul Monroe, editor, "A Cyclopedia of Education," Vol. V (New York: Macmillan, 1913), p. 257.

thought. But it was the Roman playwright Plautus, *c.* 213 B.C., who connected via translation the Latin *ludus* with the Greek *schole* in the sense of a place of study.[7]

Jewish tradition also identified the relationship of leisure and learning. In the post-biblical literature of the Apocrypha, one reads as follows: "The wisdom of a learned cometh by opportunity of leisure; and he that hath little business shall become wise. How can he get wisdom that holdeth the plough, and that glorieth in the goad, that driveth oxen, and is occupied in their labors, and whose talk is of bullocks?"[8] The Talmud, too, admonishes the individual not to overengage himself in business, since such hyperactivity is a barrier to wisdom.[9] From the standpoint of Jewish educational philosophy, each person was to complete his work obligations as soon as possible and then devote his leisure hours to the study of the Torah.

Throughout the history of Western education, leisure — and, hence, formal education — was available to those who were able to satisfy their needs and wants and still have time and energy to do what interested them. Generally, only relatively few, the affluent and the aristocratic, could afford leisure-time activities of an educational and cultural nature. As far as children were concerned, they usually helped their parents and so had virtually no leisure of their own. The long working day of young children in the 19th century may be a distant memory, but the child workers of the earlier 20th century still weigh on many a social conscience. Also painful is the fact emphasized by Unesco that close to 50% of the children of the world have little or no accessibility to primary school.

During recent centuries, there has taken place an increase of opportunities for leisure by the rise of the middle classes. Most recently, as already indicated, the automated revolution has extended farther the limits of leisure to laborers and farmers who already had been included among the participants in the free-time pursuits which had resulted from the constantly growing trend toward total industrialization.

One illustration of how changes in the economy and society altered the leisure-education pattern might be the Grand Tour of the

---

[7] *Ibid.*, p. 258.

[8] Ecclesiasticus, 38: 24-25.

[9] Aboth (Ethics of the Fathers), chap. II, Mishnah 5. *Cf.*, chap. II, Mishnah 4; chap. IV, Mishnah 10; chap. VI, Baraitha 5. For a convenient translation, see Herbert Danby, "The Mishnah" (London: Oxford University Press, 1933), pp. 448, 454, 460.

18th century.[10] As can well be understood, both the investment of time and of finance was considerable, and the Grand Tour, consequently, could be enjoyed, in the main, by young people with ample means. Since World War II, many have noted the multitudes of young students flocking to Europe from the U.S. and the vast movements of young people within Europe. Transportation, time, personal funds, and stipends have become increasingly available to larger numbers of young people.

The importance of leisure in a well-balanced educational experience was recognized in modern America by the Commission on Reorganization of Secondary Education, National Education Association. In its famous listing of the seven "Cardinal Principles of Secondary Education," this group mentioned "worthy use of leisure time" as the sixth outstanding educational objective of the American high school.[11] More instances might be cited, but the basic point about the interrelatedness of leisure and education has been made. With the greater availability of leisure time, one might expect a corresponding increase in educational interests and activities. Indeed, without an adequate amount of time beyond that consumed in existence and subsistence efforts, it is almost futile to think of any adult or young person as steeping himself in lore and culture. As Woody remarked, "Liberal education is impossible without plenty of leisure, and suitable employment of that leisure time." [12]

The education-leisure relationship must be considered from the standpoint both of education *for* leisure and of education *through* leisure. A curriculum that is reasonably broad and is derived from the traditions and significant thought and activities of the human race is a likely source of inspiration for the continuance into life of what has been learned at school. No attempt will be made here to specify the kinds of learning experiences which furnish the motivation for leisure-time education. This form of curriculum construction requires more time and space than is presently available. Let it suffice to say that the so-called functional and practical courses in secondary school and college are designed, generally, for a vocational or professional end. This, of course, is not education for leisure, but

[10] William E. Mead, "The Grand Tour in the Eighteenth Century" (Boston: Houghton Mifflin, 1914).

[11] "Cardinal Principles of Secondary Education," Bulletin 1918, No. 5, U.S. Bureau of Education (Washington: Government Printing Office, 1918), pp. 10-11.

[12] Thomas Woody, "Liberal Education for Free Men" (Philadelphia: University of Pennsylvania Press, 1951), p. 236.

rather for work. One might recognize, however, the avocational attribute of some how-to-do-it courses. Bookbinding, for example, is a skill that can be imparted in a special course for leisure-time activity. The objective, to be sure, is not the sale of bound books but the pleasure of working in one's free time at an intrinsically satisfying activity which, incidentally, might help one interested in books to preserve his literary possessions.

In thinking about education *for* leisure, it is essential to be aware not only of learning content, of *scientia gratia scientiae,* but of the teacher as well. The kind of teacher admired by Henry Adams in the famous quotation — he who affects eternity — is the one who provides the foundation for education for leisure. It is his personal example which becomes the driving force upon an individual to carry on in a similar spirit. The teachers who instil in their students the love for study now and the lifelong pursuit of learning and wisdom after formal education is completed are the best guarantors of a generation which will know how to use leisure to its fullest and worthiest extent.

It should be stressed that reading or study is an eminently worthwhile activity in one's leisure time. It is very significant because it enables the individual to maintain and extend his basic school education. With the explosion of knowledge on all sides, it is obvious that one cannot remain long content with the educational equipment of college and university, even when it is capped with a Ph.D. degree. Knowledge rapidly becomes obsolete and out-of-date in many areas of learning. One has only to think of the geography of Africa as an example of the inadequacy of the knowledge obtained at school. Consequently, the updating of what one has learned becomes a fundamental objective of using leisure time. But one must develop also new intellectual and cultural interests beyond those to which he was exposed as an adolescent and youth. The leisure period is the ideal time for developing new listening or performing habits in music, visual patterns in the pictorial arts, and audio-visual-mental competence in drama. Different types of literature might be sampled and evaluated. Some might venture into a scientific laboratory or workshop. There are, indeed, numerous possibilities.

Perhaps we should make it clear that we do not insist upon intellectual activity as the sole type in the leisure situation. Certainly, in a nearly thoroughly automated world, prudence and balance dictate that the intellect be cultivated to the fullest possible extent.

However, we should not fail to recognize the fact that the appeal of leisure-time study may be less than universal. In instances where it is difficult to cultivate a lasting love of learning, an effort should be made by scholars and educators to get every adult interested in doing some studying during his free time. This might be in the form of adult classes, discussion groups, forums, lectures, reading circles, and the like. Or, one might be motivated to read and study on his own or in the company of a friend. Or, one might be tempted to practice some of what Prof. Harry A. Overstreet has called "civilized loafing."

At this point, the writer may be pardoned for riding hard one of his favorite viewpoints. The leisure time may be suitable for a scholar to learn the languages he did not have time for in the overcrowded college curriculum. Too many Ph.D. recipients and holders of advanced academic appointments tend to let their foreign linguistic skills fall into disuse, assuming that passing their language examinations for the doctoral degree was an indication of ability. We are not thinking merely of keeping up with the French, German, or Russian that one has learned in college or in a special graduate crash program. What we are proposing is that every responsible scholar should learn to read (and to speak if he should serve abroad) at least one new language. The acquisition of fluency in other languages will extend the scholar's range of competence in his own area of inquiry and will reduce the parochialism and provincialism that is too frequently characteristic of many learned men in this country and, perhaps to a lesser extent, in other countries. Lest the inference be drawn that such study is work rather than leisure, we should make it clear that an understanding of a foreign language brings with it more than a narrow professional interest. Once there is an acquaintanceship with another language, the door is open to a comprehension of another literature and a different system of cultural values. Under such circumstances, the act of study takes on an avocational slant. In any event, it is not always possible to draw a definite line between what is a professional and what is a nonprofessional act during leisure time. As a matter of fact, the making of such a distinction is not a prime necessity.

Some paragraphs ago we mentioned education *through* leisure. This might be interpreted as the educational outcome or dividend of the wise and worthy use of leisure. If one should carry on in his leisure what he has learned while at school and add to his learning, he should become educated in some depth. The proper utilization of leisure is the one which builds one form of education upon the other, the new upon the old.

The benevolent use of leisure is characterized further through the exercise by each person of his prerogative of planning his cultural and educational experiences. He has the freedom to choose intelligently and responsibly how to allot his time to what is of interest to him. In this way, he can express his individuality, his uniqueness as a person, in an age where the mass mind and the collective act seem to prevail. The growth of the individual *qua* individual is a source of strength to a society which all too frequently is prone to conformism, emotionalism, and unprincipled action. The human mind thus is enabled to function in a channel which is distinct from that of the mass. Man the thinker, *homo cogitans*, is encouraged, and, in fact, he has a chance of becoming man of the inquisitive, experimental mind, *homo rogitans*.

In conclusion, the education of the human race and of the people of its constituent societies is a paramount responsibility of all leaders and thinkers in society. This has been going on, in various stages of efficiency and comprehensiveness, for many centuries. To say this is to repeat what is well-known to all students of the history of mankind. However, we must emphasize that we should not be content at this point. Society today is undergoing momentous changes, and more pervasive changes are in the foreseeable future. Forces already have been unleashed in the incipient age of automation, and these are but a mere fraction of what is yet to come.

Unless scholars, educators, government officials, and others with a genuine concern for the fate of man, his works, and his spirit are alert to the possible dangers to man in an era of automated ethics and values, there, indeed, can be grounds for fear as to the future. The value of the individual must be upheld *vis-à-vis* the machine and the mass. This can be done not by palaver or pious pronouncements, but rather by constant action of a specific sort. Our educational effort must be so reconstituted as to provide every student with the intellectual baggage which will enable him to travel through life with comfort and to enrich further his initial equipment. We must imbue each individual with the desire to know better himself, his society, and his world so that he will serve his fellow man better on the basis of his own selfhood. Man should be, as Aristotle once said, the rational living being.

The function of leisure is to advance the case of the individual and, through him, the cause of humanity. Good use of leisure advances the preparation possessed by the person and furnishes him with a lifelong incentive to learn and to serve.

Automation, indeed, may be the wave of the future. Proper leisure, in league with a sound education, will ensure the ultimate triumph of the spirit of man over the machine.

Part IV

MAN, MIND, AND SOUL IN A TECHNOLOGICAL AGE

30. TECHNOLOGICAL CHANGE AND HEALTH

JOHN MacIVER

IT IS A HOMILY, but nonetheless apt, that the first wealth is health. From healthy, vigorous individuals, families, and communities we can expect much, not only in the way of continuing progress and improvement, but also, in times of adversity, the strength to cope with reverses. In contrast, given smoldering illness among the population and communities environmentally blighted, we can expect to use up much energy and wealth in dealing with a multitude of problems that never should have occurred in the first instance.

There is unquestionably a cultural lag in our thinking about individual and public health—and for a simple reason. We have not had scientifically based medicine and public health for very long—certainly for a far shorter time than, as a culture, we have developed, nurtured, and passed on from generation to generation many others of our values and beliefs which may be in conflict. The theory on which modern medicine, both curative and preventive, is based was developed in the 19th century; implementation in technology and in practice is mostly a 20th century phenomenon. The triumphs have been many and spectacular—so much so that limitations of theory and programs (limitations which not infrequently have led to the emergence of new health problems) have largely been overlooked.

What is needed, first of all, is better theory, better conceptualization, for dealing with the many-sided problems presented by the existence of various states of health and illness, with the focus at times on individuals and at other times on groups or whole communities. I should like to put forward the concept of an ecological framework as the proper place to begin. Ecology is the study of the totality of the interrelationships of organisms within the environment. Human ecology studies the interrelationships of humans with each other and within their total environment, all other living matter included. Kurt Lewin, the social psychologist, coined an apt phrase in this connection. Humans, he said, should be perceived of as operating within a life-space. In the investigation of human problems of various sorts, initially all factors that can be conceived of as influential should be included. Further along, reductionistic outlooks and methods become permissible, but never without frequent reconsideration of an ecological, holistic point of view.

A simple diagram may be helpful for clarification; it has the merit of introducing all the known categories which impinge on the human and which exert a multitude of influences on his states of health and illness. The diagram encourages a dynamic, as opposed to a static, point of view. It also should be noted that in the process of "playing with" this diagram, in individual thought and in dialogue, one's definition of what health is or is not may undergo radical revision. Here, then, is the diagram, a 16-cell matrix (modified from L. Simmons and H. G. Wolff, "Social Science in Medicine," Russell Sage, 1954):

CATEGORIES RELEVANT TO STATES OF HEALTH AND ILLNESS IN MAN

	Effects			
	Physical	Psychological	Societal	Cultural
Physical	A	B	C	D
Psychological	E	F	G	H
Societal	I	J	K	L
Cultural	M	N	O	P

(Causes)

Classical, Hippocratic medicine was restricted almost completely to A, physical causes with physical effects. A simple example is pneumonia: the multiplication of the pneumococcus in the lung tissue of the susceptible individual with subsequent physical changes in those tissues—inflammation, thickening, etc. We can take the year 1900, which saw the publication of Freud's "Interpretation of Dreams," as marking the introduction of psychological factors in health and illness. Psychoanalysis and its offshoot, dynamic psychiatry, can be placed, therefore, in F. The development of psychosomatic medicine (the interplay of psychological and bodily factors) gathered speed in the 1930's, and as a formal discipline (by no means wholly absorbed into medical practice), it is not yet 40 years old. Psychosomatic medicine is located in boxes B and E. We can conclude that in the medical profession, and certainly in the public at large, considerations of health and illness are largely conceptualized within the confines of the four boxes in the upper left-hand corner of the matrix: A, B, E, and F. It should be added that the discipline of public health (including sanitary science, communicable disease control, maternal and child health, and vital statistics) developed empirical methods which took it from box A to boxes C, I, and K— the interplay of physical and societal forces. An example in I would be the concept of "crowd disease," one instance being overcrowding leading to an increased incidence of rheumatic fever. On the whole, however, this foray into the societal area was not a self-conscious one on the part of public health practitioners; it is becoming so.

A word on the "cultural" boxes, M-P and D-P. Someone aptly has said that the discovery of culture was one of the greatest discoveries of the 19th century. It is probably fair to say that little of the learning of this new and highly important area has filtered into the professions or influenced the thought-processes of our decision makers. It would be rash to predict whether an increased awareness of cultural factors, upon which much depends, will occur with sufficient rapidity in the next several decades. There are some grounds for optimism; there is also reason to be gloomy.

We now are in a position to make some statements on the relationship of technological change and health. One, the most general and comprehensive, is that significant technological change may (and usually does) have influences on health, individually and in the group, which impinge on all 16 boxes in the matrix. Further, we may say that we can not afford to ignore the societal and cultural parameters, which happen to be those which are least understood and for whose elucidation our investigative methods, borrowed in the main from the physical sciences, are least applicable. However, awareness that these factors exist is an incalculably important initial advantage.

An example or two will illustrate the new breadth which is required. Malnutrition, in the form of obesity, is a major health problem in this country. We value ease in the matter of creature comforts; how do we reconcile this with power-steering in cars, the introduction of which lowered drivers' caloric requirements in a significant and measurable amount? Will the necessities of international economics and the balance-of-payments dictate that the American people develop a supersonic transport and learn to adjust their central nervous systems to sonic boom? Can we avoid becoming, in Samuel Butler's phrase, "machine-tickling aphids" in this computer age? Can we maintain the values which are really aspects of cultural health: individuality, healthy nonconformity, and the inner feeling of being "one's own man"? The population explosion, mainly a result of technological development in agriculture and the health sciences, has fostered urbanization and, in many areas of the world, led to crowding and overcrowding. What is optimal population density for humans in terms of health and over-all potential—productive, creative, and self-actualizing? Nobody knows, and yet there are few questions to which the answers are more important.

Heretofore we have welcomed, on the whole uncritically, penicillin, the transistor, the internal combustion engine, DDT. . . . The list, as we all know, could go on for pages. We must change. We must learn—and learn soon—to fit these gifts of science and technology with more care and foresight into the existing fabric of society. Humans have great adaptability, but we must not be misled into thinking that human adaptability is without limits. These limits exist, even if we do not know just where and what they are. Especially in their societal and cultural dimensions, humans are far more complex than is commonly appreciated.

The potentials of man as a creator and artist are barely realized today. Technology, as his master, may well destroy much that is now innate and hidden, not yet in flower. Technology, as his servant, will bring him closer to the self-realization he has always sought.

31. AUTOMATION, EDUCATION, AND CREATIVITY

STANLEY FOSTER REED

SEVERAL young men recently were questioned on the relationship of their schooling to their present jobless condition. All reported that they had been unable to relate school to job in a meaningful way during their school years. One, a dropout, offered this testimony:

> But I mean none of the classes design you for anything like, you know, one certain thing—you don't know what you're going to *be*. I mean it doesn't show you anything on how you're going to live in the *future*. When you get out of school, you don't know where you're going from there and even now *I* don't know and *you* don't know where I am going from *here*. But it's not anything that I can change because, you know, the *system* is set up that way. (Emphasis supplied.)

Note the use of the word "system"—the belief that there are great forces at work in the educative universe over which the student has no control.

In some degree, this is true of any of us. There *are* systems which we do not understand—political systems and supporting institutions which seem to be designed for someone else. In this sense, we are all dropouts from "the system" because of our lack of identification with the system. This causes retreat into technological super-specialization, scholasticism, party-lining, and other easy activities at the expense of intellectual engagement with the real world. We know that the ancients invented gods to explain the unknowns in the physical universe. We now have created some new gods to explain the unknowns in the societal universe. In this neo-theism, the modern equivalent of Zeus is "The System." How can the formal school, with deicide the object, relate its function to the real world?

The ancient functions of a formal school are to preserve, disseminate, and create new knowledge. In these time when the total mass of recorded knowledge doubles every seven years, when the half-life of a technical education is 10 years, when the number of people in school doubles every 15 years, the entire educative establishment from pre-school to post-retirement staggers under the increasing logistical load. The response has been a mix of the old and the new. It has been the creation of new and better standards along with the unfortunate exhumation of some that were long dead. It has been the long-delayed elevation of the specialist in education to a position at least on a par with the academician, along with the equally unfortunate ascendancy, as a logistical necessity, of the administrator over the pedagogue.

Along with the new gods, we create new myths. One such myth is known as "The Myth of Growing Complexity" and stems from an awareness of systems and from the frustrations arising because we should have, but do not have, a part in them.

As a result of the System-God and the accompanying myth, we have the problem of how to develop a "sense of future"—an identification with some destiny over which there is personal control; for, with the System-God in more control of the future, why have a destiny of your own?

Does not our dropout and do not many of the rest of us lack such a "sense of future"? Do we not suffer from an inability to relate, in the educative process, many things we are doing today to anything real in our lives? Ortega y Gasset spoke of "taking a stand within oneself," and said, "It is impossible to speak of action except insofar as it will be governed by a previous contemplation; the stand within oneself is nothing but a projection of (the consequences) of future action."

Who can speak of the educative process in general without relating it to the idea of future in specific? Who can advise a student about anything unless he has some basic understanding of the student's idea of the future? Is not the most important function of the educative process to get the student to understand that education is for the future? And can there ever be a compatibility among the orientations to the future of the teacher, of the administrator, and of the student, respectively? Do teacher and administrator, in fact, have a sense of future? And if they have, is it one that will hold up and help in the future? Or do they believe that, during their time, they at last have uncovered the great truths, the great universalities, and have been taken in by what William James referred to as "the pretense of finality in [that] truth"?

Of course, how does one generate a standard except out of the past? Many of the keepers of the keys of our educational institutions have had a quick brush with posterity. But they have abandoned this all too soon, for it has conflicted with the problem of "making money" or "keeping up." Service to posterity has proved all too often to be a swindler. It raises the question: should a value system have a posterity variable? If so, what is the time scale? In the educative process, what are we educating for?

What do we know of the processes that go on in the creation of behavior patterns in the student where a "sense of future" is as important as a textbook or a teacher? The educative process is, or should be, future-oriented. There is no reason to learn if there is no reason to apply. If there is no sense of future, there can be no sense of learning. The sense of learning, then, is in direct proportion to the sense of future. It is not so much what a student sees, but how much he sees, how far, and if at all. To have a "sense of future," must one not have a sight or a "feeling" of oneself in the future?

The formal educative process must be customized so that it can accommodate anyone's idea of future, no matter what it may be. If it cannot be so related, formal education can become largely a waste of time, for it may be replacing the informal educative process; and this could prove to be a far more marketable quantity.

The prediction of one's own future and its interaction with the real world of the educative process is the very stuff of which actual educative behavior is made. Additionally, it must be admitted that it is difficult to talk of "values" in any sense except that of the future because, leaving aside completely irrational compulsive behavior, the word "values" has no meaning except in the sense that it involves some future action in support of those values. This, incidentally, Ortega y Gasset saw very well.

The questions to be asked of the educative establishment are these: can behavior (in this case, the future orientation of behavior) be modified by or with the educative process or some derivative of it? Is there some way to tie the learning act in with its potential use at some future time? What kind of ethic does the student generate from the educative process itself? Does he see any "idea of future" in it? What can we supply in the place of the "System-God"?

The second myth is "The Myth of Acceleration of the Absolute Amount of Knowledge"—otherwise known as the "Knowledge Explosion." This myth is based on the fact of the fantastic increase in the mass of recorded words and the fancy that this equates to "knowledge." The amount of absolute knowledge contained within this great mass of written words is small, indeed. The problem is in abstracting, classifying, and codifying for ready access a great mass of printed information in which very little new knowledge is contained. How much better if we could learn to classify knowledge. For instance, in the recent past, some 3,000 papers have been written in the field of hydrodynamics. Marjorie Evans of Stanford Research Institute says that the total amount of knowledge in these 3,000 papers can be boiled down to a series of variations on 12 basic equations. The whole mass of words thus can be reduced to a small fraction of a percent of that contained in the 3,000 papers. Yet, Dr. Evans claims that no one is interested in supporting the reduction of this "information" to "knowledge."

In the age to come, the educative establishment must learn to classify knowledge rather than information. And the form and manner must be such that it is readily accessible to staff and to student so that the triadic function of the formal school may be properly served. Certainly, the efficiency of the storehouse function will be vastly increased; the dissemination function will be accelerated, for we will be disseminating knowledge itself instead of information about knowledge; and, lastly, we finally may have a better definition of the interface between the known and the unknown—a definition that will enable us to separate the trivial research result or project from the basic.

The third myth is "The Myth of the Total Replacement of Man by Machine." This one is simple to defeat: machines thrive on mass production; mass production thrives on mass taste. *Ergo,* eliminate the mass taste and you eliminate mass production *and* the machine. Very simple! The question is this: how does one eliminate mass taste? Here the answer is not simple. We might begin, however, by making the educative process dependent on the creative drive of the individual. If we could make creative originality the arbiter of excellence, conformity to the mass taste that is the result of the rote-learning process might disappear in a great wave of individual expression. To accomplish this, we must split the educative process into two parts—the creative process and the rote-learning process.

The creative urge should form the basis of all learning. The desire to create ever-better things should propel the student into the automated rote-learning room to acquire technological or communicative skills. These skills, however, should not be ends, but means by which to carry a true learning project to a higher point—that of creative implication or application. How much better this creatively heuristic process would be than the forced-feeding of mere facts in the dissolved hope that they some day may be used in a constructive way.

That the acquisition of large amounts of facts, as an end in itself, has become the national educative ethic was well demonstrated a few years ago in the television quiz scandals. The significant thing was not the intellectual sell-out of 100 gifted memorizers, but that 60,000,000 people in the TV audience thought that the recall and repetition of unapplied facts was "excellence" in action. And why should they not think this? They were conditioned to this attitude from their first toddling steps into their school buildings.

Some of the participants thought of it as a game—a method of entertainment; and to this day they do not believe that what they did was wrong. This idea of education as a game has been created in recent years by a sentimental confusion. This confusion carries the notion that, in order to make learning attractive, it should be made pleasant through a large associative content with happy play. The true notion should be, rather, that the attractiveness of learning should spring from the desire to be original. In an atmosphere of happy play, the acquisition of knowledge *per se* by any method is thus condoned. It needs no tie to living, only to existing. And grading on ability to repeat rote-acquired non-applicabilities is merely existing.

If it matters not how the knowledge was obtained or why it was obtained, but just that it is obtained, the line between cheating and non-cheating becomes very confusing, indeed. It would be impossible to cheat if grades were based exclusively on the ability to create and to criticize. But this is not the case. They are based on the administrative system that not only has to grade students, but, as collateral demands, has to grade the teacher and to rate itself as an institution.

The fourth myth is "The Myth of Alienation in a Leisure Society." Here again, if there is a widespread fear of footlessness in a leisure world, it is the conventional educative process that is at fault.

Take, for instance, the de Grazia film, *Of Time, Work, and Leisure,* produced by National Educational Television. It features a recently retired man, left to his own devices and confronted by another 25 years of existence, sitting on a park bench with a vacant "why am I here?" expression on his face. Can you see him asking, "Mommie, please give me something to do"? This is the kind of question we hear over and over from the young after several years of exposure to the educative ethic of ritualistic repetition of rote-acquired knowledge has drained them of their natural talents for innovation. Regrettably, the influence of later years at higher levels of learning, where the creative acts do become important and are stimulated, is insufficient to provide the needed de-conditioning.

If there is to be a leisure age with the threatened consequent alienation for the individual, the threat may be annulled by instilling in the student, at all levels, the conviction that the arbiter of excellence is originality. Thus, if leisure is imposed on one, it will be welcomed as an opportunity to give full force and effect to one's innate creative drives which have been reinforced continually throughout the educative life.

There must be some way to instill in the student the concept that he is an originative part and parcel of the system, that he can make and mold his own environment in his own image, that there is a great universe of possibilities out there through which to be creative or originally critical. If only we can get man to appreciate that there is enormous opportunity for original, individual expression—that, with 40 notes on a piano, for instance, he can play more different tunes than there are particles in the universe, and that, with the words available to him in any language, there is an infinity of new prose and poetry yet to be written. As it is with all sound, so it is with all thought. As it is in the arts, so it is in the sciences. "Truth," as Buckminster Fuller says, "is a verb." How can we teach that it is man's task to seek out the fullest expression of his nature as a human being, that it is his task to discover the order in the universe, to release his talents for love and learning, and finally, as he must die, to leave some little thing, some tiny try, some little thought, some tiny rationality to add to the universal order as his particular monument to the ages?

But compare this view of mature man with the conditioning he receives in childhood. Think, for a minute, of the child who comes home and says, "Mommie, I told teacher that six times six is 36 and I got a gold star." The mother gives the child a pat on the head, a kiss, and a cookie to add to the kudos. The next moment, the child, secure in his knowledge but striving to express himself in some meaningful way, draws a picture on the living-room wall and, for reward, gets a rap on the head. Future kisses and cookies are denied; he gets a long lecture about "responsibility"; and one more little rote-learner, TV-watcher is born. He has learned his lesson. Cookies, kisses, and kudos are needed for survival, and the child knows it. There never has been any doubt in a child's mind about the methods he will use to accomplish his ends; moral sense is generated out of behavior. So the child henceforth will optimize the production of cookies, kisses, and kudos in the safest manner possible—and this means suppression of creative drives and conformity with the mass ethic.

If the learning process has such little sense of living in it, it *ipso facto* must be something else. What else could it be? It must be like a play, something that one can sit back and watch and not get involved in as a part of living. The acquisition of knowledge has been turned into a game, generally divorced from the process of living except to the extent of optimizing the production of cookies, kisses, and kudos.

But great numbers of successful people never have been remarkable rote-learners except in institutions such as the service academies, where the student hierarchy tends to be perpetuated in the actual working hierarchy of the profession. In the case of the service academies, the conformity that produces success in academe is applied successfully in later life. This is not generally true of business, government, and the professions, where rote-learning in itself does not bring the best professional rewards.

This leads us to the problem of the generation of standards in education. The regent or school board member very seldom has acquired his position by virtue of his ability to recite rote-acquired facts. Very often, success has depended on the fact that he has been highly creative, an innovator. Yet—and here is the rub—he often approves of getting back to the "good old 3 R's" to which he was conditioned in childhood. He goes all out for reinstalling a system that he knows was not good for him. But the conditioning that he received is still so powerful that, in spite of his own success through other means, he seeks to recreate a situation to produce more of what, in early boyhood, he had been led to believe was excellence. Meanwhile, the teachers who know that early conditioning to the idea of rote-learning as excellence makes a mess of lives can do nothing about it. They do not have the power.

What have machines to do with all this? Why this disquisition on our educative ills in a book that is supposed to be about automation and human values? Well, certainly human values are involved where there is cheating. Certainly human values are involved when knowledge *per se* is the *sine qua non* of the educative process. And as for the machine, it may offer a solution to the problem of cheating that has been rendered acute by stress on sheer rote-learning as excellence in itself and entitled to the rewards of excellence.

One of the great problems in education is the time of the teacher. The easy way to administer the teaching process is to give out a set of carefully controlled facts and to require that they come back in exactly the same form in which they went out. The burden of grading is thus reduced to a mechanical operation. As such, this becomes a job for machines, not people. This is a basic job for programmed learning.

The problem in the use of programmed learning, however, is that knowledge is not yet completely organized to be stuffed into a computer with sufficient packing density to provide the necessary universe of knowledge so that most questions that need to be asked can be answered. That is the reason that "The Myth of the Acceleration of the Absolute Amount of Knowledge" must be refuted. Then we may get on with the task of automating the teaching of factual knowledge.

With the advent of proper programmed learning, the potential to use the innate "teaching sense" of our national educative staff can be tapped for truly creative learning. No matter that there is opposition to the teaching machines by the professional educator. He has been so frustrated and neglected all his life that he often sees the teaching machine as a threat. "Not only do they not believe I'm important, not only will they not listen when I talk, not only will they not pay me properly when, through my service, I help create the great wealth of this nation. Not only have I been neglected. But now comes more: I am being replaced by machines. Will the machines do the job better?"

The answer to the teacher is a gentle yes. The machine *can* do a better job of teaching facts. Let the machine take on the job of answering the universe of questions that no one person, regardless of intellectual capacity, could answer. Let the machine answer the questions that the teacher does not understand. Let the machine answer the questions of the ugly child the teacher unconsciously may dislike. Let the machine answer the questions of the lame, the stutterer, the abnormal, the poorly or skimpily or garishly dressed. Let it answer the questions of the garrulous and the taciturn alike. And let the judgments as to rote-learning competence be made *ex persona* to the greatest extent possible.

The machine can do all this. And then what does the teacher do? The answer is *teach*. The teacher instructs in method and stimulates the desire for creative scholarship. The teacher concentrates on the learning process in the individual, as this makes for originality and creativity.

This is the tutorial process that was thought to be too expensive. Perhaps so. But with the advent of broad-based programmed learning, it may well be more efficient. Certainly, programmed instruction by machine, in combination with the tutorial process, should result in the development of truly knowledgeable people; and by this is meant people who, through original and creative effort, are able to solve problems both assigned and self-generated.

What, finally, of the concept of change and the idea of progress? If we agree that change is taking place, if we agree that it is important to sense change, if we agree that teaching sensitivity to change is important for original, creative learning, then where is the place for the rote-acquisition process? If learning depends on it, it can do little but stifle the educative process in its more telling function—the development of creative sensitivity to the new relationships that are forming about us in the physical and societal universe. The facts of the forming cannot be told; they are not discovered as yet. But the methods by which the facts are discovered *can* be taught. They must be taught by the actual process of factual discovery, and this only can be done by solving problems to which neither teacher nor pupil has the answer.

32. TECHNOLOGICAL CULTURE, THE UNIVERSITY, AND THE FUNCTION OF RELIGIOUS FAITH

MYRON B. BLOY, JR.

T HIS CHAPTER will suggest a working model for the function
of religious faith—in the Judeo-Christian tradition—in the university's struggle to achieve a significant role in our technological culture. The strategy has three stages: first, a brief description of several
leading characteristics of technological culture, including what seems
its most dangerous flaw; second, a description of the crucial role
the university has to play in healing this flaw in our culture and the
difficulties it has in assuming this role; and third, some suggestions,
based on my experience as a Protestant chaplain at the Massachusetts
Institute of Technology, of how religious faith can assist the university to assume its appropriate cultural role.

LEADING CHARACTERISTICS OF TECHNOLOGICAL CULTURE

C. P. Snow's "The Two Cultures," although neither the first nor
the best of the descriptions of our contemporary cultural schizophrenia, nevertheless has provided some of the leading terms for the
discussion of this situation (*cf.*, *Daedalus*, Winter, 1965, on "Science
and Culture"). C. P. Snow's argument, essentially right in its "two-
ness"—in its insistence on the grossly *simple* confrontation which
the situation reveals—but seriously askew in its actual descriptions
of those confronting cultures, will serve as a beginning and a foil

for the subsequent observations. Snow argues that the two cultures, which have "almost ceased to communicate," are those of the "literary intellectuals" or "traditionalists," who live mostly in the past and eschew the present or future, and the "scientists," who are basically future-oriented. Traditionalists, says Snow, have a subdued literary tone, are centered on the tragic state of the individual, and are lacking in foresight, while scientists are flamboyant, are centered on the social possibilities of mankind, and sometimes betray a shallow optimism. The upshot of this lack of cross-cultural communication is that both cultures are impoverished, and this impoverishment is the root cause of our failure to have the wisdom necessary to solve the world's great problems, *i.e.*, H-Bomb war, overpopulation, and most importantly for Snow, the gap between the rich and the poor. The most effective way to change this situation is to devise better educational programs which will educate each individual in both cultures. Snow ends his argument with this pulpit-style summary:

> For the sake of the intellectual life, for the sake of this country's special danger, for the sake of the Western society living precarious rich among the poor, for the sake of the poor who needn't be poor if there is intelligence in the world, it is obligatory for us and the Americans and the whole West to look at our education with fresh eyes.[1]

The urgency of Snow's tone is well taken, but the description of the two cultures is too narrowly academic and their relationship to each other is too statically conceived. Snow's fundamental error is in lumping into one so-called "scientific culture" everything from the most elegant theorizings of the mathematician to the most practical decisions of the field engineer. That is, Snow fails to see the fundamental difference between the scientific and the technological world views. Judging from personal experience at M.I.T., the traditional-literary and the scientific ways of apprehending reality are much closer to each other than either is to the technological outlook. The kind of scientific intelligence which delights in the richness and coherence of reality as seen through "The Second Law of Thermodynamics" and which is essentially contemplative and reflective in its search for truth has a spiritual kinship with the traditional-literary intelligence which delights in the richness and coherence of reality as seen through "King Lear" or a Bach fugue or St. Thomas' "Summa" and which is also essentially contemplative and reflective in its search for esthetic or metaphysical or moral truth. Both stand

---

[1] C. P. Snow, "The Two Cultures: And A Second Look" (New York: Cambridge University Press, 1964), p. 50.

in a reverential, awed, wonder-filled attitude before the always surprising glory of Truth revealed; both, that is, participate in the
ancient quest for the beatific vision. In rejecting the confusion of
technology with science, Michael Polanyi says flatly, "No important
discovery can be made in science by anyone who does not believe
that science is important—indeed, supremely important—*in itself*"
(italics added).[2]

But this traditional mode of apprehension, which includes both
the literary and the scientific, is generically different from the drive
for workability, for practical solutions to practical problems, which
characterizes the technological spirit. The technological spirit sees
in nature not the reservoir of the beatific vision—of Truth—but the
raw stuff for its practical fashioning. Its satisfactions are more
Faustian, in the manipulation rather than in the contemplation of
reality, in successfully turning the stuff of nature into means for
contingent ends rather than in uncovering the existent but hidden
ends of nature or man.

Here, then, are the two cultures as they really exist: a traditional
culture, including the liberal arts and sciences, representing a contemplative, ends-focused stance towards natural, social, and metaphysical reality, and a technological culture, including most professional disciplines (especially engineering) and the social sciences,
representing an activist, means-focused stance towards reality.
Furthermore, these cultures, contrary to Snow's static picture of
non-communication, are joined in a death-battle which is clearly
being won by the technological forces. They draw their lines against
each other throughout society and not just in the academic world;
and their conflict exists not simply between individuals of differing
professional persuasions, but within each one of us.

The difficulty of communication between these two cultures, the
traditional and the technological, is seen very clearly in the following scene from "The Spy Who Came in From the Cold," in which
the Communist agent, Fiedler, is interrogating the English agent,
Leamas. Fiedler asks Leamas what motivates the English agents in
their fight against the Communists. What, Fiedler wants to know, is
their philosophy?

"What do you mean, a philosophy?" Leamas replied. "We're not Marxists,
we're nothing. Just people."
"Are you Christians then?"

---

[2] Michael Polanyi, "Personal Knowledge" (Chicago: University of Chicago
Press, 1958), p. 183.

"Not many, I shouldn't think. I don't know many."

"What makes them do it, then?" Fiedler persisted: "They must have a philosophy."

"Why must they? Perhaps they don't know; don't even care. Not everyone has a philosophy," Leamas answered, a bit helplessly.

"Then tell me what is your philosophy?"

"Oh for Christ's sake," Leamas snapped, and they walked on in silence for a while.[3]

The Marxist in this scene represents the traditional culture: in Marxism he has a vision of the Ultimate Truth of history, and this vision determines the loyalties, the values, the style of his life. He cannot conceive of living at all except around some passionately held "philosophy of life." Leamas, on the other hand, is a true denizen of the technological culture. His loyalty is simply to the job at hand, to good workmanship. He is non-reflective, having no drive for a beatific vision—not even of the nationalistic or patriotic type. His satisfactions are in the immediate experience, not in the vision of some grand design which is presumed to lie behind the façade of experience. When these two encounter each other, they are a source of deep puzzlement and frustration to each other. It is as if they spoke different languages.

This little scene actually reveals the central theme of the novel. The traditionalists, those with loyalties to Truth, all go down to defeat before the single-mindedness, the dispassionate and inexorable skillfulness of the technological "pro's"; Fiedler, Leamas' girl, and even Leamas himself (as a result of his conversion to the traditionalists in the last scene) are all defeated. Technological culture, as Daniel Bell pointed out several years ago, marks the "end of ideology" in the contemporary East-West political scene just as it does in the novel. Clearly, one of the reasons for the so-called "thaw" both in the West and in many Marxist countries of East Europe is not simply an upsurgence of goodwill, but the breakdown of ideological passion under the inexorable power of the technological spirit. For example, economists on both sides of the iron curtain are less and less concerned about economic ideology and more and more concerned with the technical problems of raising the Gross National Product, and so they are increasingly discovering themselves in a common effort using a common language, mathematics. Technological culture is clearly on the way to becoming a world culture, sweeping before it every form of traditional culture in the way.

At this point, it is appropriate to summarize conclusions pre-

---

[3] John LeCarré, "The Spy Who Came in From the Cold" (New York: Dell Publishing Co., 1963), p. 123.

sented elsewhere concerning the "gracefulness" of technology.[4] If Jesus of Nazareth is taken as the norm of human maturity, then technology is a stage in man's development towards that maturity. Technology is first of all a means of Western man's growth into a deeper measure of freedom, for it has freed us from an absolute preoccupation with survival and has opened up a whole range of possibilities, such as justice, friendship, political and economic equality, and esthetic enjoyment. Before the advent of the technological revolution in the West, this richness of choice was not possible except for the aristocratic few. Furthermore, as Daniel Bell points out, even the often-adduced negative characteristics of technological or mass culture have a positive effect on the growth of man's freedom. Mr. Bell says,

If it is granted that mass society is compartmentalized, superficial in personal relations, anonymous, transitory, specialized, utilitarian, competitive, acquisitive, mobile, and status-hungry, the obverse side of the coin must be shown, too—the right to privacy, to free choice of friends and occupation, status on the basis of achievement rather than exclusive and monopolistic social controls of a single dominant group. For if, as Sir Henry Maine once put it, the movement of modern society has been from status to contract, then it has been, in that light, a movement from a fixed place in the world to possible freedom.[5]

This is, of course, a psychically painful kind of freedom because it threatens the security and integrity of the person, but this pain finally should be understood as the birth pangs of a new evolution in man's growth towards his maturity. (This aspect of technological culture will be touched on again later.)

Continuing the summary, there are other signs of grace in technology. Technological man has a kind of tough humility, a flatfooted honesty before the contingencies of reality. If the traditionalist deplores the naivete of technological man's devotion to facts, he also must acknowledge in him what Mumford calls "a certain decent self-effacement, which is in the best style of our epoch."[6] There is also a strong utopianism and dynamism in technology, a sense that hard technical work and honesty before the immediate facts will carry mankind through to "the good life." And if traditionalists point to such utopian technological horrors as Franken-

---

4 Myron B. Bloy, Jr., "The Crisis of Cultural Change: A Christian Perspective" (New York: Seabury Press, 1965).

5 Daniel Bell, "The End of Ideology" (Glencoe, Ill.: The Free Press of Glencoe, 1960), pp. 29-30.

6 Lewis Mumford, "Art and Technics" (New York: Columbia University Press, 1960), p. 54.

stein's monster or B.F. Skinner's "Walden II," then it must be acknowledged that the willingness to risk change, to push through the frontiers in the reach for some better version of life, is another way of describing this dynamism. This courage to risk change is, in fact, a revelation of deep trust in the sustaining character of creation, which is the seedbed of courage. Finally, to take a cue from Fr. Walter Ong, there is the "play" aspect of the technological spirit. The fascination with a mechanical toy, the delight in building a good fire or solving the *Times* "Double-Crostic," the exhuberant clapping and backslapping in the moon-flight control room when the rocket hits its target—all are aspects of this spirit. And, again, if the traditionalist criticizes this as infantilism, then he is the loser, because this play-spirit of technology is really an unself-conscious ebullient homage to life itself, an uncalculated celebration of existence, and, as such, is an authentic aspect of man's maturity. In summary, Fr. Ong says,

Seen in larger historical, and prehistorical, perspectives, the age of technology is part of the great and mysterious evolution of the universe devised by God. It can be considered as an epoch in what we may call the "hominization" of the world, that is, the taking over of our planet by mankind.[7]

This eschatological promise is, contrary to many traditionalists, the most fundamental characteristic of the technological culture. This means that, although we must counter those perversions of the technological spirit which we see against the foil of other marks of man's maturity inherited from the traditional culture, our technological culture is not essentially anti-human but, rather, an evolutionary stage in our growth to maturity.

The fundamental problem which is increasingly plaguing our technological culture and inhibiting its best features from being fully realized is its difficulty in finding a judgment-empowering perspective from which it can reflect sensitively on itself. If the British spy, Leamas, is free from the metaphysical fanaticism of his Marxist counterpart so that his world is immensely richer in its possibilities for him, then we also must say that this very richness, when there is no means of value discrimination except workability, becomes his prison. He must change his color, as does the chameleon, with his environment. Daniel Bell described this phenomenon well in a recent article when he said,

---

[7] Walter J. Ong, S.J., "Technology and New Humanist Frontiers," in "Frontiers in American Catholicism" (New York: Macmillan, 1957), p. 88.

The underlying social reality, the stylistic unity of the culture of the past hundred years lies, I would argue . . . , in a structural form of expression that I have called "the eclipse of distance," of psychic, social and esthetic distance. Modern culture began as an effort to annihilate the contemplative mode of experience by emphasizing *immediacy, impact, simultaneity,* and *sensation.* It is today at the point of breaking up all fixed points of reference in formal genres.[8]

In his brilliant phenomenology of our culture in "Understanding Media," Marshall McLuhan points to the role of technology in this development. He says,

This is the Age of Anxiety for the reason of the electric implosion that compels commitment and participation, quite regardless of any "point of view." The partial and specialized character of the viewpoint, however noble, will not serve at all in the electric age. At the information level the same upset has occurred with the substitution of the inclusive image for the mere viewpoint. If the nineteenth century was the age of the editorial chair, ours is the century of the psychiatrist's couch. As extension of man the chair is a specialist ablation of the posterior, a sort of ablative absolute of backside, whereas the couch extends the integral being. The psychiatrist employs the couch, since it removes the temptation to express private points of view and obviates the need to rationalize events.[9]

The problem of our time is how to get enough "psychic, social, and esthetic distance" on our seductively *involving* culture to be able to exercise some discriminating leverage on it, to be able to ensure that its promise as the epoch of "hominization" is fulfilled. The price of cultural growth is, to recoin an old phrase, eternal vigilance, and that is why the situation described by Bell and McLuhan is so frightening. In the process of rapid cultural change, the old norms that formed a common, coherent vantage point for reflecting and making discriminate judgments on our culture have fallen apart and we are presently in danger of fulfilling Yeats' prophetic vision in "The Second Coming":

> Turning and turning in the widening gyre
> The falcon cannot hear the falconer;
> Things fall apart; the centre cannot hold;
> Mere anarchy is loosed upon the world,
> The blood-dimmed tide is loosed, and everywhere
> The ceremony of innocence is drowned;
> The best lack all conviction, while the worst
> Are full of passionate intensity.

The freedom we have gained can be lost if we are unable to achieve the personal collectedness or coherence to take its risks with-

---

[8] Daniel Bell, "The Disjunction of Culture and Social Structure: Some Notes on the Meaning of Social Reality," in *Daedalus,* 94: 220, Winter, 1965.

[9] Marshall McLuhan, "Understanding Media" (New York: McGraw-Hill, 1964), p. 5.

out being centrifugally pulled apart. Honest humility before the contingent character of reality becomes fatuous pride if we continue to drift into a closed rationalism which is blind to love or art or the richly ambiguous character of existence. Utopian dynamism can lose its potentiality for cultural growth if its vision of man's maturity is corrupted by that same rationalism. "Walden II" is a real possibility if we cannot articulate a more human hope. Play, unbalanced by other human ends, becomes rather small beer for the sustenance of the human spirit. In short, although the promise of a new epoch of human maturation is given to us in our technological culture, it will be realized only if we are able to grasp it and make it ours, only if we are able to develop a coherent, yet flexible point of view from which we can exercise real judgments.

THE CRUCIAL ROLE OF THE UNIVERSITY —AND ITS DIFFICULTIES IN ASSUMING THIS ROLE

Historically, Western universities have had a double role in society: they have tested, elaborated, and taught both the perceptions of Truth which determine the fundamental norms of society and also the professional skills that are needed for the practical operation of society. (Contrary to some contemporary apologists for the liberal arts, the practical purposes were there from the beginning, too; it is only difficult to see, from the contemporary perspective, that theology, within the world view of the Middle Ages, was just as "practical" as, say, engineering within our world view.) The university was, then, a place where the debate between means and ends went on constantly so that each was modified by the other. The contemplative, reflective mode of apprehension lived in close relation with the activist, manipulative mode so that there was constant interaction. It is astounding to us that Leonardo Da Vinci could be both a painter and an engineer, but not to his own contemporaries in the 15th and 16th centuries. They recognized, as we do, the greatness of his talent; but, unlike us, they saw nothing unique in its multiplicity.

Today, the university itself has been victimized by the same "eclipse of distance" that characterizes the whole society, so that its traditional role is in deep jeopardy. The liberal arts and sciences of the traditional culture, often called "humanities" today, traditionally focused on the basic perceptions of Truth, against which all human action and experience could be defined, and developed the skills of reflection and judgment. Now, they either have been so alienated from or seduced by the technological culture that the means/ends dialogue has been disrupted. The voice of alienation can be heard in the jeremiads of Robert M. Hutchins, or Paul Tillich, or Jacques Ellul. They consider the technological spirit to be simply anti-human and, therefore, see no point in dialogue. (Tillich and Ellul explicitly have advocated total detachment from technological society, and Hutchins' Olympian retreat in Santa Barbara implicitly makes the same point.) This alienation deprives the technological culture of the help it needs to achieve its maturity in the evolutionary history of man and pushes the liberal arts and sciences even further into effeteness and futility.

This is not to deny that there are real psychological grounds for such alienation. The liberal arts professor is likely to become somewhat bitter about being treated as more or less dispensable frosting for the university's real task of training professionalists of one kind or another. But the increasingly notorious irony is that the form this alienation from technological culture is taking is the defense of a technology; alienation is apparently the path to seduction. For what are these arcane terminologies, fusty methodologies, and esoteric minutiae, which are the treasure so many liberal arts scholars ardently defend and teach, but a somewhat aged technology? A classical sign of the loss of substance and power in any discipline is this cabalistic concern with the "apparatus" of the discipline.

Such courses as "Business English" and "Survey of Western Culture" represent, as a rule, a more straightforward acquiescence of the liberal arts to a passive, rather than dialogical, role in our technological culture. The liberal arts and sciences become part of the passive background of culture, rather than the ground for making discriminating judgments on the culture. Prof. Marshall McLuhan attributes this phenomenon to electronic media:

It is useful to notice all the arts and sciences as acting in the role of anti-environments that enable us to perceive the environment. In a business civilization we have long considered liberal study as providing necessary means of orientation and perception. When arts and sciences themselves become environments under conditions of electric circuitry, conventional liberal studies whether in the arts or sciences will no longer serve as an anti-environment. When we live in a museum without walls, or have music as a structural part of our environment, new strategies of attention and perception have to be created.[10]

---

[10] Marshall McLuhan, "The Relation of Environment to Anti-Environment," unpublished essay, March, 1965.

The liberal arts increasingly become a subservient function or gingerbread façade for our technological culture.

But, even if the liberal arts and sciences were freed from the pitfalls of alienation from or seduction by technological culture, there are certain difficult limitations that would have to be overcome before they significantly could help our society to recover some "psychic distance" or, to use McLuhan's term, some anti–environmental viewpoints. In the first place, the formal structures of liberal studies have come to emphasize the mastery of certain blocks of information rather than the skill to reflect on our culture from and with the help of this knowledge. That is, as Paul Goodman often has pointed out, the dynamic character of the liberal arts and sciences has been broken into pieces by the university's penchant for rationalistic (rather than organic) order and close tolerances of judgment on performance. But until faculties of liberal studies are persuaded that the art of reflecting on contemporary technological culture in terms of the various liberal disciplines is a primary teaching goal, this condition will not change and their courses will remain so many undigested lumps in the student's educational life.

In the second place, dispassionate inculcation in the multiplicity of mankind's commitments emerges as a relativism which seems to prohibit any intellectually honest person from adopting any particular point of view at all. The scholarly effort to break down intellectual gaucheries and childish commitments by teaching respect for evidence and hard thinking should be understood as a helpful tool for arriving at viable perspectives on contemporary culture. It should not be understood, as it often is, as an end in itself. If liberal arts faculties are unwilling to undergo the risk and imaginative effort of developing the functional relevance of their own cultural commitments in the terms of their own disciplines, then the liberal arts are seen to be not only irrelevant to our struggle for the commitments which will enable us to grasp and shape our culture, but actual roadblocks to that effort. Vague, scholarly gnosticism is weak medicine for a culture in the midst of revolutionary change.

It often is argued that personal commitments distort scholarly efforts, and this might be a telling argument in an age where strong cultural norms exist. But in our time, where such norms are swallowed up in a quicksand environment, scholarly efforts are meaningless if they do not help to build personal commitments. Acquiescent cynicism and convulsive opinionism are the typical styles of those who have not been helped to discover that liberal intelligence and deep commitments are correlates rather than antagonists. Until the necessity of helping our culture commit itself to coherent perspectives from which to reflect on itself is accepted as a central responsibility by the liberal arts and sciences, their weight in the educational process will be negligible.

Fortunately, there is a growing awareness of the university's failure to fulfill its *raison d'être* as the agent for bringing into clear focus the age's most mature visions of Truth and for helping the culture to reflect on itself. Pres. Julius Stratton of the Massachusetts Institute of Technology has pointed out that, although we once could assume that technological innovation could be absorbed by culture without very severe dislocations, the rapid pace and extensive reach of innovation nowadays compels us to seek new "systems of understanding," through collaboration of professional and liberal disciplines, which can cope with these changes. At M.I.T. and elsewhere, experiments in interdisciplinary teaching and research, attempts to develop more functional designs and contents for the humanities, and new extracurricular and para-curricular forms of education are being tried in the attempt to recover the university's *raison d'être*. The problem is massive, but the will to solve it is evident in the many new experiments that are presently under way. Religious faith has a role to play in this hopeful development.

RELIGIOUS FAITH AS HELP TO THE UNIVERSITY

Our technological culture has the promise of being a "great leap forward" in mankind's growth towards its maturity, and the university has the potentiality of playing a critical role in the realization of that promise. Religious faith, likewise, has the promise or potentiality to help the university to realize its appropriate role. This religious function has a provisional character because it is not being fulfilled now with any great power in the university. Those in the university who hold a religious faith reserve its significance for familial and personal dimensions of their lives and see little relevance for it in the vocational and intellectual spheres outside of such personal aspects as being sensitive to a colleague's personal problems or honest in one's research results. Religious faith is much more profoundly alienated from a viable role in the university's struggle for a cultural role than are the liberal arts and sciences.

How, in principle, can the holders of religious faith within the university (and here the reference is to the Judeo-Christian tradition at the very most) help the institution to recover its perspective-focusing and reflective role in the culture? The answer (which is simple enough, although its realization certainly is not) is by recovering the historical and cultural perspectives of their faith and by giving these perspectives play in their intellectual lives—in the very terms of their disciplines—as viewpoints for reflecting on the state of our culture. In the present intellectual style of non—commitment and narcissistic reflection, such stances would be risky and revolutionary. It would demand religious imagination which is rusty with disuse. It would be so demanding of faith and intellect that both probably would be changed beyond recognition alongside their current models. The Judeo-Christian faith would recover some of the deeply cultural and historical commitments of the Old Testament prophets, and the intellect would become a means of cultural definition and direction rather than a victim of cultural drift. Most importantly, such an effort would serve the university as one model of the kind of struggle for cultural perspectives and reflective skill which should be its central concern. It would serve as further encouragement to others in the university to uncover and clarify their own often unarticulated commitments and to test them as perspectives for reflection on our culture.

As a chaplain at M.I.T., with a mandate from the Protestant Ministry to be concerned especially with the faculty, I have attempted to work from this model. In the university, a chaplain, of course, has special advantages and disadvantages which others do not have. The main disadvantages are that, because of his anomalous, unstructured role, he does not usually participate in policy-making, and his opinions always can be discounted easily as special pleading. The main advantages are simply the obverse of the disadvantages. His anomalous, unstructured role allows him a certain freedom and breadth of perspective, and his public viewpoint gives explicit definition to his actions. From this standpoint, with the help and advice of several M.I.T. faculty members, I have been able to convene a Faculty Seminar on Technology and Culture whose purpose is simply to search, through interdisciplinary reflection, for viable perspectives on our technological culture. The seminar is a good example of the kind of occasions which the university needs to develop to recover its *raison d'être* in our culture: it grew directly out of a religious perspective; and it is a strategem which easily could be used in other universities. It is, therefore, worth further description.

The first meeting of several M.I.T. faculty members and administrators to consider such a seminar considered its possible purpose in the following way, as stated by this writer:

The fact of technology—works and spirit—is so much a part of the air we breath, so much a pre-supposition in our contemporary understanding of self, that it is extremely difficult to step back from it, reflect on its power, appraise its character and weight, and find perspectives for creative judgments on it. Although there are many articles on individual aspects of technologically induced cultural change, there has not been enough of a sustained effort to walk around the whole issue, to see it whole if possible, and this is the basic reason which has prompted several of us to begin thinking about this seminar.

In particular, we need to try to bring some light to bear on M.I.T.'s role in this matter as an institution for educating technologists. That is, we have to discover ways of making students more sophisticated in their approach to technology, to help them find ways to use technology according to some conscious criteria rather than to be used by it, to help them gain some *authority* over the fact of technology. I speak here of students, but I really am suggesting that the whole Institute, as well as our whole culture, could benefit by such an ongoing attempt to gain some intellectual sophistication vis-a-vis technology. We can only control what we understand.

At that first meeting, several important decisions were made. The membership of the seminar should be as broadly interdisciplinary as possible. We would meet monthly for papers and discussion, with topics and speakers chosen by a representative Steering Committee. We would attempt to gain cumulative, rather than random, insight through careful planning and by transcribing from tapes the talk and discussion of each session and sending copies to each member before the next session. The seminar should not be in any way "official," but, rather, an *ad hoc* gathering of those whose interest in the issues brought them together.

This format derives fundamentally from the Columbia Seminars, but the differences of intention and membership are crucial. Because the Columbia Seminars' primary purpose is to build a body of public knowledge about a given subject, they tend to involve mainly the specialized range of disciplines which is directly pertinent to each topic, and a majority of their members come from outside Columbia University. The primary concern of the M.I.T. Seminar is simply to educate the membership by developing perspectives and reflecting from them on our technological culture, thereby serving as a kind of paradigm to focus the collective consciousness of the Institute on this responsibility. Therefore, it has limited its membership to the M.I.T. faculty and administrators. Within this limitation, however, it has tried to get the broadest disciplinary range possible.

The Steering Committee decided that the first year should be devoted to a broad survey of technology and culture issues. Institute members who led sessions were Elting Morison (Department of Industrial Management) on a historical example of technology as a force for social change; Robert Wood (Chairman, Department of Political Science) on the effects of technology on political processes; Richard Douglas (Chairman, Department of Humanities) on the role of humanities in a technological school and culture; and Pres. Stratton on the problem of developing "systems of understanding" to cope with technological change. Others who led sessions were Melvin Kranzberg (Editor of *Technology and Culture*) on technology and human values; Donald Michael (Institute of Policy Studies) on the social effects of "cybernation"; Emmanuel Mesthene (Director, Harvard Program on Technology and Society) on science and technology as means and ends; and Roger Revelle (Director, Harvard Center of Population Studies) on technology and population.

During the course of the first year, the seminar grew to 40 members, including junior and senior faculty from every department, many among the most seminal minds at the Institute. Only those are invited as new members who can bring to the discussion some particular perspective not yet represented. Discussion is always lively and sometimes extremely painful and clumsy, as the most fundamental assumptions of each discipline are tested against those of other disciplines and as untried dimensions of thought are demanded of participants. It is evident, however, that ground is being gained in terms of the purposes of the seminar.

There is a hunger for such basic and serious dialogue in the university today—a real readiness to undertake the exhilarating but painful task of recovering the university's cultural *raison d'être* as the place where fundamental commitments and perspectives are developed and tested in the course of reflecting on our culture. A proliferation of new occasions to exploit this readiness for growth is needed, and those such as the adherents of the Judeo-Christian faith, who already have certain defined perspectives on culture and who are willing to bring them into the open air of the intellectual market place, can help to develop such occasions. Our technological culture, despite its great promise, tends to subvert the commitment to broad perspectives from which men can reflect and make judgments on the culture; and the university, once a bastion for perspective delineation and judgment-making, has been weakened seriously in its role. Mature religious faith can be a valuable stimulus and aid in the university's struggle to regain its true role.

33. Conclusion

...AND SEE IT WHOLE

MAXWELL H. GOLDBERG

"**W**HIRL IS KING, having driven out Zeus.**"** Fixety is deposed. Daniel Bell declares that modern culture "is today at the point of breaking up all fixed points of reference in formal genres" (cited by Myron B. Bloy, Jr.). In our troubled phantasies, Fickle Change rides a precarious throne on shifting seas—aimlessly or toward some as yet unsighted goal. Toward a Baconian New Atlantis, with its scientific and benevolent House of Solomon? Toward a Swiftian Laputa, like the TV vehicle of "Lost in Space," of busy projectors researching this and that, and, like the TV characters, leaving basic decisions as to their very survival "up to The Computer"? Toward a grimly mechanized robot port of no recall, a submarine Walden II? Toward a Milltown of vegetating Lotus Eaters and partakers of hallucigens? Toward a Soma Shangri-La or the Blessed Isles? Toward a celestial city for the creative spirit of fully hominized (not homogenized) man?

In the boundless realms of technological change, Whirl is King. It presides over changes that, in degree of novelty, in rate of speed-up and magnification, in penetrative power and pervasiveness, are exponential.

A realistic expert on projection, Arnold Barach, himself bullish by temperament and conviction, acknowledges that, only three years after a series of his predictions, it is clear he sadly has underestimated the rate of change. Just one of the technological innovations—the computer—realistically is claimed to be more revolutionary than the wheel, the printing press, the steam engine, the electric motor, or atomic energy; and it is stated, as fact, that "certainly no other single item of capital goods has changed the basic terms of so many human activities in so short a time."[1]

Even those who accept recent arguments against automation as the villain in job dislocation and displacement[2] often acknowledge that, for our whole way of life, technological progress is effecting a "deep transformation"—a "sea change into something new and strange." The question is not *whether*, but *when*. The further question is: "What to do about changes that not only are breathtaking in themselves, but are communicated, around the world, like a supersonic boom and all at once, so that we live within a grotesquely magnified kaleidoscope of *here-and-now?*"[3]

Rejecting a passive role, the contributors to this book manfully reply, as does Pres. Johnson: "If we have the brainpower to invent these machines we have the brainpower to make certain that they are a boon and not a bane to humanity." "Let us never forget that the economic system and the technology upon which it is based were created to serve man. . . . We make them and we shall remake them" (August Heckscher). "Today, for the first time in human history, we have the right to human dignity"; and we have the duty to respond to that distinctive human demand: "I want to be treated like a man" (Luther Harshbarger).

---

[1] Gilbert Burck, "The Boundless Age of the Computer," *Fortune*, 69:101, March, 1964.

[2] *Cf.*, R. A. Gordon, "Has Structural Unemployment Worsened?" *Industrial Relations*, 3:53-77, May, 1964; Charles E. Silberman, "The Real News about Automation," *Fortune*, 71:124-127, 220-222, 227-228, January, 1965; "The Comeback of the Blue Collar Worker" ("The Unemployment Problem: It's Not What You Think"), *ibid.*, 71:153-155, 210-216, February, 1965; "What Hit the Teenagers?" ("The Real Cause of Teenage Unemployment"), *ibid.*, 71:130-133, April, 1965; and E. K. Faltermayer, "The Drift to Early Retirement," *ibid.*, 71:112-115, 218, 222, May, 1965. For refutation of Mr. Silberman's strictures against her "Computers and Cyberculture," see Alice Mary Hilton's "Letter," *feedback*, 2:1, February, 1965. See also, Peter F. Drucker, "Automation Is Not the Villain," *New York Times Magazine*, Jan. 10, 1965, pp. 26-27, 75-77, 82 (identifies improved education as the villain); and *Newsweek*, "The Challenge of Automation," Jan. 25, 1965, pp. 73-80. *Cf.*, "Triple Revolution: Cybernation-Weaponry-Human Rights," issued May 22, 1965, by the Information Service, Department of Research, National Council of Churches, New York City; and Daniel Bell, "The Bogey of Automation," *The New York Review*, 5:23-25, Aug. 26, 1965.

[3] *Cf.*, Maxwell H. Goldberg, "The Displacement of Human Labor," *The Evolving Society*, ed. Alice Mary Hilton, Institute for Cybercultural Research, New York, 1965, *passim*.

"Whirl is King, having driven out Zeus," and the question for educators, too, is: *What are we to do about it?* In response, hundreds of voices—from that of a scholarly Margaret Mead to that of a popular woman's magazine—blend into a swelling chorus: *Educate for radical change.* Yet, this is but the Alpha, not the Omega. What fills in the rubric? What is the paradigm? How can the schools prepare students for a future as yet unknown? First, obviously, we must help cultivate a receptivity to continuous and heavy change. Also to sudden change. But how?

For one thing, by generalistic education: "Our time demands that we raise the broad educational level of all our people, that we deny to no one education's passport to the future. General education is the foundation of all learning. It can be neglected only at our peril" (Francis Keppel). It is such education that makes "well-rounded citizens in a democratic society, who have to understand many things in order to take active part in the decision-making process" (George Arnstein). It is such education that meets the challenge of the sign: "No Room at the Bottom."

There is no room at the civic bottom and no room at the vocational bottom; and the generalistic emphasis is recommended for both. "Let us assure every child the opportunity of attending a comprehensive high school of sufficient size to give reasonable choices with reference to vocational interests and personal needs." "Let us delay intensive, specialized skill training until past high school or on-the-job training" (Virgil Rogers).

Nor, for personal living, is there room at the bottom. And, again, we have the generalistic prescription—with emphasis on cultural enrichment for adulthood as well as for the present: "recreational skills, hobby interests, familiarity with the rich resources of the library and how to make the fullest use of them." Education which prepares for the world of work likewise will "encourage greater appreciation of the fine arts and volunteer services to the community" (*ibid.*).

In-service training, too, will have its generalistic emphasis. Increasingly, jobs are being designed that combine skills from a number of crafts. Increasingly, we must provide programs to make educated people quickly into combined-skills people who quickly can master new combined skills. This means that men on the job, too, must be prepared for "a dynamic and fluid situation." Hence the question: "How do you learn to see a job as 'becoming' and not as 'being'?" The answer, in part: "As static thinking must give way to dynamic thinking, so linear thinking must give way to process thinking" (Ball, Croft, Lloyd).

To do this, moreover, is to move to a wholly different way of sizing up problems:

Teaching must face a problem of action as a set of many elements where each interacts with all the others now and continuously. Human "control" of these elements consists of trying to shove the whole system slightly one way or another while it is in motion, with an eye always to the fringe effects (*ibid.*).

Nor is this wholly different way of sizing up problems limited to operation training:

This same structural intersection of variables exists in higher level business decisions, in human relations, in complicated accounting practices, in laboratory experiments . . . and in everything. Following Whitehead, Bridgman, and others, this kind of thinking has virtually remade the physical sciences. It now is beginning to have a similar effect on behavioral sciences (*ibid.*).

How do we educate for meteoric change? Educators have to resolve, for themselves and their students, the resulting crisis in human values. One answer is: nothing less than utter innovation. We must have a new dialectic and semantics of *work* as well as a new ethic for it. We must free the idea of work from the notion that its value can be gained only at the plant and through the market economy; we must free it from bondage to the calvinistic doctrine: *Laborare est orare* (to work is to pray). We must change both the idea of work and that of prayer.[4] "We will need new programs which will prepare children for a world in which they will work, not under threat, but as part of their membership in society" (Margaret Mead).

Similarly, according to the advocates of axiological innovation, we must have a whole new dialectic and semantics of leisure—a new ethic and a whole new vocabulary: *idleness, indolence, sloth, laziness, loafing, daydreaming, boredom, ennui, apathy, withdrawal, retreat, brooding, ruminating, meditating, contemplating, fun, play, diversion; unallocated time, spare time, left-over time, vacant time, blank time, open time, free time, pastime, killed time, recreational time, re-creative time*, and so on.

Some advocates of axiological innovation either reject or ignore the ultimately self-denying, self-sacrificial set of the traditional Judeo-

---

[4] At the Second Annual Conference on the Cybercultural Revolution (New York City, May 1, 1965), Prof. Aaron Levenstein pointed out that the Hebrews "linked their work with worship," "by using the same term *avodah* to represent both," and thus found "in their economic activities an identification with life's basic meaning."

Christian ethic or of the heroic or tragic view of life in classical humanism. They blandly assume, as altogether fitting and proper, an easy-come, easy-going hedonism. The traditional ethic of austerity asks, with the Jewish sage, "Where stands it written that we must be happy?" The new ethic—the "fun morality"—has one commandment: *Enjoy! Enjoy!* Thrill to the marvels of technological change! Enjoy its bountiful blessings! Take as your model Carnation's contented cow! *Consume! Consume!*

But there are some who view this easy-does-it interpretation of leisure as paving the way for "serious social confusion." They insist on something more than this fair-weather formula for the good man, the good life, and the good society. They call for some fundamental reinterpretation of the nature of work and leisure. They insist that this "must go deeply into concepts which undergird our entire culture." They call for radical probes and complete revisions (Dale Harris).

In place of the definition of work as "activity involving muscular and/or mental effort to produce effects which are valued by others, and hence are rewarded by pay," they suggest a definition which "embodies any effort leading to the development of potentiality considered very broadly," and without reference to pay as major motivation or reward. Thus revised, the concept of work and the concept of leisure will be much closer together, with the result that intellectual and social activities which lead to enhancement of the self will constitute the "leisure-work" in the world of tomorrow. This, in time, will mean that "we blend somehow the notion of the personally and socially enhancing with the idea of the economically productive" (*ibid.*).

Such re-definitions and re-conceptualizations, it is admitted, will pose real dilemmas as to human values: "it will take a subtle value system to insure that, on the one hand, those who can excel are encouraged to do so and that, on the other hand, the limits of others will not result in their discouraged withdrawal into trivial leisure," the mediocrity of cheaply pre-fabricated products, the apathy of routinized services, and the passivity of spectator amusements (Donald Michael). Yet, this entropic lowering of energy and motivation for the individual's pursuit of excellence is not inevitable: "the threat may be annulled by instilling in the student, at all levels, the conviction that the arbiter of excellence is originality. Thus, if leisure is imposed on one, it will be welcomed as an opportunity to give full force and effect to one's innate creative drives which have been reinforced continuously throughout the educative life." For this there is an important proviso—namely, that "the forced-feeding of mere facts in the dissolved hope that they some day may be used in a constructive way" will be replaced by another sort of education, the goal of which will be "creative implication and application"— through a "creatively heuristic process" (Stanley Foster Reed).

Dynamic rather than static in their intellectual habits, the contributors to this book generally favor creative reconcilement of divergences. With Dr. René Dubos, they favor energetic response, not passive adjustment.[5] They favor responses that prove—that is, test— the limits of creative accommodation within the constraints of substantive, personal, and social integrity. They reject simplistic reductions, dichotomies, and polarizations. They favor strenuous, versatile, and ingenious *both-and* rather than *either-or* strategies: "I cast my lot with those who are seeking a middle way . . . " (G. Bruce Dearing).

Even some of those who declare that "we have to build a new society (if not a great society, then surely a better one) with an entirely different functional pattern of values" (Walter Davis), wish to have us follow the *both-and* habit of creative reconcilement. "The Judeo-Christian ethic of an outgoing concern for the welfare of our fellow men is a pretty fair base on which to start." For, in "the society of abundance which cybernation will produce, the well-being of all is the key to human relationships powered by justice and compassion." Yet, in shaping the new education—both for youngsters and for adults—"we will have to invent new means for making these traditional ethical powers freshly functional for our radically altered, and even more radically altering, industrial and social situation—both as it confronts the individual and as it confronts the community" (*ibid.*).

Indeed, the great business now, of the humanist, is "inventive inter-meshing"—creative mediation. He must mediate between the past and the present-future. He must mediate creatively between our easy acceptance of technologies and our tendency, in ethics, to be anachronistically conservative or blind to the problems of ethical realignment caused by this cultural lag. He must mediate creatively those problematic discrepancies or divergences caused by our habit of moving "different parts of our lives into the future at different speeds." He must mediate creatively the divergences caused by the

---

[5] "Humanistic Biology," *The American Scholar*, 34:179-198, Spring, 1965.

lag between the latest knowledge of the experts and the going moods of the artists and writers entrapped in now outmoded lore and impacted sensibilities. He must help bring about those mediative decisions arrived at through weighing social gain and social loss in proposed solutions to problems of human concern (Warner Rice).

One of the processes on which the mediative propensities of humanists are to be brought to bear is that of paradoxic confrontation and resolution. They are to be brought constructively to bear on such paradoxes as are described in the following: "Some of us have a feeling that our bodies are moving too fast for our souls to keep up" (William Mather). "Man's belief in himself is weakest in the very age when control of his environment is greatest" (Luther Harshbarger). More specifically, we have in the very title of Charles Bowen's chapter, "The Paradoxes of Abundance," a key to how this humanistic mediation works. Through dialectic processes of thought, policymaking, programming, and action, one bends the antithetic poles of a paradox toward each other until the yoke becomes a closed circle and circuit and the extremes fuse to form a new and potent unity.

Thus, we have a call for a new humanistic education that creatively reconciles rigor and resiliency and education for technical competence with education for emotional or psychic competence (Peter Siegle). Such twofold competence enables us, as Clarence Randall expressed it in the 1957 *Lectures* of the Fund for Adult Education, to move with confidence into an uncertain future. Again, we have the call for a new humanistically educated executive who, within the constraining principle of quality, combines both "literacy" and "numeracy" and excellence in limited areas with proficiency in the rest (Charles Peters). Again, as Donald Michael indicated in his December, 1963, CCLE-IBM Humanities Conference talk, we have a call for a humanistic education to produce leaders who are not only technically proficient, but also men of deep understanding, wisdom, justice, and compassion to resolve the very paradoxes of abundance in our teeming and turbulent time.

In this same mood of creative mediation we are told that the scholar "will refrain, in all likelihood, from full acceptance or rejection of the new phenomenon in pedagogy"—that is, the teaching machine (William W. Brickman). Again, we have the recommendation that we are to mediate the shock of automational job dislocation and displacement by such devices as earlier retirement and the second career and by cultivating the economy of the craft side by side with the economy of the machine (August Heckscher). In some instances, we have a paradoxic dilemma posed for resolution: "One way of looking at this entire problem is to ask the question, 'How can . . . social needs be converted into economic jobs?' " (*ibid.*). Again,

The main difference between unemployment and leisure lies in the attitude taken toward being not-gainfully employed. Let us encourage the unemployed to become a leisure class rather than an unemployed group. . . . We ought to find ways of using their presence among us to develop ways of enjoying leisure to greater advantage (Luther Evans).

And still another paradox: " . . . regulation is not necessarily the opposite of freedom. . . . Life must be much more regulated, but I think this should and can produce greater freedom in areas where freedom counts most" (*ibid.*).

Indeed, concerning the very nature of a humanistic education suited to an age of advanced technological and social change, we have a pervasive paradox. It is that the humanities, as historically transmitted, as conventionally conceived and defended, as conventionally organized and taught, just will not do. Paradoxically, it is insisted, if they are to gain their life, they must lose it. The traditional humanities must steel themselves to jettisoning a great deal of the classical *impedimenta*—as distinguished from the essential spirit and enduring vitality—inherited from the glory that was Greece and the grandeur that was Rome, as well as from the vast cultural turbulences and treasure houses of the Renaissance. Much of this heritage is hard to render freshly viable to our technological times; even if rendered viable and available, it too often turns out to be—whether to the world of action or to man's inner needs—irrelevant.

Again, paradoxically, if the traditional and conventional humanities are to gain their life, they must lose their inherited forms. They must learn to absorb into their own organism modifying increments from other academic disciplines and non-academic spheres of human creativity. For *the wind bloweth where it listeth,* and the enduring humanistic spirit within the humanities breathes through the various voices of man's changing efforts, experiences, and aspirations.[6]

This, for example, is the meaning of Ralph Burhoe's allegory. When the humanist, Jack, first looked into the wondrous Black Book that the Angel of Death gave to him, his face fell. Contrary to his excited expectations, it was neither a new Bible nor a new Plato. It

---

[6] *Cf.,* Maxwell H. Goldberg, "The Impact of Technological Change on the Humanities," *Educational Record,* Fall, 1965.

was "The Book of Science." "And Jack woke up in a sweat and vowed never to sleep again." But, later, when Jack did look into this strange new book, he was "most electrified." For, "he suddenly felt he was reading the most magnificent dramatic poem in any literature, revealing hitherto hidden but now overarchingly significant values of man and his world."

Put in non-allegorical language,

concepts of the good are as much the property of history or sociology as of philosophy or literature; beauty belongs as much to mathematics as to art history; and truth both transcends and eludes all our formulations and organizational patterns (G. Bruce Dearing).

In this statement we move toward the encompassing paradox of this entire volume: education for a technological age must provide at once for the increasingly refined specialization essential to such an age and for the interrelative, integrative, synthesizing efforts without which our specialties become mutually repellent particles. Briefly, but in no creedal or dogmatic sense and without implying a mystique, a formal metaphysic, or theology, our education must be resolutely and pervasively holistic.

This goes for our vocational or technical training as well as for our general or liberal education. "We find vocational and general education to be far too often as separate streams in the development of secondary schools"; "we would make a grave error to set vocational education apart from the basic fabric of education" (Francis Keppel). "Interdisciplinary research, drawing together such fields as psychology, social psychology, sociology, anthropology, and linguistics, is just beginning to show its relevance to practical training needs." To be noted, also, is "the growing interest in such interdisciplinary fields as communication, organization theory, information theory, learning theory, open systems theory, international development theory, computer-based business decision-making, and many others." "The behavioral scientists begin to understand each other and grope toward unified views of man in an industrial society" (Ball, Lloyd, Croft).

This groping marks a reaction from the "free-enterprising entre-preneurship of professors eager to stake out specialities in the land-scape of truth" and from the dominant current practice of education and the intellectual vocations "patterning themselves after the tech-nological content of culture" (Roy C. Buck). This groping toward unified views of man in an industrial society marks a recognition clarified through the image of the exploded drawing of a power lawnmower to be put together by the purchaser. "The drawing, the analysis, make the parts visible, but it is the synthesis of the parts that produces the power and the manicured lawn." It is "the relationship of the parts" that makes for the meaningful whole (*ibid.*). More than that, as Albert Browne-Mayers has observed, such a synthesis, in education for human competence, yields "a total configuration in which the whole appears to be more than the sum of its parts."[7]

This same holistic impulsion gives fresh force to the reiterated conviction that, for our technological times, continuing education through all of adulthood is essential.[8] Lip service or casual treatment as educational by-product, afterthought, or sideshow is not enough. Merely exploitive treatment of continuing education as a money-raiser for other activities of an educational institution, or as a means for the advancement of the institution's public favor and public support—this, too, is not enough.

It is not enough partly because of the principles and necessities of American democracy and the aspirations of the still vigorous American Dream: "To deny educational opportunity to any of us diminishes us all" (Francis Keppel). It is not enough, also, because of the totalistic impact of exponentially accelerating technological change and because of the need for correspondingly totalistic (not to be confused with totalitarian) response on the part of education: "The impact of change and the knowledge explosion are not limited to the professions, but are setting off shock waves felt in varying degrees in virtually every form of human endeavor. It is a compelling fact of life that we must commit ourselves to being students all our lives. A continuing education—training and retraining—is our primary response to the challenge of automation and technological change" (Anthony Celebrezze). Again: "our schools . . . must respond to the need of education as a lifelong process—indeed, as a lifelong necessity" (Francis Keppel). Or again: "Changing technology, in fact, has made it a necessity that all of us make education a lifelong activity," a "high percentage" of which should be in the humanizing liberal

---

[7] "The Uses of Experience," *Saturday Review*, 47:24, Dec. 12, 1964.

[8] *Cf.*, Maxwell H. Goldberg, "Continuous Education as a Way of Life," *Adult Education*, Fall, 1965; Maxwell H. Goldberg, "Leisure, Education, and the Formative Nature of Man," in "Symposium on Leisure," ed. Richard E. Wentz, University Park, Pa., 1965; and Maxwell H. Goldberg, "Meaning and Metaphor: On Teaching Human Values through Poetry at a Steelworkers Institute," Center for the Study of Liberal Education for Adults at Boston University, Brookline, Mass., 1965.

arts (Hubert H. Humphrey).

This means that in the remainder of our century—to consider just one sector of adult education—"nearly as many adults will be working for college degrees on a part-time basis as will undergraduates enrolled full-time in our higher institutions."[9] It means the encompassing need for "an extension of educational opportunities to every segment of the population of a variety and even quality never before possible and at a cost per student hour of instruction at least comparable with, if not greatly below, present costs."

To meet these great needs—both quantitative and qualitative—of continuing education for adults, we already have at hand the instrumentalities: above all, in plans for great learning resource centers—one of which can service a whole city, a whole state, or even a whole region; and in plans for corresponding study-space receiving "stations" for the student. Here we have a twofold picture: of the master computer at the learning resource center; of the small-scale, moderate cost ($400-$500) computer at the receiving end for the student. Indeed, "it is the addition of a computer which transforms a useful additional teaching tool [programmed instruction] into something which, next to the human teacher, may prove to be the most effective teaching instrument yet devised."

Moreover, far from rendering the live teacher obsolete in adult education, this new system "undoubtedly would generate great demand for direct contact with teachers." For "once people get a taste for education through independent study, they generally want the experience of sharing ideas with others." Hence: "Whether in privately arranged group meetings or in specially organized formal seminars and workshops, individuals would find ways to satisfy the need to exchange ideas with fellow human beings."

While the versatile new instrumentalities would be applied, as appropriate, all along the educational front, they might best be concentrated, in the near future, on advanced adult study. For "the system would be entering a field now serviced by a wide variety of institutions, none strong enough to resist the program," and, in any case, few of which "are doing anything in the areas in which the system would be most important" (*ibid.*).

Of course, advanced adult education would not be limited to the computer-coupled complexes of resources and instrumentalities. The

---

[9] This and the following citations on continuing education are drawn from the chapter by Norman D. Kurland.

small, high-level, person-to-person seminar in continuing liberal education for adults would continue to have its place—either by itself or as an educational experience to be "beamed out" to large numbers of other adults by way of the new instrumentalities. The Columbia Seminars, the Humanities Center Institutes on industry and liberal education as at Corning, N.Y., and Delaware, Ohio (with du Pont), the American Humanities Seminars (at the University of Massachusetts), the Washington Colloquium on Science and Society, the Summer Conference on Science and Society set up by the Oak Ridge Institute for Nuclear Studies, the programs at Aspen and "Aspen East," at the Brookings Institution, and the leadership conferences, seminars, forums, institutes, and study-discussion courses of the Center for Continuing Liberal Education, College of the Liberal Arts, The Pennsylvania State University—all are working models for such leadership-level, non-degree programs in continuing liberal education for adults.

All in all, as far as continuing education is concerned, "we somehow must engrain it into the culture more widely and more deeply than we have succeeded to date" (Dale B. Harris). As far as general, liberal, and humanistic education is concerned, we must treat continuing education as a "vital continuum," and we must start, in the education of the child, to make him adequately self-motivated and adequately competent in learning as a lifelong, heuristic process of inner growth in wholeness.

This devotion to wholeness as a cultural and educational criterion and goal, and as furnishing models for pragmatic process and production, takes various forms and moves in various directions.

The very word, *health*, as Thomas Carlyle pointed out, has a root meaning of *wholeness*. So it is aptly a physician, a psychiatrist from public health and industry, who stresses the wholeness approach. He sets an ecological framework within which to consider education, technological change, and health. He defines ecology as "the study of the totality of the relationships of organisms within the environment." He insists that segmented, reductionist outlooks and methods never should be employed "without frequent reconsideration" of an initially established "ecological, holistic point of view." Such a holistic point of view, however, takes into account the interactions—or, to go back to Polybius, the transactions among the physical, the psychic, the societal, the cultural components within what Kurt Lewin called the individual's total "life-space" (John MacIver).

Similarly holistic thinking is seen in this declaration: "if the use of machines by the government does not result in the improvement of the whole man . . . the United States will have lost its way"; for the "whole theory of the universe is directed unerringly to one single individual"—namely, in this context, to each individual within the "American compact" (James A. Donovan, Jr., citing Walt Whitman). The "education of the whole man will have to come from inside out as more and more thousands of people are faced with the frightening prospect of increased leisure" (*ibid.*).

This cosmically and socially activated, yet internally and individually originative impulse toward education in and for wholeness becomes an antidote to that sort of anomie, in Durkheim's term, which we experience as cultural dropouts because of our lack of identification with "the system"—political or economic—and partly, at least, because we have not come to understand it earlier (Stanley Foster Reed). The anomie of the systemic dropout expresses itself in education for technological super-specialization—whether in personal, professional, or civic endeavor, or whether in the sciences or the arts—and by no means excluding the humanities.

As antidote, we must "instill in the student the concept that he is an originative part and parcel of the system, that he can make and mold his own environment in his own image, that there is a great universe of possibilities out there through which to be creative or originally critical" (*ibid.*). There are, thus, two intersecting spirals toward wholeness to which education should habituate the individual: (1) the fullest expression of his own nature as a human being; (2) the order in the universe which it is the individual's duty freshly to discover and formulate. If successful, this combined creative, holistic effort of the individual will "leave . . . some little try, some tiny rationality to add to the universal order as his particular monument to the ages." (*Cf.*, William Henry Henley's "I have a bit of fiat in my soul"; and Ralph Waldo Emerson's "The world globes itself in a drop of dew.")

The need to be "originally critical" through internal wholeness is all the more urgent in an epoch of meteoric technological change. The freedom we have gained by technological advances "can be lost if we are unable to achieve personal collectedness or coherence to take risks without being centrifugally pulled apart." It can be lost if we are unable to "develop a coherent, yet flexible point of view from which we can exercise real judgments."[10]

While this is an individual quest, it involves collaborative effort. "Although we once could assume that technological innovation could be absorbed by culture without very severe dislocations, the rapid pace and extensive reach of innovation nowadays compels us to seek new 'systems of understanding,' through collaboration of professional and liberal disciplines, which can cope with these changes" (citing Pres. Julius Stratton of M.I.T.). The university's *raison d'être* is for nothing less than "bringing into clear focus the age's most mature visions of Truth"—not Truth as contemplative vision merely, but Truth, rather, as a criterion and goal for wise and responsible action as applied to the whole culture.

Those who hold religious faith (Judeo-Christian) should include, within this holistic habit of projective enquiry, evaluation, and application, the "historical and cultural perspectives of their faith." They should give "these perspectives play in their intellectual lives—in the very terms of their disciplines—as viewpoints for reflecting on the state of our culture." An example of this sort of effort is the M.I.T. Seminar on Technology and Culture, which is "a search, through interdisciplinary reflection, for viable perspectives on our technological culture"—perspectives "growing directly out of a religious perspective." Through the reactivated religious imagination, now "rusty with disuse," the academic who holds religious faith should apply these religious perspectives in the shaping of models for the future development of our culture within the constraints and potentialities of technological change.

Indeed, "until the necessity for helping our culture commit itself to coherent perspectives from which to reflect on itself is accepted as a central responsibility by the liberal arts and sciences, their weight in the educational process will be negligible." At least two serious deterrents to such acceptance present themselves. The first is found in the circumstance that, as Paul Goodman has pointed out, "The dynamic character of the liberal arts and sciences has been broken into pieces by the university's penchant for rationalistic (rather than organic) order." The second is to be found in the "contemporary cultural schizophrenia" which has reduced to a minimum the active, "dialogical" role, in our technological culture and with technology itself, that the liberal arts and sciences should play. This, in turn, has produced an alienation which deprives the technological

---

[10] This and the following quotations are from the chapter by Myron B. Bloy, Jr.

culture of the help it needs to achieve its maturity—as Teilhard de Chardin has conceived it—in the evolutionary history of man and as a current expression of divine grace and divine purpose.

What we have here is related to the traditional humanistic effort, as formulated in Matthew Arnold's tribute to Sophocles:

> . . . whose even balanced soul
> From first youth tested up to extreme old age
> Business could not make dull, nor passion wilt,
> Who saw life steadily and saw it whole.

Yet, this contemporary holistic emphasis bears the stamp of our technological times. For both its imagery and its instrumentalities, as well as its urgencies, are drawn directly from technology itself. They are drawn from the instantaneous pictures we have had of the Gemini missions, "where the intricate interrelationship of complicated electronic systems was immediately in great part understood and accepted by millions throughout the world."[11] They amount to "the application of the implications of a systems approach" to many aspects of education and the applying of "rigorous comprehensiveness" and of "manipulating models of systems and subsystems" to help solve problems of an educational institution, however complex.

This systems approach to the problems of education in a technological epoch calls for a certain degree of sophistication. It calls for recognition that it "is perfectly possible within a system to achieve a steady state, where inputs and outputs are so balanced that an equilibrium, not a stasis, is established"; and this equilibrium can be a vital, a dynamic, a creative equilibrium. This approach "has also the virtue of taking into account the fact that education is a lifelong process."

The preceding citations, illustrative of the emergent systems approach to education in an advanced technological epoch,[12] are the words of a Ph.D. in English. They are the words of a humanist scholar who has held positions of high esteem and responsibility in

---

[11] This and the following quotations are from "Schools, Styles, and Systems in Thinking," inauguration address by G. Bruce Dearing, president, State University of New York at Binghamton, Sept. 25, 1965.

[12] For an elaborate presentation of a systemic concept of the modern university, *cf.*, Paul Weiss, "Science in the University," *Daedalus*, 93:1184-1217, Fall, 1964. What Dean Weiss advocates is a pattern of "efficient super-universities, communities of scholarly institutions," the "Integrated University Compact," achieved through "the linking of existing autonomous institutions of higher learning into self-regulatory networks." "Such an ideal university system," maintains Dean Weiss, "is both conceivable and practicable. It would achieve the restoration of the very principle of *continuity, unity, and universality of knowledge,* the loss or abandonment of which our universities bemoan."

his profession and who, "at risk of the revocation of his membership in the fraternity of humanists," nevertheless spoke thus—and in his inaugural address as president of an institution priding itself on its college of liberal arts and sciences.

We find the systemic imagery in other significant contemporary thinking about education as a lifelong process for continuing and humanistic self-renewal—both individual and social. "In the ever-renewing society," declares Secretary John W. Gardner, "what matures is a system or framework within which continuous innovation, renewal, rebirth occur." And, again—this time in biological terms: "for an ever-renewing society the appropriate image is a total garden, a balanced aquarium or other ecological system. Some things are being born, other things are flourishing, still other things are dying— but the system lives on."[13]

This effort toward wholeness, so important in American education, may be, in part, the latest expression of the traditional humanist's yearning for that rational, esthetic, and, in some instances, ethical symmetry which Leonardo da Vinci, for all his Renaissance versatility and virtuosity, felt he lacked: *Mihi una defuit: symmetria prisca.* It is the expression of a sense of urgent need for an encompassing, complex, and magnanimous instrumentality of the imagination and the intellect adequate for coping with the encompassing and complex ethico-social and cultural crises of our time.

Leaders in technology and technological education are among those most eloquently voicing this need. In his commencement address[14] to the M.I.T. graduates of 1964, M.I.T. Pres. Julius A. Stratton cited the "massive industrial technology" the engineer has created:

And now, suddenly—almost within your own generation—the whole sweeping line of advance seems to have taken fire. In some strange unforeseen way, we have come to a critical threshold, beyond which the forces of technical progress appear to be self-sustaining. The processes of discovery, invention, and production feed upon each other. . . . The translation of ideas into action is taking place at an ever-accelerating pace, so that the functional line of demarcation between scientist and engineer has about vanished. . . . The stupendous revolution of the twentieth century is doing more than adding theories, data, and apparatus to the accumulated store of the past. It has provided an entire new dimension to human affairs and a total change of scale.

This change of scale, moreover, is not merely an "expanding scale of discovery and appreciation." Its distinctiveness "lies rather in the

---

[13] "Self-Renewal: The Individual and the Innovative Society," Colophon Books, Harper & Row, New York, Evanston, and London, 1965, p. 5.

[14] *Daedalus,* issue on "The Contemporary University: USA," 93:1238-1243. *Cf.,* too, Vannevar Bush, "Science Pauses," *Fortune,* 71:116-119, 167-168, 172, May, 1965.

complete penetration of science and technology into every domain of human affairs."

According to Dr. Stratton, this "stupendous revolution" has done even more: ". . . science, technology, and society now form a tightly coupled system. Each new technical advance adds a component to that system." It is this totalistic and systemic change of scale that calls for corresponding change in education: ". . . because such components are coupled into an immensely complex system on a huge and massive scale, it is only by an examination of the impact upon society as a whole that we can pass judgement on the degree of progress." To drive home his point, Dr. Stratton, like Secretary Gardner, draws upon a biological analogy: ". . . We must advance from the anatomy of components to the physiology of the organic whole."

As Dr. Stratton sees it, these new pressures toward seeing "the great new socio-technical problems and the systems they represent" complexly—and seeing them whole—are "now also generating strongly countervailing forces" against the increasingly widespread "fragmentation of knowledge and the proliferation of multitudes of specialties" and "toward new unities, bringing together many different resources, and giving rise to a new synthesis of knowledge."

For this constructive, vastly complex, and large-spirited holistic effort, Dr. Stratton places central responsibility upon the modern university man and the modern university—particularly of the type of M.I.T. It is such a university which, in the solution of problems that "touch most deeply upon the total welfare of our society," and in "the synthesis of knowledge—as well as in the creation of new learning" upon which such solutions depend—"must lead the way." It "is only within the framework of the modern university that one finds the wide range of interests, common ground for the exchange of ideas, a forum of discussion for scholars who draw upon the arts and the humanities as well as upon science and engineering."

Thus, through shared idiom and imaging, analogy and instrumentalities, conceptualization, imaginative vision, and magnanimity, the difficult, yet crucial dialogue toward wholeness among technologist, scientist, and humanist must be advanced. This contributes to the much-needed educative process of communicational exchange (Lawrence Williams). It must be accompanied by energetic criticism—ethically, socially normative—as prelude to wise and humane collaboration. It must involve an ethic, as well as a politics and a technology, of expectations. If successful, this dialogic collaboration may bring man to the point where he may stand with dignity "on the brink of a newer and fuller life" (Stanley Lehrer). It will help assure that the National Foundation for the Humanities and the Arts will be, in the words of Frederick H. Burkhardt, president of the American Council of Learned Societies, a "visible, living monument" both to humane knowledge and to humane action; that it will have the "unprecedented effect in the arts and humanities" of the United States which Pres. Johnson has predicted; and that it will make major contributions to American education, which the President has declared to be "at the core" of his hopes for a Great Society.

APPENDIX

POINTS OF VIEW
—More or Less Predictive
and/or Provocative

EDUCATION AND THE INDIVIDUAL

Education is both the root of technological change and the basis for successful adaptation. We must become a more versatile people, with more skills and broader understanding of the modern world. A new national attitude, in which education is universally prized and innovation universally welcomed, is the key to the progress of the American people in the age of automation.—"Final Report of the Twenty-first American Assembly," *Automation and Technological Change* (1962).

Education in its broadest sense is the process of enabling a person to live in his own society.—ROBERT THEOBALD, *The Challenge of Abundance* (1961).

What is the task of the liberal college for adults? . . . Its first and continuing task is to help develop the bold and sensible individual who cannot be overwhelmed by the burdens of modern life. . . . What the college ought to do for the individual is to turn personal troubles and concerns into social issues and rationally open problems.

EDITORS' NOTE: This section was compiled by Alan Trachtenberg, Assistant Professor of English; Stephen H. Knox, Graduate Assistant in English; Annette Leavitt, Instructor in English; and John Low, Graduate Assistant in English—all of The Pennsylvania State University.

... The task is to help him become a self-educating man.—C. WRIGHT MILLS, "Mass Society and Liberal Education," *Power, Politics and People* (1963).

It is no longer sufficient to tell a person *what* he should think— what theories have already been developed—he must be taught *how* to think so that he can make sense of an altering world and plan a sensible course of action whatever the conditions. This will require a revolution in education, but this drastic change must take place.—ROBERT THEOBALD, *The Challenge of Abundance* (1961).

So if I feel free to speak disparagingly of the still current ideological background for the automation of knowledge, it is with the assurance that the more alert scientific minds of our generation have themselves led the way. Today our fundamental irreducible unit is not the atom but the human personality, in all its biological complexity and cultural multiformity. And it is now plain that only by restoring the human personality to the center of our scheme of thought can mechanization and automation be brought back into the service of life. Until this happens in education, there is not a single advance in science, from the release of nuclear energy to the isolation of DNA in genetic inheritance that may not, because of our literally absent-minded automatism in applying it, bring on disastrous consequences to the human race. These consequences would have no parallel in previous history, since in both cases they would be irreversible and irretrievable. For that possible miscarriage, our educational institutions would have to take no small share of the blame.—LEWIS MUMFORD, "The Automation of Knowledge," *Current Issues in Higher Education* (1964).

THE TECHNOLOGICAL THREAT TO HUMANISTIC STUDIES

In its essence a liberal education is an education for thought and for aesthetic appreciation. It proceeds by imparting a knowledge of the masterpieces of thought, of imaginative literature, and of art. The action which it contemplates is command. It is an aristocratic education implying leisure.—ALFRED NORTH WHITEHEAD, *The Aims of Education* (1929).

Technology is a ruthless tyranny, and its processes demand from the educational system a training directed exclusively toward conceptual modes of thought. "Money, mechanization, algebra. The three monsters of contemporary civilization." So wrote Simone Weil.—SIR

HERBERT READ, "Art and Life," *Saturday Evening Post*, CCXXXII (1959).

At present, education means nothing in the U. S.; it is a vast personnel system for the use of employers . . . a technology assisting a technology.—ROBERT M. HUTCHINS, "Achieving a Perspective on the Technological Order: Commentary," *Technology and Culture,* III (1962).

Where emphasis is placed on facts, education strives for a handbook knowledge, imparted to the student through surveys, profiles, graphs, and statistics of the subject matter. True education is incompatible with this kind of knowledge and with this method of instruction, for the crude empiricism into which such training has fallen is a purely mechanical piling up of facts. The training lays no foundation, it contains no forming principle, which would be superior to, and would master, the subject matter.—FRIEDRICH GEORG JUENGER, *The Failure of Technology* (1956).

Citing Nathan Pusey: "We live in a time of such rapid change and growth in knowledge that only he who is in a fundamental sense a scholar—that is, a person who continues to learn and inquire —can hope to play the role of guide. Indeed it is not too much to believe that we may now be coming into an Age of the Scholar, for we have created for ourselves a manner of living in America in which a little learning can no longer serve our needs."—ROBERT THEOBALD, *The Challenge of Abundance* (1961).

Citing Henry David: "Education is a mechanism for inducing change and for providing the means of accommodation and adjustment to change. At the same time, as an institution, education is given responsibility for insuring the preservation and transfer and therefore the continuity of the society's knowledge, skills, traditions and values."—LUTHER H. EVANS and GEORGE E. ARNSTEIN, eds., *Automation and the Challenge to Education: Proceedings of a Symposium* (1962).

The long-range stability of the social system depends on a population of young people properly educated to enter the adult world of tasks and attitudes. Once, the pace of change was slow enough to permit a comfortable margin of compatibility between the adult world and the one children were trained to expect. This compatibility no longer exists. Now we have to ask: What should be the education of a population more and more enveloped in cybernation? What are the appropriate attitudes toward the training for participation in government, the use of leisure, standards of consumption, particular occupations?—DONALD N. MICHAEL, *Cybernation: The Silent Conquest* (1962).

The highest end of government is the culture of men.—R. W. EMERSON.

THE NEED FOR ON-GOING EDUCATION

The man whose whole life is spent in performing a few simple operations, of which the effects too are, perhaps, always the same, or very nearly the same, has no occasion to exert his understanding, or to exercise his invention in finding out expedients for removing difficulties which never occur. . . . His dexterity at his own particular trade seems, in this manner, to be acquired at the expense of his intellectual, social and martial virtues. But in every improved and civilized society this is the state into which the labouring poor, that is, the great body of people, most necessarily fall, unless government takes some pains to prevent it.—ADAM SMITH, "The Education of the Worker," *Of Men and Machines*, ARTHUR O. LEWIS, JR., ed. (1963).

Citing Lewis Mumford, *Brainpower Quest*: "The man who has been educated in 1965 and hasn't gone on with his self-education, beyond his immediate day-to-day activities, will be uneducated in 1976. We have to think of revising the education curriculum, along with our whole scheme of work, to plan for a life-time education for all of us who are capable of taking advantage of it. The professions may even have to organize sabbatical years for study to accomplish their larger purpose of maintaining a high level of technical efficiency without debasing, through inaction and neglect, the human values we must nourish and cherish."—ROBERT THEOBALD, *The Challenge of Abundance* (1961).

Learning should be a lifelong, conscious activity . . . failure to educate in terms of new developments can only mean unemployment and social disorientation. . . . Vocational education has been slow in adapting to changing needs, operating largely within the boundaries of concepts formulated around the time of World War I. Only recently has it begun to receive even a measure of the attention it sorely needs. Adult education, as traditionally carried on, must be broadened and many of its former concerns modified. It must assume a much greater role in updating skills and promoting continued learning. The notion of refresher or extension courses, so well accepted in many professions, must become a routine course of action for people in industry and government and must be applied to workers in the lowest as well as in the highest echelons. Further, there is a great need for better facilities for counseling, guidance, and placement at the adult level.—LUTHER H. EVANS and GEORGE E. ARNSTEIN, eds., *Automation and the Challenge to Education: Proceedings of a Symposium* (1962).

In the past, educators could plan reasonably well to prepare the student for a lifetime career as a clerk, factory worker, mechanical engineer, or salesman. Most jobs and the qualifications were fairly constant. For example, the likelihood of radical change being required of a machinist or clerk was remote. New types of jobs were quite rare and generally involved very few people. Today this is no longer true. Educators at all levels now realize that education must enable graduates to undertake later career changes and be flexible enough to meet them successfully. Education and reeducation must be a continuing process throughout the careers of most young people in school today. The range of problems facing them in the next ten years, in economics, space science, automation, life science, and almost every other field will demand far more open minds, and far better trained ones, than ever before in man's history.—THOMAS J. WATSON, JR., "Technological Change," *Of Men and Machines*, ARTHUR O. LEWIS, JR., ed. (1963).

As a remedy, it has sometimes been proposed that, in addition to their technical and special instruction, workers be given a general education. . . . No doubt, it is good for the worker to be interested in art, literature, etc., but it is nonetheless bad that he should be treated as a machine all day long. Who cannot see, moreover, that two such existences are too opposed to be reconciled, and cannot be led by the same man! If a person has grown accustomed to vast horizons, total views, broad generalities, he cannot be confined without impatience, within the strict limits of a special task. . . . —EMILE DURKHEIM.

The peddlers of persuasion have now developed such techniques of sophistication and grown themselves into such large-scale enterprise that they engage the talents and the creative passions of a substantial segment of young college graduates in the fields of sociology, psychology, economics, and the English language itself. They regard the worker-consumer as a manipulatable object, rather than as a human being with individual needs and aspirations; they address him, in consequence, with a cynicism that can only be described as shameless, and they exploit him culturally as ruthlessly as he was exploited economically a generation ago.—HARVEY SWADOS, *A Radical's America* (1962).

HUMANISTIC STUDIES FOR A TECHNOLOGICAL AGE

Science interprets the phenomenal world with reference to the coherences of structure and behavior. Art transforms the phenomenal world into poetic metaphors with reference to experience unique to man. Both are indispensable to the enrichment of life in our civilization, and each can only benefit from a mature reciprocity with the other.—JULES LANGSNER, "The Artist and the Scientist," *Art and Architecture*, LXXIX (1962).

The cultivation of the arts is an education of the sensibilities, and if we are not given an education of this kind, if our hands remain empty and our perception of form is unexercised, then in idleness and vacancy we revert to violence and crime. When there is no will to creation the death instinct takes over and wills endless, gratuitous destruction.—SIR HERBERT READ, "Art and Life," *Saturday Evening Post*, CCXXXII (1959).

Scientific and technological knowledge and its applications have brought new security, new comforts, new dignity within the reach of human beings. They have brought in sight the day of elimination of most kinds of unskilled hand labor—and have thus elevated the status and the dignity of the working man—if he is suitably educated to perform more skilled and more interesting tasks. They have also increased the need for and social importance of the highly talented and the well educated—the teachers, the scientists, engineers, doctors, lawyers, industrial managers. Our educational system and our social and political institutions and practices face a great challenge in helping us—and all the world—meet these new opportunities.—LEE A. DUBRIDGE, "Educational and Social Consequences," *Automation and Technological Change* (1962).

The habit of apprehending a technology in its completeness: this is the essence of technological humanism, and this surely is what we should expect an education in higher technology to achieve.

It should be our business in higher technological education to persuade students that they cannot practice technology without continually reflecting upon its social implications, and that some understanding of the humanities is essential to this reflection.—SIR ERIC ASHBY, "Technological Humanism," *Journal of the Institute of Metals,* LXXXV (1957).

Man in the future world community will increasingly base his thoughts and actions on a view of nature, of himself, and of his works arising from the findings of science. Youths will be taught, with copious examples, the dire consequences of wishful, "rationalized" thinking, of uncritical following of authority, and of allowing symbols to mask the realities that are supposed to be represented. They will be trained in the evaluation of evidence in varied fields, in the designing of texts, in the criticism of the methods and conclusions of their own and others, and so far as it may be open to them, in creative thinking applied in diverse directions. At the same time they will be taught, both in its grand outlines and in the form of specific, vivid illustrations, what kind of a world they live in, how it operates, how it has come about and is still changing, man's nature and possibilities, and their own roles as active participants in the inspiring human enterprise. These teachings will be presented not as dogmas but with an appraisal of the grounds for them and for the evolutionary view of things in general.—H. J. MULLER, "The Human Future," *The Humanist Frame,* Julian Huxley, ed. (1961).

The antithesis between a technical and a liberal education is fallacious. There can be no adequate technical education which is not liberal, and no liberal education which is not technical: that is, no education which does not impart both technique and intellectual vision.—ALFRED NORTH WHITEHEAD, *The Aims of Education* (1929).

BIBLIOGRAPHY

Bibliography

I. SOME RESOURCES
A. Bibliographic

Bancroft, Nancy, and Henry Clark, *Bibliography on Poverty, Unemployment, Work, Automation and the Cybercultural Ethos,* Union Theological Seminary, New York, July, 1965 (mimeo.).

Casebier, Marjorie L., *An Overview of Literature on Leisure,* The Institute of Ethics and Society, San Anselmo, Calif., 1963.

Committee on Education and Labor, House of Representatives, 88th Congress, *Hours of Work,* hearings before Select Subcommittee on Education and Labor, Washington, D. C., 1963.

————, *A Survey of Current Literature on Automation and Other Technological Changes,* Washington, D. C., 1964.

————, *Toward Full Employment: A Report.* Washington, D. C., 1964.

Committee on Labor and Public Welfare, U. S. Senate, *Nation's Manpower Revolution,* a series of volumes of hearings before the Subcommittee on Labor and Public Welfare, Washington, D. C., 1963-1964.

EDITORS' NOTE: This bibliography was compiled by Stephen H. Knox and John R. Low, Staff Assistants, Center for Continuing Liberal Education, The Pennsylvania State University, with Maxwell H. Goldberg advising.

————, *Selected Readings in Employment and Manpower*, a series of volumes, Washington, D. C., 1964.

Continuing Education for Adults (bibliography included in issue devoted to "Automation," April 30, 1964), Center for the Study of Liberal Education for Adults, at Boston University, Brookline, Mass.

Doty, William G., *Meaningful Leisure: An Interpretative Bibliographic Essay*, The Institute of Ethics and Society, San Anselmo, Calif., 1963.

Hilton, Alice Mary, ed., *feedback*, newsletter of The Institute for Cybercultural Research, New York.

International Labour Office, *Automation Programme*, a review of recent Soviet literature on the social aspects of automation and technological change in the U.S.S.R., Geneva, Switzerland, 1964.

————, abstracts of articles on the social aspects of automation. A collection based on selected literature published in leading industrialized countries, Geneva, Switzerland, 1964.

Labor & Industry Research Council, *Economic & Social Implications of Automation: An Annotated Bibliography*, 2 vols. (Vol. 1, ed. Gloria Glick, covers the period before 1957; Vol. 2 covers the period, 1957-1960), Michigan State University, East Lansing, Mich.

Library of Congress, *Human Engineering: A Selected Bibliography and Guide to the Literature*, Washington, D. C., 1953.

Manpower Administration, Office of Manpower, Automation, and Training, *Technical Manpower Publications and Services* (OMAT, Washington, D. C.).

National Science Foundation, *Current Projects on the Economic and Social Implications of Science and Technology* (annual publication), Washington, D. C.

Pollock, Friedrich, *Automation: Materialien zur Beurteilung ihrer Okonomischen und Sozialen Folgen*, Europaische Verlaganstalt. (Via NEA Project: Educational Implications of Automation, Washington, D. C.)

U. S. Department of Labor, *Implications of Automation & Technological Development* (a selective and annotated bibliography), Bulletin No. 1319.1, December, 1963, Washington, D. C.

Way, Phillip S., *A Bibliography of Materials Relating to the Appalachian South*, The Council of the Southern Mountains, Berea, Ky.

Yale Computer Center, Morris S. Davis, director, *Beginner's Intro-*

duction to the Literature of the Computer (mimeographed), New Haven, Conn., 1965.

B. Signs of the Times

Bueker, Mrs. W. E., "Letter from a Housewife," *This Week*, Aug. 2, p. 12, 1964.

Kenkizer, J., "What is a Computer?," *Science Digest*, 57: 75-78, January, 1965. (First in a series on computers.)

Leisure, first issue, January, 1960, New York City. Articles by Charles Van Doren, H. Allen Smith, Ernie Kovacs, David Bazelon.

Life, Inc., "Astronauts' Personal Stories about Their Gemini Flight," *Life*, Sept. 24, 1965, Pete Conrad, pp. 84C-84D; Gordon Cooper, pp. 87-88.

Man on Earth, Vol. I, No. 1, 1964, a periodical of writings on *Human Ecology*—man's interrelationship with his total environment. Ed. S.P.R. Charter, Olema, Calif.

Playboy, "The Uses and Abuses of the New Leisure" (a panel discussion with Steve Allen, Cleveland Amory, John Diebold, Paul Goodman, Walter Kerr, Norman Podhoretz, Jean Shepherd, and Terry Southern), 12: 51-64, March, 1965.

Schrieber, Flora Rheta, and Melvin Herman, "The Computer Age in Psychoanalysis," *Science Digest*, 57: 18-19, January, 1965.

Sevareid, Eric, "Instantaneous News on Television May Manipulate Tide of Events," *The Sunday Bulletin*, Philadelphia, Sect. 2, Editorials, March 22, 1964.

Smith, Sherwin D., "50 Years Ago—," *The New York Times Magazine*, Feb. 16, 1964, pp. 62-64.

Weir, Frank H., "Horizons Unlimited," *The Philadelphia Inquirer*, Oct. 7-Nov. 1, 1963.

Wingo, W., "Automation's Impact," *Science Newsletter*, 84: 278, Nov. 2, 1963; "Automation's Surge," 84: 294, Nov. 9, 1963; "Galloping Automation," 84: 310, Nov. 16, 1963; "Automation Changes Jobs," 84: 326, Nov. 23, 1963; "Can Americans Adjust?," 84: 346, Nov. 30, 1963.

C. Signs of the Trends

Ad Hoc Committee on the Triple Revolution, *The Triple Revolution: An Appraisal of the Major U. S. Crises and Proposals for Action*, Maurer, Fleischer, Zon and Associates, Inc., Washington, D. C., 1964.

American Association of University Women, *AAUW Journal*, Vol.

57, No. 4, May, 1964, issue devoted to "AAUW and the Future."

Asimov, Isaac, "Life in 1990," *Science Digest*, August, 1965, pp. 63-70.

Auer, Bernard M., *et al.*, *The Environment of Change*, Time, Inc., New York, 1965.

Barach, Arnold B., *1975: And the Changes to Come*, Harper & Brothers, New York, 1962.

————, *U. S. A. and Its Economic Future*, Macmillan Company, New York, 1964. (Twentieth Century Fund Survey.)

Bell, Daniel, "The Bogey of Automation," *The New York Review of Books*, 5: 23-25, Aug. 26, 1965.

Boulding, Kenneth, *The Meaning of the Twentieth Century*, Harper & Row, New York, 1965.

Bush, Vannevar, "Automation's Awkward Age," *Saturday Review*, 45: 10-11, 47, Aug. 11, 1962.

Center for the Study of Democratic Institutions, *Change*, Vol. I, No. 1, February, 1965, Santa Barbara, Calif.

Detroit Industrial Mission, *Automation and Unemployment: A Debate*, Detroit, Mich., February, 1965.

Diebold, John, *Beyond Automation*, McGraw-Hill, New York, 1964.

Drucker, Peter F., "Automation Is Not the Villain," *The New York Times Magazine*, pp. 26-27, 75-77, 82, Jan. 10, 1965.

Dunne, George H., S.J., ed., *Poverty in Plenty*, P. J. Kenedy, New York, 1965.

E. I. DuPont de Nemours & Company, *Automation and Employment*, Wilmington, Del., 1964.

Fuller, Buckminster, *Ideas and Integrities*, Prentice-Hall, Englewood Cliffs, N. J., 1963.

————, "The Prospect for Mankind," *Saturday Review*, 47: 26-27, Sept. 19, 1964.

————, "Notes on the Future," *Saturday Review*, 47: 26, Oct. 3, 1964.

Galbraith, John Kenneth, *The Affluent Society*, Mentor Books, New York, 1962.

Harrington, Michael, *The Accidental Century*, Macmillan Company, New York, 1965.

————, *The Other America: Poverty in the United States*, Penguin Books, New York, 1962.

Helstein, Ralph, Gerard Piel, and Robert Theobald, *Jobs, Machines and People*, Center for the Study of Democratic Institutions, Santa Barbara, Calif., 1964.

Hilton, Alice Mary, ed., *The Evolving Society*, Institute for Cybercultural Research, New York, 1965. (Spartan-Macmillan Co., New York, distributors.)

——, "Letter," *feedback*, 2: 1, February, 1965. Reply to Charles E. Silberman, *Fortune*, January, 1965.

Institute on Man and Society, *That Man May Survive*, Rensselaerville, New York, 1965.

International Labour Office, *Automation: A Discussion of Research Methods.* Bulletin No. 1 on *Labour and Automation*, Geneva, Switzerland, 1964.

Killian, James R., Jr., "Lift the Human Spirit," *Saturday Review*, 48: 58-60, May 1, 1965.

Lebergott, Stanley, ed., *Men Without Work: The Economics of Unemployment*, Prentice-Hall, Englewood Cliffs, N. J., 1964.

Life, Inc., "Control of Life," a four-part series on the frontier achievements of medical science and their implications for individuals and society, *Life*, Sept. 10-Oct. 1, 1965.

Linowitz, Sol M., "The Prosperity Gap," *Saturday Review*, 48: 42, Jan. 9, 1965.

McLuhan, Marshall, *Understanding Media*, McGraw-Hill Book Company, New York, 1964.

Manpower Report to the President: 1965, U. S. Government Printing Office, Washington, D. C., 1965.

Mesthene, Emmanuel G., "Learning to Live with Science," *Saturday Review*, 48: 14-17, July 17, 1965.

Michael, Donald N., *Cybernation and Social Change*, Seminar on Manpower Policy and Program, Office of Manpower, Automation and Training, Manpower Administration, U. S. Dept. of Labor, Washington, D. C., 1964.

——, *The Next Generation: The Prospects Ahead for the Youth of Tomorrow*, Random House, New York, 1965.

Myrdal, Gunnar, *Challenge to Affluence*, revised and expanded edition, Vintage Books, Random House, New York. (First copyright 1962.)

Newsweek, issue on "The Challenge of Automation," pp. 73-80, Jan. 26, 1965.

New York State School of Industrial and Labor Relations, *The Engineering of Human Behavior in Industry: A Conference*, Ithaca, N. Y., 1964.

Piel, Gerard, "Abundance and the Future Man," *Atlantic Monthly*, 213: 84-90, April, 1964.

————, "The Acceleration of History," *Current Issues in Higher Education: 1964*, pp. 22-32, Association for Higher Education, Washington, D. C., 1964.

Raskin, A. H., "The Great Manhattan Newspaper Duel," *Saturday Review*, 48: 58-60, 69-72, May 8, 1965.

Sarnoff, David, "By the End of the Twentieth Century," *Fortune*, 49: 116-119, May, 1964.

Scientific American, issue on "The Urbanization of the Human Population," 213: 40-219, September, 1965.

Seidenberg, Roderick, *Post-Historic Man: An Inquiry*, University of North Carolina Press, Chapel Hill, N. C., 1950.

Seligman, Ben, "Automation and the State," *Commentary*, 37: 49-54, April, 1964.

Skinner, B. F., "Freedom and the Control of Men," *American Scholar*, 25: 47-65, Fall, 1964.

Silberman, Charles E., *Technology and the Labor Market* (a series in *Fortune*): "The Real News About Automation," 71: 124-127, 220-222, 227-228, January, 1965; "The Comeback of the Blue Collar Worker" ("The Unemployment Problem: It's Not What You Think"), 71: 153-155, 210-216, February, 1965; "What Hit the Teenagers?," 71: 130-133, April, 1965 (article on "The Real Cause of Teenage Unemployment").

Solow, Robert M., *Unemployment in the United States*, Almqvist & Wiksell, Stockholm, Sweden, 1964.

SR/Research: Science & Humanity, "Building the American Dream," *Saturday Review*, 48: 49-60, Feb. 6, 1965.

Terborgh, George, *The Automation Hysteria*, Machinery and Allied Products Institute, Washington, D. C., 1965.

Theobald, Robert, "The Great Non-Debate on Automation and Cybernation," *Current Issues in Higher Education, 1963*, Association for Higher Education, Washington, D. C., pp. 102-106, 1963.

————, "Needed: A New Definition of Work," *New University Thought*, 3: 9-14, July, 1963.

Toffler, Alvin, "The Future as a Way of Life," *Horizon*, 7: 108-115, Summer, 1965.

Tournier, Paul, *The Adventure of Living*, trans. Edwin Hudson, Harper & Row, New York, 1965.

D. Collections

Lewis, Arthur O., Jr., ed., *Of Men and Machines*, Dutton Paperback Original, E. P. Dutton, New York, 1963.

Obler, Paul C., and Herman Estrin, eds., *The New Scientist*, Anchor Books, Doubleday, New York, 1962.

Phillipson, Morris, ed., *Automation: Implications for the Future*, Vintage Books, Random House, New York, 1964.

Ruitenbeck, Hendrik M., *The Dilemma of Organizational Society*, Dutton Paperback Original, E. P. Dutton, New York, 1963.

Walker, Charles R., ed., *Modern Technology and Civilization*, McGraw-Hill Book Company, New York, 1962.

Weeks, Robert, ed., *Machines and the Man: A Sourcebook on Automation*, Appleton-Century-Crofts, New York, 1961.

II. TECHNOLOGICAL CHANGE, AUTOMATION, AND HUMAN VALUES

Allen, F. R., ed., *Technology and Social Change*, Appleton-Century-Crofts, New York, 1957.

American Scholar, issue on "The Problems that Unite Us," Vol. 33, No. 4, Autumn, 1964, Washington, D. C.

Asbell, Bernard, *The New Improved American*, McGraw-Hill Book Company, New York, 1965.

Bagrit, Sir Leon, *The Age of Automation*, Mentor Books, New York, 1963. (Introduction by Daniel Bell.)

Battelle Memorial Institute, *Automation and Technological Change*, Proceedings of the Battelle-American Assembly, Cleveland, Ohio, July, 1963.

Bloy, Myron B., Jr., *The Crisis of Cultural Change: A Christian Viewpoint*, The Seabury Bookstore, New York, 1965.

————, "The Gracefulness of Technology," *The Church Review*, 22: 2-4, April-May, 1964.

Bowen, C. R., and Dwayne Orton, *Automation and Your Future*, in *The Christian Controversy Series, 1964*. General Board of Christian Social Concerns of the Methodist Church, Washington, D. C.

Buck, Roy C., "An Interpretation of Rural Values," *A Place to Live: The Yearbook of Agriculture, 1963*, pp. 1-12, USDA, Washington, D. C., 1964.

Center for the Study of Liberal Education for Adults, *Meanings of Work*, (Notes and Essays No. 39), Brookline, Mass., 1964.

Colby College, *Three Lectures: The Heritage of Mind in a Civilization of Machines* (Frank Stanton, Gerard Piel, Oscar Handlin), Colby College, Waterville, Me., 1963.

Cook, Clair M., "Technology's Impact on Religion," *The Christian Century*, 81: 1083-1085, Sept. 2, 1964.

Cowan, T. A., "Decision Theory in Law, Science and Technology," *Science*, 140: 1065-1075, June 7, 1963. (See also: Ivor Kraft, "Automated Decision Making: A Threat or Promise?" "Letters," *Science*, 143: 99-100, Jan. 10, 1964.)

Dunlop, John T., ed., *Automation and Technological Change*, Proceedings: American Assembly on Automation, Prentice-Hall, Englewood Cliffs, N. J., 1962.

Ellul, Jacques, *The Technological Order*, trans. John Wilkinson, Alfred A. Knopf, New York, 1964.

Epernay, Mark (pseudo.), *The McLandress Dimension*, Houghton Mifflin Company, Boston, 1962. (See, especially, "The Fully Automated Foreign Policy" and "The Confidence Machine.")

Friedmann, George, *The Industrial Society: The Emergence of the Human Problems of Automation*, reissue, No. 91090, Free Press, New York. (First publication 1955.)

General Electric Management Development and Employee Services, *Automation in General Electric: The Human Side of the Story*, New York [n.d.].

George Washington Law Review, issue on "Technology, Social Change, and the Constitution," Vol. 33, No. 17, October, 1964. Includes: Arthur Selwyn Miller, "The Engineering of Change in the U. S. Constitution."

Giedion, Siegfried, *Mechanization Takes Command*, Oxford University Press, New York, 1948.

Ginzberg, Eli., ed., *Technology and Social Change*, Columbia University Press, New York, 1964.

Goldberg, Maxwell H., "The Displacement of Human Labor," *The Evolving Society*, ed. Alice Mary Hilton, Institute for Cybercultural Research, New York, 1965 (Spartan-Macmillan Co., New York, distributors).

Handlin, Oscar, "Men and Magic: Encounters with the Machine," *American Scholar*, 33: 408-419, Summer, 1964.

Heckscher, August, *The Individual and the Mass*, The Twentieth Century Fund, New York, 1965.

————, *The Public Happiness*, Atheneum, New York, 1962.

Hirschfeld, Gerhard, "Technology and the Idea of Mankind," *Technology and Culture*, 5: 43-56, Winter, 1964. Report of Conference sponsored by The Council for the Study of Mankind.

Holton, Gerald, *et al.*, in *Daedalus*, issue on "Science and Culture," 94: 1-262, Winter, 1965.

Huxley, Aldous, *Brave New World*, Bantam Books, New York. (First copyright, 1932.)

Juenger, Friedrich Georg, *The Failure of Technology*, Gateway Books, Chicago, 1956.

Kouvenhoven, John A., *Made in America*, Anchor Books, New York, 1961.

Lichtheim, George, "A Nous la Liberté," review of Jacques Ellul's *The Technological Society*, George Friedmann's *Ou va le travail humain*, etc., *The New York Review*, 3: 22-25, Nov. 19, 1964.

McLuhan, Marshall, *The Gutenberg Galaxy: The Making of Typographic Man*, The University of Toronto Press, Toronto, 1962.

Mead, Margaret, *Cultural Patterns and Technological Change*, Mentor Books, New York, 1963.

Michael, Donald N., *Cybernation: The Silent Conquest*, Center for the Study of Democratic Institutions, Santa Barbara, Calif., 1962.

Mumford, Lewis, "Apology to Henry Adams," *Virginia Quarterly Review*, 38: 196-217, Spring, 1962.

————, *Art and Technics*, Columbia University Press, New York, 1952.

————, "Authoritarian and Democratic Technics," *Technology and Culture*, 5: 1-8, Winter, 1964.

————, "Automation of Knowledge," *Current Issues in Higher Education: 1964*, Association for Higher Education, Washington, D. C., 1964.

————, *Technics and Civilization*, G. Routledge & Sons, London, 1934.

National Council of Churches, *Triple Revolution: Cybernation—Weaponry—Human Rights*, National Council of Churches, New York, June, 1965.

New York Times Magazine, issue on "Hiroshima and the Atomic Age" (articles by A. M. Rosenthal, Hanson W. Baldwin, William L. Laurence, Clinton P. Anderson, W. H. Auden, Betty Jean Lifton), Aug. 1, 1965.

Oak Ridge Institute of Nuclear Studies (University Relations Division), *A Report on Science and Contemporary Social Problems* (one-month conference, June 15-July 15, 1964), Oak Ridge, Tenn., September, 1964.

Pi-Sunyer, O., and T. De Gregor, "Cultural Resistance to Technological Change," *Technology & Culture*, 5: 247-253, Spring, 1964.

Quinn, Francis S., S.J., *The Ethical Aftermath of Automation*, Newman Press, Westminster, Md., 1962.

Renewal, "From Cybernation to Ad Man's Ethics: An Exploration," pp. 2-16, June, 1965.

Reuther, Walter P., *The Values We Cherish,* keynote address: Fifth Constitutional Convention, Nov. 7, 1963, Industrial Union Department, AFL-CIO, Washington, D. C.

Royal Bank of Canada, "Professionals' Concern for Values," December, 1962. Reprinted in *Journal of Cooperative Extension,* 2: 67-74, Summer, 1964, University of Wisconsin, Madison, Wis.

Royce, Joseph R., *The Encapsulated Man: An Interdisciplinary Essay in the Search for Meaning,* Van Nostrand Insight Book, Princeton, N. J., 1964.

Simon, Herbert A., *The Shape of Automation: For Men and Management,* Harper & Row, New York, 1965.

Tillich, Paul, "The Person in a Technical Society," in *Christian Faith and Social Action,* ed. John A. Hutchison, Charles Scribner's Sons, New York, 1953.

Time, Inc., *The Environment of Change,* a conference at Sterling Forest, Tuxedo, N. Y., June 14-17, 1964. Privately printed.

Tournier, Paul, "The Person in a Machine Age," *The Christian Century,* 81: 793-796, June 17, 1964 ("Mindful of Man Series").

Vickers, Geoffrey, *The Undirected Society: Essays on the Human Implications of Industrialization in Canada,* University of Toronto Press, Toronto, Canada, 1959.

Watson, Thomas J., Jr., "Technology," *Think,* 26: 17-19, December, 1960.

III. CYBERNETICS, COMPUTERS

Auerbach, Isaac L., *et al.,* "The Information Revolution," *New York Times,* Sect. II, May 23, 1965 (a special supplement).

Arbib, Michael A., *Brains, Machines, and Mathematics,* McGraw-Hill Book Company, New York, 1964.

Bell, Arthur David, *Intelligent Machines,* Random House, New York, 1962.

Berkeley, Edmund C., *The Computer Revolution,* Doubleday, New York, 1962.

Bernstein, Jeremy, *The Analytical Engine: Computers, Past, Present and Future,* Random House, New York, 1964.

Bessinger, Jess B., Jr., Stephen M. Parrish, and Harry F. Arader, eds., *Literary Data Processing Conference,* Sept. 9-11, 1964. Issued through Modern Language Association, New York.

Bronowski, J., Review of *Brains, Machines, and Mathematics,* by Michael A. Arbib, in "Books," *Scientific American,* 210: 130-134, June, 1964.

Burck, Gilbert, and The Editors of *Fortune, The Computer Age and Its Potential for Management,* Harper & Row, New York, 1965.

Feigenbaum, E., and J. Feldman, eds., *Computers and Thought,* McGraw-Hill Book Company, New York, 1964.

Greenberger, Martin, ed., *Computers and the World of the Future,* M.I.T. Press, Cambridge, Mass., 1962 (also published under the title, *Management and the Computer of the Future).*

Halacy, D. S., Jr., *Computers: The Machines We Think With,* Harper & Row, New York, 1964.

Hilton, Alice Mary, *Logic, Computing Machines, and Automation,* Meridian Books, New York, 1964.

Leedham, Charles, "The 'Chip' Revolutionizes Electronics," *The New York Times Magazine,* pp. 56-57, 62, 64, 66, 68, Sept. 19, 1965.

Mack, Raymond W., and Dennis C. McElrath, "A Computerized View of the World" (Series: "The Study of Man"), *Transaction,* 2: 27-28, January-February, 1965.

Maruyama, Magoroh, "Cybernetics," *NEA Journal,* 53: 51-56, December, 1964.

Michael, Donald N., "Speculations on the Relation of the Computer to Individual Freedom and the Right to Privacy," *The George Washington Law Review,* 33: 270-286, January, 1965.

Pfeiffer, John, "Man's Brain Child," *New York Times Book Review,* pp. 1, 25, April 18, 1965.

————, *The Thinking Machine,* J. B. Lippincott Co., Philadelphia, 1962.

Time, Inc., issue on "The Computer in Society," April 2, 1965.

von Neumann, John, *The Computer and the Brain,* Yale University Press, New Haven, Conn., 1959.

Wiener, Norbert, *Cybernetics, Or, Control and Communication in the Animal and the Machine,* John Wiley & Sons, New York, 1961.

————, *Ex-Prodigy: My Childhood and Youth,* M.I.T. Press, Cambridge, Mass. (First copyright, 1953.)

————, *God & Golem, Inc.,* M.I.T. Press, Cambridge, Mass., 1964.

————, *The Human Use of Human Beings,* Anchor Books, New York, 1956.

IV. WORK AND LEISURE

Anderson, Nels, *Work and Leisure,* Free Press, New York, 1962.

Arendt, Hannah, *The Human Condition*, Anchor Books, New York, 1960.

Brightbill, Charles K., *The Challenge of Leisure*, Spectrum Books, Prentice-Hall, Englewood Cliffs, N. J., 1962.

Buckingham, Walter, *Automation: Its Impact on Business and People*, Harper & Brothers, New York, 1961.

Charlesworth, James C., *Leisure in America: Blessing or Curse*, monograph in a series sponsored by American Academy of Political and Social Science, Philadelphia, April, 1964.

————, "To Make Leisure Time Worthwhile," *The Pennsylvania Gazette*, April, 1964.

de Grazia, Sebastian, *Of Time, Work, Leisure*, Anchor Books, Doubleday, New York, 1964.

Faltermayer, E. K., "The Drift to Early Retirement," *Fortune*, May, 1965.

Friedmann, George S., *The Anatomy of Work, Labor, Leisure and the Implications of Automation*, Free Press, New York, 1964.

Gabor, Dennis, *Inventing the Future*, Alfred A. Knopf, New York, 1964.

Havemann, Ernest, "Too Much Leisure," *Life*, 56: 76-90, Feb. 14, 1964; 56: 84-94, Feb. 21, 1964.

Heckscher, August, "Reflections on the Manpower Revolution," *The American Scholar*, 33: 568-578, Autumn, 1964.

Larrabee, Eric, and Rolf Meyerjohn, eds., *Mass Leisure*, Free Press, Glencoe, Ill., 1958.

Lobsenz, Norman, *Is Anybody Happy?*, Doubleday, New York, 1962.

Rideau, Émile, "Theology of Leisure," *Theology Digest*, 12: 184-188, Fall, 1964.

Steere, Douglas V., *Work and Contemplation*, Harper & Brothers, New York, 1957.

V. AUTOMATION (TECHNOLOGY, CYBERNATION) AND EDUCATION

American Child, "Automation: Outlook for Youth," 44: 1-16, November, 1962.

American Education, "The White House Conference on Education," 1: 13-28, July-August, 1965.

Ashby, Eric, "Education as an Investment in Man," *Overseas*, 3: 8-14, March, 1964.

————, "Technological Humanism," *Journal of the Institute of Metals*, 85: 461-467, 1957.

————, *Technology and the Academics: An Essay on Universities and the Scientific Revolution*, Papermac, St. Martin's Press, New York, 1963.

Baskin, Samuel, ed., *Higher Education: Some Newer Developments*, McGraw-Hill Book Company, New York, 1965.

Brameld, Theodore, and Stanley Elam, *Values in American Education: An Interdisciplinary Approach*, Phi Delta Kappa, Bloomington, Ind., 1964.

Brown, James W., and James Thornton, eds., *New Media in Higher Education*, National Education Association, Washington, D. C., 1963.

Bruner, Jerome S., *On Knowing: Essays for the Left Hand*, Atheneum Paperback, New York, 1965.

Center for Study of Liberal Education for Adults, *Perspective on Automation: Three Talks to Educators* (Notes and Essays No. 43), Boston University, Brookline, Mass., 1964.

Curle, Adam, *et al.*, *Some Educational Implications of Technological Development: A Report Presented by the Committee of the Harvard University Program on Technology and Society*, Cambridge, Mass., 1965. Contains detailed bibliography.

de Grazia, Alfred, and David A. John, eds., *Revolution in Teaching: New Theory Technology and Curricula*, Bantam Books, Matrix Edition, New York, 1964.

————, *Programs, Teachers and Machines*, Bantam Books, Matrix Edition, New York, 1964.

Deikhoff, John S., "Adam, Automation, and the American College," *Journal of General Education*, 16: 215-225, October, 1964.

DeVane, William Clyde, *Higher Education in Twentieth-Century America*, Harvard University Press, Cambridge, Mass., 1965.

Dillard, Irving, "A Report: On the Humanities," *The American Scholar*, 34: 274-291, Spring, 1965.

Dubos, René, "Humanistic Biology," *The American Scholar*, 34: 179-198, Spring, 1965.

Educational Services Incorporated, *A Review of Current Programs: 1965*, Watertown, Mass.

Evans, Luther H., and George E. Arnstein, eds., *Automation and the Challenge to Education*, Project on the Educational Implications of Automation, National Education Association, Washington, D. C., 1962.

Frank, Robert W., and Harrison Meserole, eds., *The Responsible*

Man: The Insights of the Humanities, Doubleday, Garden City, N. Y., 1965.

Friedman, Albert B., ed., *Creativity in Graduate Education*. Addresses by Milton S. Eisenhower, Louis T. Benezet, Robert R. Sears. Commentary by W. T. Jones, Albert B. Friedman, and Stanley Foster Reed. Claremont, Calif., 1964.

Fuller, Buckminster, *Education Automation*, Southern Illinois University Press, Carbondale, Ill., 1962.

General Electric Management Development and Employee Services, *Training in General Electric: The Human Side of the Story*, New York (n.d.).

Goldberg, Maxwell H., "General Education and the Explosion of Knowledge," *General Education: Current Ideas and Concerns*, ed. James G. Rice, Association for Higher Education, Washington, D. C., 1964.

————, *Meaning and Metaphor: On Teaching Values Through Poetry at a Steelworkers Institute*, Center for the Study of Liberal Education for Adults, Boston University, Brookline, Mass., 1965.

Hadas, Moses, *Old Wine, New Bottles—A Humanist Teacher at Work*, Pocket Books, New York, 1962.

Harbison, Frederick, and Charles A. Myers, *Education, Manpower and Economic Growth*, McGraw-Hill Book Company, New York, 1964.

Hersey, John, *The Child Buyer*, Bantam Books, New York, 1962.

Horn, Francis, *Improving Humanistic Education*, The Wemyss Foundation, Wilmington, Del., December, 1964.

Hurwitz, H. L., "What Shall We Teach Our Children about Automation?," *Social Education*, 27: 301-304, October, 1963.

Humanities Center for Liberal Education in an Industrial Society, Inc., *Human Competence in the World of Change; Business and the Humanities: A Symposium*, E. Lansing, Mich. Reprinted from *The Michigan Quarterly Review*, 4: 77-105, Spring, 1965.

Jaspers, Karl, *The Idea of the University*, ed. Karl W. Deutsch, introduction by Robert Ulich, Beacon Press, Boston, Mass., 1959. (See especially chap. VII, "The Cosmos of Knowledge.")

Lewis, Arthur O., Jr., *The Society of Men and Machines*, CCLE Humanities Study-Discussion Course, Center for Continuing Liberal Education, University Park, Pa., 1965.

Marx, Leo, *The Machine in the Garden*, Oxford University Press, New York, 1965.

NASSP Bulletin, Education and Automation: The Coming World of Work and Leisure, NASSP Bulletin, Vol. 48, No. 295, November, 1964. Special issue of publication of National Association of Secondary-School Principals. National Education Association, Washington, D. C.

National Education Association: Project on the Educational Implications of Automation. Numerous articles by George E. Arnstein, Luther Evans, and Virgil Rogers. Also a clearing-house for bibliographical and other resources. Washington, D. C.

—————, Technological Development Project, A Series of Occasional Papers, 1962-1963, Washington, D. C.

Pacific Northwest Conference on Higher Education, *Human Values in a Technological Age,* Oregon State University Press, Corvallis, Ore., 1958.

Rickover, Hyman G., "A Humanistic Technology," *The American Behavioral Scientist,* 14: 3-8, January, 1965.

Saturday Review, symposium, "Technology's Challenge to Education," 47: 21-25, 77-79, Dec. 12, 1964. Selections from Delaware Seminar on Education for Human Competence in the Face of Technological Change. Co-sponsored by the Humanities Center for Liberal Education in an Industrial Society, Inc., with the University of Delaware, the Wemyss Foundation, and E. I. DuPont de Nemours and Company.

Smallwood, Richard D., *A Decision Structure for Teaching Machines,* M.I.T. Press, Cambridge, Mass., 1962.

Stern, Bernard H., "Automation and Adult Education," *Educational Forum,* 29: 304-311, March, 1965.

Stern, J. L., "Automation: End or a New Day in Unionism," annals, *American Academy of Political Science,* 150: 25-35, November, 1963.

Stover, Carl F., ed., *The Technological Order: Proceedings of the Encyclopaedia Britannica Conference on the Technological Order,* Wayne State University Press, Detroit, Mich., 1963. (Originally published in *Technology and Culture,* Vol. 3, No. 4, Fall, 1962.)

Subcommittee on Education, Committee on Labor and Public Welfare, United States Senate, *White House Conference on Education: A Milestone for Educational Progress,* U. S. Government Printing Office, Washington, D. C., 1965.

Sviridoff, Mitchell, "Labor, Humanities, and the New Technology," *Basic College Quarterly,* Michigan State University, Summer, 1959.

Swenson, May, "The Poet as Anti-Specialist," *Saturday Review*, 48: 16-18, 64, Jan. 30, 1965.

Trachtenberg, Alan, *The Brooklyn Bridge: Fact and Symbol*, Oxford University Press, New York, 1965.

Venn, Grant, *Man, Education, and Work*, American Council on Education, Washington, D. C., 1964.

Watson, Goodwin, ed., *No Room at the Bottom: Automation and the Reluctant Learner.* Project on the Educational Implications of Automation. National Education Association, Washington, D. C., 1963.

Wolfbein, Seymour L., "Automation, Education, and Individual Liberty," *Teachers College Record*, 66: 27-36, October, 1964.

VI. PUBLICATIONS RELATED TO CCLE-IBM HUMANITIES PROJECT: TECHNOLOGICAL CHANGE AND HUMAN VALUES

American Association of University Women, *General Director's Letter*, Vol. 32, No. 1, September, 1964.

Arnstein, George E., "The Mixed Blessings of Automation," *School and Society*, 92: 311-313, Oct. 31, 1964.

Brickman, William W., "The Scholar-Educator in an Age of Automation," *School and Society*, 92: 314-315, Oct. 31, 1964.

Burhoe, Ralph W., "Human Values in an Age of Science and Technology," *Current Issues in Higher Education: 1964*, pp. 33-35, Association for Higher Education, Washington, D. C., 1964.

Davis, Charles T., "Humanistic Imperatives in an Age of Technology," *Pennsylvania Library Association Bulletin*, 20: 7-11, August, 1964.

Dearing, G. Bruce, "Education for Humane Living in an Age of Automation," *School and Society*, 92: 305-308, Oct. 31, 1964.

Evans, Luther H., "Some Neglected Aspects of Education in an Age of Automation," *School and Society*, 92: 310-311, Oct. 31, 1964.

Gibboney, Richard, "The Pennsylvania Humanities Course," *Phi Delta Kappan*, 46: 58-59, 62, October, 1964.

Goldberg, Maxwell H., "Continuous Education as a Way of Life," *Adult Education*, Vol. 16, Fall, 1965.

————, "The Impact of Technological Change on the Humanities," *Educational Record*, Vol. 46, October, 1965.

————, "Library Services to Adults: The Educational Challenge of Technological Change," *Pennsylvania Library Association Bulletin*, 19: 17-19, May, 1964.

————, "Technological Innovation and Humanpower," *PNA Press,* Pennsylvania Newspaper Publishers Association, Harrisburg, Pa., 37: 20, May, 1964.

Groom, Phyllis P., "The Labor Month in Review," *Monthly Labor Review,* 87: iii-iv, July, 1964.

Harshbarger, Luther H., "Humanistic Imperatives and Technological Change," *Educational Forum,* 29: 313-317, March, 1965 (also published in *Spotlight,* 1: 32-36, Queens College, Ont., 1964).

Heckscher, August, "Humanistic Invention in the Post-Industrial Age," *Liberal Education,* 50: 309-320, October, 1964.

Hilton, Alice Mary, "Cyberculture—The Age of Abundance and Leisure," *Michigan Quarterly Review,* 50: 309-320, Fall, 1964.

Kranzberg, Melvin, "Technology and Human Values," *Virginia Quarterly Review,* 40: 578-592, Fall, 1964 (also, translations made and distributed by USIA).

Lehrer, Stanley, "Man, Automation, and Dignity," *School and Society,* 92: 303, Oct. 31, 1964.

Mangum, Garth, "Automation, Employment, and Human Values," *Educational Record,* 45: 122-127, Spring, 1964 (reprinted in *Spotlight,* 1: 37-43, Queens College, Ont., 1964).

MacIver, John, "Report on December 1963 CCLE Conference on Technological Change and Human Values," *Newsletter on Occupational Psychiatry,* American Psychiatric Association.

May, John, "The Myth of Human Obsolescence," *Topic: 8,* 73-82, Fall, 1964, Washington and Jefferson College, Washington, Pa.

Oliver, Robert T., "Education in the Year 2000 A.D.," *Michigan Quarterly Review,* 3: 233-236, Fall, 1964.

Peters, C. M. D., "The Education of the New Humanist," *School and Society,* 92: 304-305, Oct. 31, 1964.

Reed, Stanley Foster, "Entrepreneurship and the Depressed Area," *Yale Review,* 54: 31-40, Fall, 1964.

————, "Innovation and Human Values—The Interaction Spectrum," *The Gadfly,* April 10, 1964, pp. 3, 5-6, University of Colorado, Boulder, Colo.

Siegle, Peter, "Automation, Education, and Competency," *School and Society,* 92: 309-310, Oct. 31, 1964.

Simon, Herbert A., "The Promise of Automation," *Pennsylvania Library Association Bulletin,* 20: 7-15, February, 1965.

Theobald, Robert, "Human Rights in a Cybernated Age," *Educational Record,* 45: 113-122, Spring, 1964.

Trachtenberg, Alan, "Technology, Education, and Human Values," *School and Society*, 92: 316-318, Oct. 31, 1964.

————, "Technology and Human Values," *Technology and Culture*, 5: 359-376, Summer, 1964.

Weir, Frank H., "Changing America's Way of Life: Mankind's Most Momentous Revolution," *The Philadelphia Inquirer*, June 28, 1964.

Zeigler, Martha, "Creative Education," *Christian Standard*, 99: 9-10, Aug. 29, 1964; 99: 5-6, Sept. 5, 1964.

ADDENDA

AHE College and University Bulletin, 18: 1-6, Nov. 1, 1965. Articles on new educational media by C. R. Carpenter and Wilbert J. McKeachie.

Computers for Humanities?, Yale University Press, New Haven, Conn., 1965.

Platt, John R., "The Step to Man," *Science*, 149: 607-613, August, 1965.

The Use of Computers in Humanities Research, New York, 1965. Available through Center for Information Processing, Rutgers, The State University, New Brunswick, N. J.

RELATED
WRITINGS

CHANGE AND CHALLENGE IN AMERICAN EDUCATION

James E. Russell, Educational Policies Commission

An articulate analysis of the modern educational dilemma and a sound prescription for its solution, written by an expert in the field. Mr. Russell claims we must change our conventional modes of "practical" pedagogy or else face mass unemployment and social unrest. He maintains that the *central* role of education must be to develop the rational potential and theoretical insights of all men.

115 pages   *1965*   *paper*   *$1.95*

THE CHEERFUL PROSPECT

A Statement on the Future of American Education

Charles S. Benson, University of California, Berkeley

A fresh and well-reasoned solution to two main administrative problems in American education: the need to obtain a more effective use of school revenues and the need to reduce inequalities of educational opportunity. The author suggests a scheme (actually a modification of the English system of administration and finance) for changing the structure of state-local relations in education and for modifying the structure of local government.

134 pages   *1965*   *paper*   *$2.25*

MAN IN A WORLD AT WORK

Edited by Henry Borow, University of Minnesota

For the National Vocational Guidance Association

A collection of 24 writings—nearly all of them in original form—contributed by distinguished social scientists and educators, providing the first book that is a comprehensive interdisciplinary analysis of the human work experience. Several chapters treat the changing state of the American social order and its effect upon the education, counseling, and vocational development of American youth, as well as the adjustment of the worker on the job.

606 pages   *1964*   *$8.50*

Houghton Mifflin Company

BOSTON · NEW YORK · ATLANTA · GENEVA, ILL · DALLAS · PALO ALTO

INDEX

INDEX

Index

Adams, Henry, 309

Administrator(s), and decision-making, 45; and "sense of Future," 320-321

Adolescence, in American culture, 275-276; income as symbol of sense of identity, 278; qualities and attitudes, 280-281; transition to adult status, 280-281; *see* Youth

Adolescents, attitudes toward tasks, 279; developing behaviors and attitudes, 278-279; increasing financial resources of, 277; money as key to wants, 277-278; prime characteristics of, 283; reinterpreting place of work, 281-282; unemployment among slum, 281; upward movement in class structure, 275-276; value of work experience, 278-279; world-wide unrest among, 305; *see* Children

Adult(s), continuing liberal education for, 353; free time pursuits of, 297-298; humane leadership, 24; increased return to school, 298; increased travel, 298; increasing cultural pursuits, 297-298; innovational programs for, 24; work role and social status, 275; youth's work relationship to, 280

Adult education, 207-210; advantages and disadvantages, 208; causes of upsurge in, 208-209; continuing, 108; correcting traditional weaknesses, 208; evening schools and correspondence courses, 209; faults of leadership, 210; future of, 352-353; increasing demands for, 63; innovation in, 209-210; liberal, 23, 24; *see* Continuing education

Advertising, and ethics, 42; sales resistance to, 42; in technological age, 238

Aerospace industry, audio-visual instruction in, 76; *see* Boeing; Communications Satellite Corp.; Satellite Corp.; *and* Space

Aeschylus, 127

"Affluent Society, The," 283

Africa, 298; changing geography of, 309

Age of Anxiety, 334

"Age of Thunder," 123

Aged, development of free-time activities for, 299; relationship with youth, 297; *see* Elderly

Agriculture, revolution in productivity, 73-74; stimulated, 62; *see* Farmer(s) *and* Farming

cation; Liberal education; National Defense Education Act; New Education; Programmed learning; Robbins Report; Rote-learning; School(s); Teaching machines; University; *and* Vocational education

Educational establishment, 206, 210

Educational Facilities Laboratories, 59

Educational Policies Commission, NEA, 81

Educational television, Federal financing of, 246; *see* National Educational Television; Television; *and* WVIZ

Educative process, and human values, 326; knowledge as *sine qua non* of, 326

Educator(s), American, 17; professional, opposition to teaching machines, 326; rising stature of, 274; *see* Faculty *and* Teacher(s)

Einstein, Albert, 21

Elba, 103

Elderly, effect of technological change on, 75; *see* Aged

Elections, national: *see* Electoral College

Electoral College, and electronic recording, 49

Electrical industry, shortened work week, 75

Electronic(s), and microminiaturization, 57; recording, Electoral College and, 49; systems, 46

Elevator operators, unemployed by automation, 37

Elite, increased free time for wives of, 295, 298-299; increased schooling, 295; increased work responsibility, 300-301; managerial and professional, less free time for, 295; style-setting by wives of, 298-299; technological and bureaucratic, in New Society, 203; working past retirement age, 295

Ellul, Jacques, 336

Emerson, Ralph Waldo, 354

Employees, and automation, 44; reducing, in supermarkets, 42; *see* Worker(s)

Employers, obligation to workers, 16

Employment, achieving full, 12; changing patterns in government, 220; changing patterns through history, 189; declining opportunities for unskilled, 267; in Post Office Department, 224; ratio of Federal to state and local government, 223-225; Senate Subcommittee on, and Manpower, 55; *see* Civil Service; Unemployment; *and* Work

Engineering, discouragement of women in, 272

England, 17, 81, 122; *see* Britain *and* Great Britain

Engle, Paul, 219

English, 356

Enrollments, increasing college, 59, 79, 81; increasing public school, 59, 251

Epictetus, 127

"Erewhon," 58, 104

"Essays for the Left Hand," 101

Essex, University of, 17

Ethic(s), in advertising, 42; of austerity, 346; "fun morality" as new, 346; man in era of automated, 311; *see* Judeo-Christian *and* Protestant

Ethic of Work, 232

Ethical norms, 23

"Ethics," Plato's, 92

Europe, 238; Central, 72; East, 331; emergence of "mixed enterprises" in, 76; immigrants from, 50; leisure class of, 300; Master of Arts degree in, 111; in Middle Ages, 81; nondiscriminatory education of women, 271; schools in, 267; Western, shortage of manpower in, 73; Western, unemployment in, 73; *see* Britain; France; Germany; Grand Tour; Greece; Sweden; *and* Switzerland

Evans, Luther, 349

Evans, Marjorie, 322

Excellence, originality as arbiter of, 324; pursuit of, and free time, 301-302; pursuit of, in mass-consumption society, 302

Executives, "cult of overwork," 104; problems of automation, 44

Factory, and automation, 44-45; *see* Manufacturing *and* Plants

Faculty, preparation for computer pilot programs, 19; *see* Educator(s) *and* Teacher(s)

Faculty Seminar on Culture and Tech-